HARPER TORCHBOOKS / The Cloister Library

Tor Andrae	MOHAMMED: *The Man and His Faith* TB/62
Augustine/Przywara	AN AUGUSTINE SYNTHESIS TB/35
Roland H. Bainton	THE TRAVAIL OF RELIGIOUS LIBERTY TB/30
Karl Barth	DOGMATICS IN OUTLINE TB/56
Karl Barth	THE WORD OF GOD AND THE WORD OF MAN TB/13
Nicolas Berdyaev	THE BEGINNING AND THE END TB/14
Nicolas Berdyaev	THE DESTINY OF MAN TB/61
James Henry Breasted	DEVELOPMENT OF RELIGION AND THOUGHT IN ANCIENT EGYPT TB/57
Martin Buber	ECLIPSE OF GOD: *Studies in the Relation Between Religion and Philosophy* TB/12
Martin Buber	MOSES: *The Revelation and the Covenant* TB/27
Jacob Burckhardt	THE CIVILIZATION OF THE RENAISSANCE IN ITALY [Illustrated Edition]: *Vol. I*, TB/40; *Vol. II*, TB/41
Edward Conze	BUDDHISM: *Its Essence and Development* TB/58
F. M. Cornford	FROM RELIGION TO PHILOSOPHY: *A Study in the Origins of Western Speculation* TB/20
G. G. Coulton	MEDIEVAL FAITH AND SYMBOLISM TB/25
G. G. Coulton	THE FATE OF MEDIEVAL ART IN THE RENAISSANCE AND REFORMATION TB/26
H. G. Creel	CONFUCIUS AND THE CHINESE WAY TB/63
Adolf Deissmann	PAUL: *A Study in Social and Religious History* TB/15
C. H. Dodd	THE AUTHORITY OF THE BIBLE TB/43
Johannes Eckhart	MEISTER ECKHART: A Modern Translation TB/8
Mircea Eliade	COSMOS AND HISTORY: *The Myth of the Eternal Return* TB/50
Morton S. Enslin	CHRISTIAN BEGINNINGS TB/5
Morton S. Enslin	THE LITERATURE OF THE CHRISTIAN MOVEMENT TB/6
Austin Farrer, ed.	THE CORE OF THE BIBLE TB/7
Ludwig Feuerbach	THE ESSENCE OF CHRISTIANITY TB/11
Harry Emerson Fosdick	A GUIDE TO UNDERSTANDING THE BIBLE TB/2
Sigmund Freud	ON CREATIVITY AND THE UNCONSCIOUS: *Papers on the Psychology of Art, Literature, Love, Religion* TB/45
Maurice Friedman	MARTIN BUBER: *The Life of Dialogue* TB/64
Octavius Brooks Frothingham	TRANSCENDENTALISM IN NEW ENGLAND: *A History* TB/59
Edward Gibbon	THE END OF THE ROMAN EMPIRE IN THE WEST [J. B. Bury Edition; Illustrated] TB/37
Edward Gibbon	THE TRIUMPH OF CHRISTENDOM IN THE ROMAN EMPIRE [J. B. Bury Edition; Illustrated] TB/46
Charles C. Gillispie	GENESIS AND GEOLOGY TB/51
Maurice Goguel	JESUS AND THE ORIGINS OF CHRISTIANITY I: *Prolegomena to the Life of Jesus* TB/65
Maurice Goguel	JESUS AND THE ORIGINS OF CHRISTIANITY II: *The Life of Jesus* TB/66
Edgar J. Goodspeed	A LIFE OF JESUS TB/1
Herbert J. C. Grierson	CROSS-CURRENTS IN 17TH CENTURY ENGLISH LITERATURE: *The World, the Flesh, the Spirit* TB/47
William Haller	THE RISE OF PURITANISM TB/22
Adolf Harnack	WHAT IS CHRISTIANITY? TB/17
Edwin Hatch	THE INFLUENCE OF GREEK IDEAS ON CHRISTIANITY TB/18
Karl Heim	CHRISTIAN FAITH AND NATURAL SCIENCE TB/16
F. H. Heinemann	EXISTENTIALISM AND THE MODERN PREDICAMENT TB/28
Stanley R. Hopper, ed.	SPIRITUAL PROBLEMS IN CONTEMPORARY LITERATURE TB/21
Johan Huizinga	ERASMUS AND THE AGE OF REFORMATION TB/19
Aldous Huxley	THE DEVILS OF LOUDUN: *A Study in the Psychology of Power Politics and Mystical Religion in the France of Cardinal Richelieu* TB/60
Søren Kierkegaard	EDIFYING DISCOURSES: A Selection TB/32

(Continued on next page)

Søren Kierkegaard	THE JOURNALS OF KIERKEGAARD TB/52
Søren Kierkegaard	PURITY OF HEART TB/4
Alexandre Koyré	FROM THE CLOSED WORLD TO THE INFINITE UNIVERSE TB/31
Emile Mâle	THE GOTHIC IMAGE: *Religious Art in France of the 13th Century* TB/44
H. Richard Niebuhr	CHRIST AND CULTURE TB/3
H. Richard Niebuhr	THE KINGDOM OF GOD IN AMERICA TB/49
H. J. Rose	RELIGION IN GREECE AND ROME TB/55
Josiah Royce	THE RELIGIOUS ASPECT OF PHILOSOPHY: *A Critique of the Bases of Conduct and of Faith* TB/29
Auguste Sabatier	OUTLINES OF A PHILOSOPHY OF RELIGION BASED ON PSYCHOLOGY AND HISTORY TB/23
George Santayana	INTERPRETATIONS OF POETRY AND RELIGION TB/9
George Santayana	WINDS OF DOCTRINE *and* PLATONISM AND THE SPIRITUAL LIFE TB/24
Friedrich Schleiermacher	ON RELIGION: *Speeches to Its Cultured Despisers* TB/36
Henry Osborn Taylor	THE EMERGENCE OF CHRISTIAN CULTURE IN THE WEST: *The Classical Heritage of the Middle Ages* TB/48
Paul Tillich	DYNAMICS OF FAITH TB/42
Edward Burnett Tylor	THE ORIGINS OF CULTURE TB/33
Edward Burnett Tylor	RELIGION IN PRIMITIVE CULTURE TB/34
Evelyn Underhill	WORSHIP TB/10
Johannes Weiss	EARLIEST CHRISTIANITY: *A History of the Period* A.D. 30–150: *Vol. I*, TB/53; *Vol. II*, TB/54
Wilhelm Windelband	A HISTORY OF PHILOSOPHY I: *Greek, Roman, Medieval* TB/38
Wilhelm Windelband	A HISTORY OF PHILOSOPHY II: *Renaissance, Enlightenment, Modern* TB/39

HARPER TORCHBOOKS / The Academy Library

H. J. Blackham	SIX EXISTENTIALIST THINKERS TB/1002
Walter Bromberg	THE MIND OF MAN: *A History of Psychotherapy and Psychoanalysis* TB/1003
G. P. Gooch	ENGLISH DEMOCRATIC IDEAS IN THE SEVENTEENTH CENTURY TB/1006
Francis J. Grund	ARISTOCRACY IN AMERICA TB/1001
Henry James	THE PRINCESS CASAMASSIMA TB/1005
Georges Poulet	STUDIES IN HUMAN TIME TB/1004

HARPER TORCHBOOKS / The Science Library

J. Bronowski	SCIENCE AND HUMAN VALUES TB/505
W. C. Dampier, *ed.*	READINGS IN THE LITERATURE OF SCIENCE TB/512
Arthur Eddington	SPACE, TIME AND GRAVITATION: *An Outline of the General Relativity Theory* TB/510
H. T. Pledge	SCIENCE SINCE 1500: *A Short History of Mathematics, Physics, Chemistry, and Biology* TB/506
George Sarton	ANCIENT SCIENCE AND MODERN CIVILIZATION TB/501
Paul A. Schilpp, *ed.*	ALBERT EINSTEIN: Philosopher-Scientist: *Vol. I*, TB/502; *Vol. II*, TB/503
Friedrich Waismann	INTRODUCTION TO MATHEMATICAL THINKING: *The Formation of Concepts in Modern Mathematics* TB/511
W. H. Watson	ON UNDERSTANDING PHYSICS: *An Analysis of the Philosophy of Physics* TB/507
G. J. Whitrow	THE STRUCTURE AND EVOLUTION OF THE UNIVERSE: *An Introduction to Cosmology* TB/504
A. Wolf	A HISTORY OF SCIENCE, TECHNOLOGY AND PHILOSOPHY IN THE 16TH AND 17TH CENTURIES: *Vol. I*, TB/508; *Vol. II*, TB/509

"Come then, excellent Sir, and banish all fear of stirring up the pygmies of our time; long enough have sacrifices been made to ignorance and absurdity; let us spread the sails of true knowledge, and search more deeply into the innermost parts of Nature than has been done hitherto" (Henry Oldenburg, in a letter to Spinoza, written in July 1662, in which he reports that the Royal Society, of which he was the first Secretary, had received its Charter.—*The Correspondence of Spinoza*, tr. by A. WOLF, 1928, p. 100).

FRANCISCI

DE VERULAMIO,

Summi Angliæ

CANCELLARII,

Instauratio

magna.

Multi pertransibunt & augebitur scientia.

LONDINI
Apud Joannem Billium
Typographum
Regium.

The Title-Page of Bacon's *Novum Organum*

A HISTORY OF SCIENCE,
TECHNOLOGY
AND PHILOSOPHY
In the 16th & 17th Centuries

———————— *Volume II* ————————

by A. Wolf

With the co-operation of F. Dannemann and A. Armitage

SECOND EDITION PREPARED BY DOUGLAS MCKIE

HARPER TORCHBOOKS
The Science Library
HARPER & BROTHERS · PUBLISHERS · NEW YORK

DEDICATED

TO

MY FATHER

LEWIS WOLF

WHOSE LOVE OF GOOD BOOKS
HAS NEVER WANED THROUGH
PREOCCUPATION WITH LEDGERS

A HISTORY OF SCIENCE, TECHNOLOGY AND PHILOSOPHY
IN THE 16TH & 17TH CENTURIES: *Vol. II*

Printed in the United States of America

Reprinted from the second edition, originally
published in 1950, by arrangement with The
Macmillan Company, New York.

FIRST HARPER TORCHBOOK EDITION PUBLISHED 1959

Library of Congress catalog card number: 59–13845 Vol. II

CONTENTS

PAGE

Preface   24

CHAPTER

XVI.   Geology

GEOGONY: DESCARTES; KIRCHER; BURNET; LEIBNIZ; WOOD-
WARD; NEWTON.   PHYSICAL GEOLOGY: AGRICOLA; STENO;
PERRAULT; LISTER; WOODWARD.   PALAEONTOLOGY: ANTE-
CEDENTS; STENO; FRACASTORO AND BRUNO; HOOKE; LHUYD.
CRYSTALLOGRAPHY: HOOKE AND BARTHOLINUS; STENO; BOYLE   350

XVII.   Geography: I. Exploration
      II. Cartography   III. Treatises

EXPLORATION: VESPUCCI; CABOT; CORTES; SOTO; PIZARRO;
ALMAGRO;   GONZALO;   VALDIVIA;   MENDOZA;   MAGELLAN;
MENDANA; DRAKE; CARTIER; WILLOUGHBY; CHANCELOR;
PET; JACKMAN; BARENTS; HUDSON; FROBISHER; DAVIS; BUTTON;
QUIROS; TORRES; JANSZOON; HARTOGSZOON; HOUTMAN; TAS-
MAN; DAMPIER; VRIES; SCHAEP; JENKINSON; ANDRADE;
GRUEBER; D'ORVILLE; SPAFARIK; GERBILLON; PONCET; LEO
AFRICANUS; CHAMPLAIN; JOLIET; MARQUETTE; LA SALLE;
BLAND; WOOD; LEDERER; NEEDHAM; ARTHUR; TEIXEIRA;
FRITZ. CARTOGRAPHY: PETER APIAN; PHILIP APIAN; MER-
CATOR; ÖRTAL; CLÜVER.   TREATISES: MÜNSTER, CAR-
PENTER; VARENIUS   372

XVIII.   The Biological Sciences: I. Botany
    II. Zoology   III. Anatomy and Physiology
            IV. Microscopic Biology

BOTANY: HERBALS;   BOTANICAL GARDENS;   CLUSIUS AND
LOBELIUS; MATTIOLI; BAUHIN; CESALPINI; JUNGIUS; MORISON
AND RAY; RIVINUS; TOURNSFORT.   ZOOLOGY: GESNER;
ALDROVANDI; WOTTON; BELON AND RONDELET; VESALIUS;
RAY.   ANATOMY AND PHYSIOLOGY: VESALIUS; SERVETUS;
FABRICIUS; HARVEY; BORELLI.   MICROSCOPIC BIOLOGY:
MALPIGHI; SWAMMERDAM; LEEUWENHOEK; GREW AND
CAMERARIUS   394

CHAPTER
XIX. Medicine

MEDICINE AND SCIENCE. THE MEDICAL HERITAGE. SCIENTIFIC INSTRUMENTS IN MEDICINE. IMPROVED TREATMENT.
NEW MEDICAMENTS. SPECIALIZED STUDY OF DISEASES.
FAMOUS DOCTORS   425

XX. Technology: I. Science and Technology
II. Agriculture   III. Textiles

SCIENCE AND TECHNOLOGY. AGRICULTURAL IMPROVEMENTS
AND INVENTIONS. TEXTILE PROBLEMS: SPINNING; WEAVING;
KNITTING   450

XXI. Technology: IV. Building Problems

THE STRENGTH OF BUILDING MATERIALS: DA VINCI;
GALILEI; WURTZ; MARIOTTE; HOOKE. STRUCTURAL
MECHANICS: BEFORE THE SEVENTEENTH CENTURY; PALLADIO;
DERAND. THE SEVENTEENTH CENTURY: WREN; HOOKE;
LA HIRE. ELASTICITY: PETTY; HOOKE; NEWTON   467

XXII. Technology: V. Mining and
Metallurgy: VI. Mechanical Engineering

MINING AND METALLURGY: AGRICOLA. GLASSMAKING.
MECHANICAL ENGINEERING: HAULING MACHINES; WATER
PUMPS; VENTILATION; WATERWORKS. ENGINEERING
SKETCHES: DA VINCI; BESSON; RAMELLI; ZONCA; D'ACRES.
ADDENDA   486
                                                            677

CHAPTER
XXIII. Technology: VII. The Steam Engine
VIII. Mechanical Calculators   PAGE

THE STEAM ENGINE: ANTECEDENTS; THE MARQUIS OF WORCESTER; HUYGENS; PAPIN; MORLAND; SAVERY. MECHANICAL
CALCULATORS: THE ABACUS; NAPIER'S BONES; THE SLIDE-RULE; CALCULATING MACHINES; PASCAL; MORLAND; LEIBNIZ 543

XXIV. Psychology

PSYCHOLOGY IN THE SEVENTEENTH CENTURY: HOBBES;
DESCARTES; SPINOZA; LOCKE; LEIBNIZ   564

CHAPTER

XXV.   The Social Sciences

ANTECEDENTS.   GEOGRAPHICAL AND CLIMATIC INFLUENCES.
BODIN.   POLITICAL ARITHMETIC: GRAUNT; PETTY; KING.
LIFE OR MORTALITY TABLES: GRAUNT; HALLEY. ECONO-
MICS: NATIONAL WEALTH; MONEY AND WEALTH; GRESHAM'S
LAW; VALUE AND PRICE; THE VALUE OF LAND; WAGES;
INTEREST.   REGULARITY IN SOCIAL PHENOMENA   582

XXVI.   Philosophy

PHILOSOPHY AND SCIENCE. BRUNO. BACON. HOBBES. DES-
CARTES.   SPINOZA.   LOCKE.   LEIBNIZ.   MORE.   BARROW.
GILBERT.   BOYLE.   NEWTON   629

Index   676

LIST OF ILLUSTRATIONS

NO.   PAGE

THE TITLE-PAGE OF BACON'S *Novum Organum*   *Frontispiece*

190. STENO'S SIX TYPES OF CRUST-STRUCTURE OF THE EARTH   . 360
191. NICOLAUS STENO .   .   .   .   .   *facing* 368
192. THOMAS BURNET .   .   .   .   *facing* 369
193. JOHN WOODWARD .   .   .   .   ,, 369
194. ACCRETIONS TO CRYSTALS 369
195. TYPES OF CRYSTALS WHOSE AXIS LIES IN ONE PLANE .   . 369
196.   ,, ,, CROSS-SECTIONS OF A CRYSTAL .   .   . 369
197. IRON PYRITES ENCLOSED BY TWELVE PLANES .   . 370
198. SKELETONS OF BIRD AND MAN COMPARED .   .   404–5
199. ANDREAS VESALIUS .   .   .   .   *facing* 408
200. A PLATE FROM VESALIUS .   .   .   ,, 409
201. MICHAEL SERVETUS .   .   .   ,, 410
202. HIERONYMUS FABRICIUS .   .   .   ,, 411
203. DIAGRAM TO ILLUSTRATE THE CIRCULATION OF THE BLOOD . 414
204. WILLIAM HARVEY .   .   .   .   *facing* 414
205. GIOVANNI A. BORELLI .   .   .   ,, 415
206. THE MECHANICS OF MUSCULAR ACTION .   .   . 416
207. THE CELLULAR STRUCTURE OF CORK.   416
208. MARCELLO MALPIGHI .   .   .   } *between* { *and*
209. ANTONIUS LEEUWENHOEK.   417
210. NEHEMIAH GREW .   .   .   .
211. THEOPHRASTUS PARACELSUS .   .   .   *facing* 426
212. THE TITLE-PAGE OF THE FIRST LONDON PHARMACOPOEIA ,, 427
213. UROSCOPY 428
214. SANCTORIUS' CLINICAL THERMOMETER.   .   . 432
215. TWO TYPES OF PULSIMETER 433
216. SANCTORIUS' WEIGHING-CHAIR 434
217. OVERALL TO PROTECT FROM INFECTION .   .   . 436
218. ANTIMONY CUP 439
219. GLAUBER AS APOTHECARY'S "SIGN" .   .   . 441
220. HIERONYMUS FRACASTORIUS 446
221. SANCTORIUS SANCTORIUS .   .   .
222. AMBROISE PARÉ .   .   .   448
223. THOMAS SYDENHAM .   .   } *between* { *and*
224. FRANCIS GLISSON .   .   .   449
225. THOMAS WILLIS .   .   .
226. A PLOUGH OF THE SIXTEENTH CENTURY .   .   . 455
227. THE NORFOLK PLOUGH 455
228. BESSON'S THREE-SHARED PLOUGH .   .   . 456
229. TWO-FURROW PLOUGH 457
230. CHINESE LOOMS 460
231. DRAW-LOOM OF THE SEVENTEENTH CENTURY .   . 461
232. AN EARLY RIBBON LOOM. 462
233. THE FULLING MILL. 464
234. AN EARLY STOCKING FRAME 465
235. RESISTANCE TO FRACTURE OF A BEAM (GALILEI) .   . 469
236.   ,, ,, ,, ,, CYLINDERS .   . 471
237.   ,, ,, ,, ,, BEAMS (MARIOTTE) .   . 474

NO.   PAGE

238. COMPARISON OF ESTIMATES OF MOMENT OF RESISTANCE. . 476
239. DERAND'S CONSTRUCTION FOR THE ABUTMENT TO AN ARCH . 479
240. CHRISTOPHER WREN . . . . . *facing* 480
241. WILLIAM PETTY . . . . . . ,, 481
242. WREN'S CONCEPTION OF THE ARCH 481
243. LA HIRE'S TREATMENT OF THE PROBLEM OF THE ARCH . 483
244. THE DIVINING ROD 488
245. VERTICAL SHAFTS 490
246. CONSTRUCTION OF A SHAFT 491
247. STANDING PLUMMET-LEVEL 492
248. SWISS COMPASS 493
249. TOUCHSTONE NEEDLES 494
250. A STAMP-MILL WORKED BY WATER-WHEEL . . . 495
251. FURNACES FOR METAL ORES CONTAINING BITUMEN OR
     SULPHUR. 496
252. FURNACES FOR SMELTING LEAD ORE 497
253. LUSITANIAN FURNACES WITH ROUND BELLOWS . . 498
254. FURNACE FOR SMELTING BISMUTH OR ORES OF IRON . 499
255. LIQUATION FURNACE 501
256. THREE-CHAMBERED FURNACE FOR GLASS . . . 502
257. GEORGIUS AGRICOLA . . . . . *facing* 502
258. A GLASS-BLOWER'S LAMP WORKED BY PEDAL-BELLOWS ,, 503
259. OLD METHOD OF GLASS-BLOWING 503
260. SIMPLE WINDLASS 506
261. WINDLASS WITH FLY-WHEEL 507
262.   ,,   WORKED BY TREADMILL 508
263. HORSE WHIM WITH BRAKE 509
264. SURFACE TRANSPORT AT THE MINE 510
265. SIXTEENTH-CENTURY RAILS 511
266. CHAIN OF DIPPERS 513
267. SIMPLE SUCTION PUMP 514
268. SUCTION PUMPS IN SERIES. 516
269. CRANK-OPERATED FORCE-PUMP 517
270. CHAIN-PUMP AND TREADMILL 519
271. POWERFUL WATER-DRIVEN HOIST 520
272. PIVOTED BARREL OVER THE FLUE 521
273. VENTILATING FANS 522
274. VENTILATING FAN DRIVEN BY WINDMILL . . . 523
275. GIANT BELLOWS 524
276. WATER-RAISING WITH BELLOWS. 525
277. THE AUGSBURG WATER MACHINE 526
278. WATER-RAISING BY MEANS OF ROCKING TROUGHS. . 529
279. THE WATER MACHINE OF JUANELO (TWO POSITIONS) . 530
280. RECONSTRUCTION OF ROMAN PUMP FOUND AT SILCHESTER . 532
281. BATE'S SKETCH OF THE LONDON BRIDGE WATERWORKS. . 533
282. FORD'S PUMP 535
283. BESSON'S SCREW-CUTTING LATHE 538
284. AN AEOLIPILE SUPPLYING A BLAST TO A COPPER-SMELTING
     FIRE 543
285. BAPTISTA PORTA'S SKETCH OF A STEAM MACHINE. . 544
286. RAISING WATER BY HEAT (DE CAUS) . . . 544
287. BRANCA'S TURBINE 546

NO.		PAGE
288.	WORCESTER'S WATER COMMANDING ENGINE	547
289.	HUYGENS' GAS ENGINE	548
290.	PAPIN'S DIGESTER, WITH SAFETY VALVE	549
291.	,, STEAM ENGINE	550
292.	SAVERY'S ,, ,,	552
293.	,, SMALLER STEAM ENGINE	554
294.	SAVERY'S FINAL STEAM ENGINE	555
295.	AN ABACUS	557
296.	NAPIER'S BONES IN USE	558
297.	,, ,, (ORIGINAL FORM)	
298.	,, ,, (CYLINDRICAL FORM)	560
299.	PASCAL'S CALCULATING MACHINE	between and
300.	MORLAND'S ,, ,,	561
301.	SAMUEL MORLAND	
302.	LEIBNIZ' CALCULATING MACHINE	
303.	THE STEPPED RECKONER	562
304.	THE PIN-WHEEL	563
305.	BILLS OF MORTALITY (1)	589
306.	,, ,, ,, (2)	590–1
307.	,, ,, ,, (3)	592
308.	,, ,, ,, (4)	593
309.	FRANCIS BACON	640
310.	THOMAS HOBBES	between and
311.	RENÉ DESCARTES	641
312.	BENEDICTUS DE SPINOZA	
313.	DESCARTES' VORTICES	647
314.	JOHN LOCKE	facing 656
315.	HENRY MORE	,, 656
316.	GOTTFRIED WILHELM LEIBNIZ	,, 657

PREFACE

IN the following pages the attempt is made to give a reasonably full account of the achievements of the sixteenth and seventeenth centuries in the whole field of "natural" knowledge. All the sciences, including several which have not hitherto been included in histories of science, receive due attention, and details are given of all the important work done in each of them during the first two centuries of the modern period. A considerable amount of space is also allotted to the principal branches of technology. The volume, moreover, includes a fairly full account of the philosophy of the period as an aid to the understanding of the general intellectual orientation of its scientists. It is hoped that the exposition is sufficiently clear, and the illustrations sufficiently illuminating to enable the general reader to profit greatly from this history. Its primary aim, however, is to meet the needs of the serious student. For this reason the work is fully documented. The plan of incorporating a select bibliography (giving precise references) in the text will probably be found much more helpful than is the usual formal bibliography, which makes it about as easy to find the authority for a particular view as it is to find a needle in a haystack. A more formal bibliography for the whole modern period will be included in the concluding volume.

The present book is complete in itself. It is, however, intended to be only an instalment of a complete history of science. The author proposes to deal with the eighteenth and nineteenth centuries next, and then with ancient and mediaeval times. But each volume will be as nearly as possible self-contained. Human history cannot, of course, be strictly correlated with exact centuries. In science, as in other fields of human activity, the events of one century have their antecedents in earlier centuries and their consequences in later ones. For the sake of greater intelligibility, and self-completeness of each volume, the author accordingly did not, and will not, hesitate to make occasional incursions into other centuries than those principally concerned.

An encyclopaedic enterprise like the present may appear to be an anachronism in an age of extreme specialization. It is widely recognized, however, that the tendency toward a narrow specialism has already gone too far. The contemporary close relationship of science and philosophy, and the growing interest in the history and development of science, may be regarded as evidence of a growing recognition of the need of a wider outlook. This work was undertaken, in the first instance, in order to meet the requirements of students pursuing courses in the History, Methods, and Principles of Science in the University of London. It is hoped, however, that its usefulness will be much more far-reaching.

Needless to say, this enterprise would have been impossible without the aid of other experts. The author has been very fortunate in receiving most valuable help from a number of colleagues. Their names are set down here in alphabetical order, with a bare indication of the general nature of the assistance rendered by each of them. Mr. A. Armitage has been unstinting in his services, not only in connection with his special subjects, astronomy and mathematics, but also in many other ways. Professor F. Dannemann has placed at the author's disposal the fruits of many years' work in this field, though conditions in Germany have unfortunately prevented the closer co-operation intended originally. Miss R. Dowling has checked the biological portions. Professor L. N. G. Filon has, in spite of the great burdens of his high office as Vice-Chancellor of the University of London, made time to go carefully through all the chapters on astronomy, and has given them the benefit of his expert knowledge of the subject. To Professor W. T. Gordon are due some very helpful suggestions concerning the geology of the period. Mr. S. B. Hamilton has been most helpful with some of the sections on technology. Professor L. Rodwell Jones has looked through the chapter on geography. Dr. D. McKie has rendered valuable help by his special knowledge of the history of chemistry. Professor L. C. Robbins has examined the section on economics. Mr. D. Orson Wood has helped with a searching criticism of the chapters on physics. The book has also benefited from Mr. T. L. Wren's expert knowledge of the history of mathematics. The author is deeply grateful to all these colleagues, and warmly appreciates their friendly interest. But he has no desire to shirk his responsibility for the whole book.

The preparation of this work has naturally involved frequent appeals to libraries for old and rare books. The librarians of the London School of Economics, of University College, London, and of the University of London have spared no pains in finding what was required; and they have laid the author under great obligation.

Special attention has been paid to the illustrations, and all possible sources have been ransacked for them. Many of the line-drawings have been copied and adapted by Miss D. Meyer, to whose skill and sympathy the author is greatly indebted. The authorities of the Science Museum, London, have kindly permitted the reproduction of some of their photographs of old engravings, etc. The proprietors of *The Mining Magazine* have given permission for the use of many of the illustrations from the Hoovers' edition of Agricola.

Messrs. John Lane have consented to the reproduction of the
facsimiles of the Bills of Mortality from W. G. Bell's *The Great
Plague in London*. Messrs. Methuen and Co. have allowed the use
of the frontispiece to *The Divining Rod* by Sir Wm. Barrett and T.
Besterman. The author is grateful for all this kindness.

The reader will not need to be told that the writing of this book
has cost the author a great deal of hard toil. What has sustained
him throughout the long and laborious enterprise, apart from the
intrinsic interest of the subject, is his belief that the world has
need of a new intellectual re-orientation, and that to this end a
close study of the history of human thought in its most objective
spheres would be the best beginning. It was in this spirit of faith
and hope that the work was undertaken and has been carried thus
far. The author hopes that it may be received in the same spirit of
faith and hope—and charity!

A. W.

UNIVERSITY OF LONDON

December 1934

CHAPTER XVI

GEOLOGY

THE terms "geology" and "geologist" did not come into general use till late in the eighteenth century, when they gradually displaced the older terms "mineralogy" and "mineralogist," which were used rather loosely. Many of the geological terms now current were either not used at all, or were used differently, during the sixteenth, seventeenth, and eighteenth centuries. The term "fossil," for example, was applied by Agricola, and nearly all other geologists in the sixteenth and seventeenth centuries, to anything dug out of the ground, and was only later restricted to the recognizable remains of organic bodies. Again, the several branches of this field of study were not usually distinguished by separate names; in fact, the boundaries even between the major Sciences were still very fluid. For the sake of convenience, however, it has been thought advisable to use geological terms in their present-day meaning, and to arrange the main topics under familiar headings, in order to prevent possible confusion.

The geological problems which interested the pioneers of modern science were chiefly those of (1) geogony, or the origin of the Earth as one of the planets of the solar system, (2) physical geology, or the nature of the different parts of the Earth's crust and the manner of their formation and transformation, (3) palaeontology, or the nature of fossils, and (4) crystallography, or the structure, forms, and properties of crystals. The early contributions to the solution of the first group of problems were highly speculative at best, and tended to be rather naïve when the attempt was made to keep strictly within the scheme of *Genesis* and to limit the story of the Earth to the six thousand years alleged to have elapsed since the Creation. The most fruitful work of the early geologists was in connection with the other groups of problems enumerated above, though the theological presuppositions just mentioned hampered them not a little in their treatment of these problems as well.

(1) GEOGONY

DESCARTES

The most interesting of the early modern geogonies is that of René Descartes (1596–1650), who dealt with the problem of the origin of the Earth as part of the problem of cosmogony or the origin of the world. Nearly the whole of Part IV of his *Principles of Philosophy* (1644) is devoted to the Earth. According to Descartes, the Earth, like the other planets, was originally a glowing mass like the Sun. In the middle of the Earth there still is a nucleus of such glowing matter. But spots like the sun-spots gathered on the surface of the Earth, and were transformed into a solid crust when, in the course of time, the Earth cooled down. When the Earth came near the Sun the crust of the Earth became differentiated into various parts, which arranged themselves into a series of strata according to their relative densities. Thus the air was on the top, below it was the water, under the water came the various solids such as clay, sand, and stone, while the innermost stratum of the Earth's crust consisted of the most dense materials such as the metals. Between the outer crust of the Earth and its central fire, or glowing mass, there is, according to Descartes, an intermediate zone filled at first with a liquid, which was subsequently changed into an opaque solid. The heat and light of the Sun, however, could at first penetrate to the inmost parts of the Earth, and so cause a fracture of the Earth's crust, parts of which consequently rose above the surface of the water and formed land. The glowing mass and other substances in the Earth give rise to exhalations which sometimes turn into oil and sometimes into dense smoke, which may burst into flame and so cause earthquakes or volcanic eruptions.

KIRCHER

In 1665 Athanasius Kircher (1602-80) published a bulky treatise on the *Subterranean World*, in which he maintained that the Earth contains innumerable centres of conflagration connected with volcanoes and numerous water cavities which feed thermal springs and are themselves fed from the sea. Kircher was the first to ascertain from a German mine official that "in dry mines the temperature steadily increases in proportion to the depth below the surface." This was naturally regarded as a confirmation of the Cartesian view of the existence of incandescent matter in the middle of the Earth, though there were not wanting people who associated the increasing temperature in the depths of the Earth with the fires of hell.

BURNET

Thomas Burnet attempted to be at once scientific and orthodox in his *Sacred Theory of the Earth* (1681). In the beginning, according to Burnet, the Earth was just a chaotic mixture of air, water, oil, and earth. Gradually these different ingredients sorted out according to their diverse weights. The heaviest of them collected at the centre. The water accumulated next above these. The oil floated on the surface of the water. The air enveloped the oily surface. And the whole Earth assumed the shape of an oval sphere. In course of time some of the fine matter suspended in the air settled on the oil, thus forming an upper layer sufficient to nourish the first plants and animals. At first the oval Earth was smooth, having neither mountains nor seas. There was no rain except at the poles. But that rain filtered into the earth, where, when the top layer of the Earth was cracked by the Sun's heat, the water was changed into vapour, burst through the crust of the Earth, and mingling with the air caused violent storms and rains, while the crumbling of the Earth's crust resulted in the formation of mountains and islands. All this happened at the time of the great Flood, when nearly all living things were drowned. After the Flood the Earth assumed its present state.

LEIBNIZ

In G. W. Leibniz (1646–1716) we meet with a more worthy successor of Descartes. In 1693 he published his views on the beginnings of the Earth, in a paper in the *Acta Eruditorum* (Leipzig). These views were elaborated in his *Protogaea* (published post-humously in 1749). The Earth, according to Leibniz, was originally an incandescent globe, which gradually cooled and contracted. After a certain amount of cooling of the outer surface a kind of glassy crust formed there. He thought that such crystalline rocks as gneiss and granite might be residues of this glassy crust. When the Earth cooled, the vapour surrounding it condensed into an ocean of water, which became salty by dissolving the salts on the surface of the Earth's crust. The great geological changes are due either to the disruption of the crust through the explosion of gases inside the Earth or to the action of water flooding its surface. Igneous rocks result from the action of the first of these causes, sedimentary formations are produced by the second.

WOODWARD

Two years after the publication of the above views of Leibniz, and more than forty years after the publication of Descartes' *Principles of Philosophy*, John Woodward, Professor of Physick in Gresham College, published his *Essay towards a Natural History of the Earth* (1695), which was typical of the orthodox views of his contemporaries. The Earth, according to Woodward, was originally full of water. At the time of the Flood, in the days of Noah, the great water reservoir burst, and the water swept over the whole Earth, mixing all things. Eventually the various substances, carried away by the rush of water and mingled with it, settled down as sediments, and they settled in the order of their heaviness—the heaviest bodies (including heavy fossils) forming the lowest strata, the lighter ones forming the upper strata.

NEWTON

British contributions to the problems of geogony did not during the seventeenth century rise above the poor level of Burnet and Woodward. John Ray's *Three Physico-Theological Discourses* (1693) and William Whiston's *Theory of the Earth* (1696) were no exceptions, though Whiston has the merit of having suggested such a liberal interpretation of the six "days" of Creation as to allow sufficient time for geological changes. The most valuable geogonic suggestion came from Newton, who, in 1692, in a letter to Bentley, then Master of Trinity College, Cambridge, indicated how the principle of gravitation might be used to explain the formation of the Earth and of all heavenly bodies. "It seems to me," Newton wrote, "that if the matter of our Sun and planets, and all the matter of the universe, were evenly scattered throughout all the heavens, and every particle had an innate gravity towards all the rest, and the whole space throughout which this matter was scattered was finite, the matter on the outside of this space would, by its gravity, tend towards all the matter on the inside, and by consequence fall down into the middle of the whole space, and there compose one great spherical mass. But if the matter were evenly disposed throughout an infinite space, it could never convene into one mass, but some of it would convene into one mass and some into another, so as to make an infinite number of great masses, scattered great distances from one another throughout all that infinite space. And thus might the Sun and fixed stars be formed, supposing the matter were of a lucid nature."

(2) PHYSICAL GEOLOGY

The more scientific departments of geology were greatly advanced and partly started in the sixteenth and seventeenth centuries by the work of Agricola and Steno.

AGRICOLA

Georgius Agricola (the Latinized equivalent of the German name Bauer) was born at Glauchau, in Saxony, in 1494, and studied at the Universities of Leipzig, Bologna, and Venice. In 1527 he commenced medical practice at Joachimsthal, in Bohemia, which was at that time the greatest mining area in Central Europe. His occupation as a doctor does not appear to have engrossed him, for he devoted an enormous amount of time and energy to the first-hand study of mining and kindred subjects. Eventually he moved to Chemnitz, of which he was elected Burgomaster in 1546. He was also greatly esteemed by such eminent contemporary scholars as Erasmus, Fabricius, and Melanchthon; and was entrusted by his sovereign with various political missions to the Emperor Charles, to King Ferdinand of Austria, and to other princes. He died in 1555, a year before the publication of his greatest work, *De Re Metallica*, the first modern classic of technology. Of this work more will be said in a subsequent chapter. Here we are only concerned with his contributions to geology and mineralogy. His *De Ortu et Causis Subterraneorum* (Basel, 1546) was the first work on physical geology; his *De Natura Fossilium* (Basel, 1546) was the first systematic treatise on mineralogy; and even in his *De Re Metallica* (Basel, 1556), which was not really concerned with geology, he managed to initiate the study of stratigraphic geology.

Agricola was the first to enunciate clearly the part played by water and wind in landscape sculpture. "Hills and mountains," he writes, "are produced by two forces, one of which is the power of water, and the other the strength of the wind. . . . We can plainly see that a great abundance of water produces mountains, for the torrents first of all wash out the soft earth, next carry away the harder earth, and then roll down the rocks, and thus in a few years excavate the plains or slopes to a considerable depth; this may be noticed in mountainous regions even by unskilled observers. By such excavation to a great depth through many ages there rises an immense eminence on each side. When an eminence has thus arisen, the earth rolls down, loosened by constant rain and split away by frost, and the rocks, unless they are exceeding firm, since their seams are similarly softened by the damp, roll down into the excavations below. This continues until the steep eminence is changed into a slope. Each side of the excavation is said to be a mountain, just as the bottom is called a valley. Moreover, streams, and, to a far greater extent, rivers, effect the same results by their rushing and washing; for this reason they are frequently seen flowing either between very high mountains, which they have created, or close by the shore which borders them. . . . Nor did the hollow places which now contain the seas all formerly exist, nor yet the mountains which check and break their advance, but in many parts there was a level plain until the force of winds let loose upon it a tumultuous sea and a scathing tide. By a similar process the impact of water entirely overthrows and flattens out hills and mountains. . . . The wind produces hills and mountains in two ways: either, when set loose and free from bonds, it violently moves and agitates

the sand, or else when, after having been driven into the hidden
recesses of the Earth by cold, as into a prison, it struggles with a
great effort to burst out. For hills and mountains are created in
hot countries, whether they are situated by the sea coasts or in
districts remote from the sea, by the force of winds; these, no longer
held in check by the valleys, but set free, heap up the sand and
dust, which they gather from all sides, to one spot, and a mass
arises and grows together. If time and space allow, it grows together
and hardens, but if it be not allowed (and in truth this is more
often the case), the same force again scatters the sand far and wide.
. . . Then, on the other hand, an earthquake either rends and
tears away part of a mountain, or engulfs and devours the whole
mountain in some fearful chasm. In this way it is recorded the
Cybotus was destroyed, and it is believed that within the memory
of man an island under the rule of Denmark disappeared. Historians
tell us that Taygetus suffered a loss in this way, and that Therasia
was swallowed up with the island of Thun. Thus it is clear that
water and the powerful winds produce mountains, and also scatter
and destroy them. Fire only consumes them, and does not produce
at all, for part of the mountains—usually the inner part—takes
fire" (*De Ortu et Causis*, Lib. II, trans. by the Hoovers in their edition
of *De Re Metallica*, 1912, pp. 595 f.).

Earthquakes and volcanic eruptions were explained by Agricola
as the explosive effects of subterranean airs, vapours, and exhalations. "Vapour," he writes, "arises when the internal heat of the
Earth, or some hidden fire, burns earth which is moistened with
vapour. When heat or subterranean fire meets with a great force
of vapour which cold has contracted and encompassed in every
direction, then the vapour, finding no outlet, tries to break through
whatever is nearest to it, in order to give place to the insistent and
urgent cold. Heat and cold cannot abide together in one place,
but expel and drive each other out of it by turns" (*Ibid.*, p. 595).

De Re Metallica contains what appears to be the first contribution
to stratigraphic geology. The passage occurs in Book V. Agricola
is attempting no generalization; he is merely describing the order
of strata which he observed in the mines in the Harz mountains,
and he mentions seventeen different strata. The account is worth
quoting as the first attempt at stratigraphic distinctions. It reads
as follows:—

"In those districts which lie at the foot of the Harz mountains
there are many different coloured strata, covering a copper *vena
dilatata* [bedded deposit]. When the soil has been stripped, first of
all is disclosed a stratum which is red, but of a dull shade, and of
a thickness of twenty, thirty, or thirty-five fathoms. Then there is

another stratum, also red, but of a light shade, which has usually a thickness of about two fathoms. Beneath this is a stratum of ash-coloured clay nearly a fathom thick, which, although it is not metalliferous, is reckoned a vein. Then follows a third stratum, which is ashy and about three fathoms thick. Beneath this lies a vein of ashes to the thickness of five fathoms, and these ashes are mixed with rocks of the same colour. Joined to the last, and underneath, comes a stratum, the fourth in number, dark in colour, and a foot thick. Under this comes the fifth stratum, of a pale or yellowish colour, two feet thick; underneath, which is the sixth stratum, likewise dark, but rough, and three feet thick. Afterward occurs the seventh stratum, likewise of dark colour, but still darker than the last, and two feet thick. This is followed by an eighth stratum, ashy, rough, and a foot thick. This kind, as also the others, is sometimes distinguished by stringers [thin veins or seams] of the stone which easily melts in fire of the second order [calcite?]. Beneath this is another ashy rock, light in weight, and five feet thick. Next to this comes a lighter ash-coloured one, a foot thick; beneath this lies the eleventh stratum, which is dark and very much like the seventh, and two feet thick. Below the last is a twelfth stratum of a whitish colour and soft, also two feet thick; the weight of this rests on a thirteenth stratum ashy and one foot thick, whose weight is in turn supported by a fourteenth stratum, which is blackish, and half a foot thick. There follows this, another stratum of black colour, likewise half a foot thick, which is again followed by a sixteenth stratum still blacker in colour, whose thickness is also the same. Beneath this, and last of all, lies the cupriferous stratum, black coloured and schistose, in which there sometimes glitter scales of gold-coloured pyrites in the very thin sheets, which, as I said elsewhere, often take the form of various living things" (Hoovers' translation, pp. 126 f.).

Agricola devotes a good deal of space to the question of the origin of ore deposits. He maintains that the channels containing ores are not coeval with the rocks in which they occur, but are of later date, having been produced by the erosion of subterranean water due either to the percolation of surface water or to the condensation of subterranean vapour by subterranean heat (caused by the combustion of bitumen and coal). Ores contained in these channels were, according to Agricola, deposited in them from "juices" [solutions] which circulated through the channels. "The force of water crushes and splits the brittle rocks; and when they are broken and split, it forces its way through them and passes on, at one time in a downward direction, making small and large *venae profundae* [fissure veins] at another time in a lateral direction, in which way *venae dilatatae* [bedded deposits] are formed. . . . Water erodes away substances inside the Earth, just as it does those on the surface, and least of all does it shun minerals" (*De Ortu*, p. 35; Hoovers' translation of *De Re Metallica*, pp. 47 f.). "Of the waters which are under the Earth, some are collected from rain, some arise from vapour, some from river-water, some from sea-water; and we know that the vapour is produced within the Earth partly from rain-water, partly from river-water, and partly from sea-water" (*De Ortu*, p. 7; Hoover, p. 48). "Juice is . . . water which . . . has absorbed 'earth' or has corroded or touched metal and has somehow become heated" (*op. cit.*, p. 48; p. 52). And "it is a juice from which metals are formed" (*op. cit.*, p. 71; p. 51). Though Agricola's view that ore channels are due to erosion was not the whole truth, it was certainly in advance of his time, and had to wait long for due appreciation.

Lastly, Agricola has the distinction of having given to the world the first detailed study of the contents of the Earth's crust. As has been pointed out already, he used the term "fossil" for anything dug out of the Earth. His book *De Natura Fossilium* accordingly deals with the whole field of mineralogy. His conception and main classification of the materials which compose the crust of the Earth may be briefly set out in the following table:—

Subterranean inanimate substances
- I. Exhalations (or Vapours) and Fluids.
- II. Minerals.
  - 1. Homogeneous
    - (a) Simple
      - i. Earths.
      - ii. Solidified juices.
      - iii. Stones.
      - iv. Metals.
    - (b) Compound (i.e. homogeneous compounds of (a).
  - 2. Mixed (i.e. heterogeneous mixtures of (a)).

"The subterranean inanimate substances," he writes, "are divided into two classes one of which, because it is fluid or an exhalation, is called by those names, and the other class is called the minerals. Mineral bodies are solidified from particles of the same substance, such as pure gold, each particle of which is gold, or they are of different substances, such as lumps which consist of earth, stone, and metal; these latter may be separated into earth, stone, and metal, and therefore the first is not a mixture, while the last is called a mixture. The first are again divided into simple and compound minerals. The simple minerals are of four classes, namely earths, solidified juices, stones, and metals, while the mineral compounds are of many sorts" (*De Nat. Foss.*, p. 180; Hoover, pp. 1 f.). Under "earths" Agricola includes clay, chalk, ochre, and anything that becomes lute when wetted sufficiently. Under "solidified juices" he classes salt, saltpetre, alum, vitriol, orpiment, sulphur, and anything that liquefies (instead of merely softening) when moistened with water. Among "stones" he groups gems and semi-precious stones, but not rocks—"stones properly so called" are usually found in veins and veinlets, rocks are found in quarries. Under metals he classes antimony and bismuth as well as gold, silver, quicksilver, copper, lead, tin, iron, and their alloys. The characteristic of a metal is that when it solidifies again after having been melted, it resumes its usual form and properties. Under "compound minerals" he groups galena, pyrite, and all those minerals which consist of two or three simple ones, "but so thoroughly mixed and alloyed that even in the smallest part there is not wanting any substance that is contained in the whole." The "mixed minerals" are those in which the component simple ones "each preserves its own form so that they can be separated one from the other not only by fire but sometimes by water and sometimes by hand" (*ibid.*). Altogether Agricola gives detailed descriptions of about eighty different minerals, at least twenty of which had never been described before. His descriptions and classifications are based on external properties such as shape, solubility, fusibility, colour, brilliance, taste, etc. But that was all that was possible in an age when there was no adequate knowledge of chemistry. Moreover, the characteristics of the various minerals which he enumerated are still used to a large extent for purposes of preliminary classification.

STENO

Nicolaus Steno (in Danish Niels Stensen or Steensen) was born in Copenhagen in 1638. He studied medicine in Copenhagen, Leiden, and Paris successively. In 1666 he settled in Florence, and was appointed Court physician to Ferdinand II, Grand Duke of Tuscany. In 1667 he forsook Lutheranism for Roman Catholicism, and even attempted to convert Spinoza (with whom he had become friendly during his Leiden days, 1660-4) to the same faith. It was during his stay in Florence that Steno studied the geology of Tuscany, and the mineralogical and palaeontological problems connected therewith. He published his results in a little book called *De solido intra solidum naturaliter contento* (Florence, 1669). The quaint title of the book was no doubt prompted by the desire to find a comprehensive description that would include such diverse phenomena as geological strata, fossils, and crystals. The essay was meant to be the forerunner of a larger work on the same subject, which was never written. The importance of the little book was recognized immediately and Henry Oldenburg published an English version of it (*The Prodromus to a Dissertation concerning Solids Naturally Contained within Solids. . . . By Nicolaus Steno. Englished by H. O.*, London, 1671. There is also a translation by J. G. Winter, New York, 1916). In the meantime Steno had become famous as an anatomist for his work on the glandular and muscular systems of the human body and on the ovaries of the shark. His name is still associated with the *ductus stenonianus* in virtue of his discovery of the exit of the parotid gland. His reputation brought him an urgent invitation from his king, in 1672, to fill the Chair of Anatomy at Copenhagen. Steno complied, but his stay there was of short duration. His change of faith caused friction, and so, in 1674, he returned to Florence, where he became increasingly absorbed in religion. In 1676 Pope Innocent XI made him Bishop of Titopolis and Vicar Apostolic for North Europe. For some time Steno lived in Hanover, then in Schwerin, where he died in 1686. He was buried at Florence, in the Basilica of San Lorenzo, where there is a monument to his memory.

Steno was the first to formulate definite principles relating to the formation of the Earth's crust. Some of these principles may be stated as follows: (1) The strata (or beds) of the Earth have been formed from the matter precipitated by the water, the said matter falling by its own weight to the bottom, and thus forming a sediment. (2) A stratum can only be formed when there is another body under it to hinder the further descent of the matter of the bed in question. Consequently when the Earth's lowest bed was formed there must have been under it either another solid body or some fluid heavier than the solid sediment of the fluid above it; and the upper strata could only have been formed after the lower strata had already obtained a solid consistency. (3) Each stratum when first formed must either have covered the whole globe or must have been bounded at the sides by another solid body. (4) The upper surface of each stratum must have been approximately parallel to the horizon. When strata are found perpendicular or inclined to the horizon, they must have been dislocated by the action of water and fire, including violent upheavals caused by subterranean ebullitions and exhalations. In this way mountains and valleys and other inequalities in the surface of the Earth must have originated. (5) If a stratum contains fragments of another kind of stratum or the parts of animals or plants, then it is not to be reckoned among the strata which "in the Creation did subside from the first fluid." (6) If a stratum contains sea-salt or anything else usually found in the sea, then the sea must have been there some time or other. (7) If a stratum contains coals, ashes, pumice-stone, bitumen, and calcined bodies, then an eruption of fire (a volcanic eruption) must have taken place near it.

A close study of the geology of Tuscany showed Steno six successive types of stratification. The information he received about the results of similar investigations carried out elsewhere led him to regard these six forms as typical of the structure of the Earth's

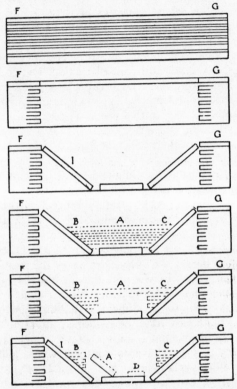

Illustr. 190.—Steno's Six Types of Crust-Structure of the Earth

whole crust. He represented the six types of the crust-structures of the Earth by means of the above six diagrams (Illustr. 190), in which dotted lines represent sandy beds, and the continuous lines represent stony beds. The first diagram shows stony beds, unbroken and parallel to the horizon. The second diagram shows vast cavities eaten out by the force of fire and water, while the upper strata are still unbroken. The third diagram shows how mountains and valleys were formed by the inthrow of the upper strata. The fourth diagram illustrates the formation of new strata by the sea overflowing the said valleys. The fifth diagram illustrates the disappearance of the lower of the new strata, and the survival of the upper ones. The last diagram shows the formation of hillocks and valleys by the subsequent inthrow of the sandy upper beds.

PERRAULT

Pierre Perrault (1608–80) was a French lawyer who took an interest in meteorology and geology. In 1674 he anonymously published, in Paris, a book on the Origin of Springs and Rivers. It attracted sufficient interest for a summary of it to be published in the *Philosophical Transactions*, 1675 (Vol. X, pp. 447–50); and this summary was reprinted in 1731, and again in 1809, when the original French book was wrongly attributed to Papin. The problem attacked by Perrault was an old one. It had already been discussed by Plato, Aristotle, and various later writers. Different views were put forward by the several writers, but they were agreed that rain could not account for springs and rivers, and that it was necessary to assume the existence of some kind of water reservoir within the Earth itself. This idea was widely accepted at the time because of its alleged confirmation in Scripture, which refers to the breaking up of "the fountains of the great deep" at the time of the Flood (Genesis vii. 11). Now Perrault ignored these traditional views, and made out a very plausible case in favour of the adequacy of rain and snow to account for springs and rivers. The main points in the summary given in the *Philosophical Transactions* of 1675 are reproduced in what follows, except that an error due to a mistranslation from the French original has been corrected.

The summary of Perrault's book bears the following title: "A particular account, given by an anonymous French Author in his book of the Origin of Fountains, printed 1674 at Paris; to shew, that the Rain and Snow-waters are sufficient to make Fountains and Rivers run perpetually." The procedure is to compare the estimated rainfall with the drainage, in the basin round the head-waters of the Seine, from its source to Ainay le Duc—a distance of three leagues—counting the breadth of the basin as two leagues. The contents of a cube 2 feet in the side being taken as 1 *muid* (= 280 French pints), hydraulic data show the rate of flow of water across unit cross-section (square inch) to be 83 *muids* a day, neglecting variations on account of the head of pressure. The average rainfall in the district is shown by observation to be 19 in. 2⅓ lines. A reservoir co-extensive with the basin considered would have an area of 6 square leagues, and, with the above rainfall, would receive during the year about 224,899,942 *muids*. The writer estimates that the Seine, at the place considered, "can have no more than a 1,000 or 1,200 [square] inches of water alwaies running," thus draining away about 99,600 *muids* a day, or about 36,453,600 *muids* a year, which is only a fraction of the 224,000,000 *muids* available. The sufficiency of rainfall and snowfall to maintain other rivers could be similarly shown. The rivers in lands where there is no rain, or very little, are generally maintained by springs rising in lands where there is rain, or by the periodical melting of snows on mountains. Perrault's views on the origin of springs and rivers were embraced by his contemporaries Mariotte and Halley, and were abundantly confirmed early in the eighteenth century by the work of Antonio Vallisnieri.

LISTER

Martin Lister (1638–1712) occupies a place of some importance in the early history of geology, inasmuch as he was the first to propose the construction of geological maps. He practised medicine at first in York, and subsequently in London. But he was interested in many things, and contributed a considerable number of papers to the *Philosophical Transactions* of the Royal Society treating of various antiquarian, biological, geological, and meteorological problems. He was made a Fellow of the Royal Society in 1671, and gained a reputation as the author of *Historia Animalium Angliae* (1678), *Historia sive Synopsis Methodica Conchyliorum* (1685–92), and *A Journey to Paris* (1698). His views on fossil shells were reactionary. He regarded them as merely curiously shaped stones, which had "no parts of a different texture from the rock or quarry whence they are taken," and "never were any part of an animal" (*Phil. Trans.*, 1671, Vol. V, p. 2282). Nevertheless, he was sufficiently interested in "these cockle-like stones" to describe and illustrate them with great care, putting the pictures of living conchylia beside them for comparison. The palpable similarity between living and fossil conchylia induced many of his readers to reject his theory of the origin of the fossils. Even more important was Lister's perception of the correlation between different kinds of rocks and their fossil contents. He observed that "quarries of different stone yield us quite different sorts or species of shells." Thus, for example, "those Cockle-stones of the ironstone quarries of Adderton, in Yorkshire, differ from those found in the lead-mines of the neighbouring mountains, and both these from the cockle-quarrie of Wansford Bridge, in Northamptonshire; and all three from those to be found in the quarries about Gunthrop and Beauvour Castle, etc." (*loc. cit.*). Pondering these and similar facts, Lister was eventually led to suggest the construction of "soile or mineral" maps, that is, geological maps. The idea of such maps appears to have occurred

to him in 1673. But it was not till 1683 that he submitted his proposal to the Royal Society; and his paper on the subject was published in the *Philosophical Transactions* in 1684 (Vol. XIV, No. 164,
pp. 739–46).

The lengthy title of the paper reads as follows: "An Ingenious
proposal for a new sort of Maps of Countrys, together with Tables
of Sands and Clays, such chiefly as are found in the North parts of
England, drawn up about 10 years since, and delivered to the
Royal Society Mar. 12. 1683 by the Learned Martin Lister, M.D."
Lister advocates examining the structure of the Earth "as far as
human art can possibly reach, beginning from the outside down-
wards," and he recommends the preparation, in the first instance,
of a "Soil or Mineral Map "of England. The basis of the map would
show districts, rivers, and the chief towns, and "the Soil might
either be coloured [or otherwise distinguished] by variety of Lines,
or Etchings; but the great care must be, very exactly to note upon
the Map, where such and such Soiles [including sub-soils and rocks]
are bounded. As for example in Yorkshire (1.) *The Woolds*, Chaulk,
Flint, and Pyrites, etc. (2.) *Black Moore*; Moores, Sandstone, etc.
(3.) *Holderness*; Boggy, Turf, Clay, Sand, etc. (4.) *Western Mountains*; Moores, Sandstone, Coal, Iron-stone, Lead Ore, Sand, Clay,
etc. *Nottinghamshire*, mostly Gravel Pebble, Clay, Sand-stone, Hall-
playster, or Gypsum, etc. Now if it were noted, how far these extended, and the limits of each Soil appeared upon a Map, something more might be comprehended from the whole, and from
every part, than I can possibly foresee, which would make such a
labour very well worth the pains. For I am of the opinion, such
upper Soiles, if natural, infallibly produce such under Minerals,
and for the most part in such order."

Lister believed that sand once formed "the most exteriour and
general cover of the surface of the whole Earth," for it still forms
the cover of the northern mountains, whence for ages rivers have
been bringing it down to the sea, so that their banks and mouths
and the shores of the sea are now covered with it. Mountain sand
seems the most fitting cover for the Earth's surface on account
of the hardness and durability of such sand. It has not originated,
as has most so-called sand, "by the Attrition and wearing of one
particle of stone against another, but is of a constant and durable
figure." The high wolds, it is true, are now topped with soft chalk
beds and not with sand, but this is because the sand on the wolds
was of such small grain that it was readily swept away long since
by the rain, and even by the wind. Our chalk wolds are continuous
with those of France, though the sea has accidentally divided them,
and the sand on the coasts of France, Flanders, and Holland is

mostly what was blown off the wolds of Yorkshire, Lincolnshire, Suffolk, Essex, and Kent by the westerly winds.

Lister concludes his paper with detailed tabular classifications of the different varieties of sands and clays, indicating the places where they are chiefly found.

Finally, mention must also be made of Lister's views on volcanic eruptions. The idea that these are due to the subterranean combustion of inflammable materials was old, but no very plausible suggestion had been made about the cause of the combustion. Lister suggested that the combustion is caused by the heating and consequent explosion of the sulphur contained in iron-pyrites. This at all events was a definite hypothesis which could be put to the test. The closing year of the seventeenth century witnessed an experimental test of Lister's hypothesis. Lemery buried in the ground a mixture of iron filings, sulphur, and water. The mixture got heated and burst into flame, disrupting the layer of earth which had covered it. (See Lemery's *Course of Chymistry*, English trans. by W. Harris, 1686, p. 140.)

WOODWARD

John Woodward (1665–1728), whose orthodox views on geogony have already been mentioned, showed a real insight into the methods of advancing physical geology. He relates that whenever he heard of the whereabouts of grottos, or of digging operations in connection with the sinking of wells, or the search for minerals or ores, he at once proceeded to the scene, took "a just account of every observable circumstance of the earth, stone, metal, or other matter, from the surface quite down to the bottom of the pit, and entered it carefully into a Journal." He also introduced the method of *questionnaires* in the service of geology. He drew up a "List of Quaeries," and dispatched copies to all parts of the world. The replies which he received convinced him "that the circumstances of these things in remoter countries were much the same with those of ours here: that the stone and other terrestrial matter in France, Flanders, Holland, Spain, Italy, Germany, Denmark, Norway, and Sweden was distinguished into strata, or layers, as it is in England: that those strata were divided by parallel fissures: that there were enclosed in the stone, and all the other denser kinds of terrestrial matter, great numbers of shells, and other productions of the sea; and in the same manner as in that of this Island." Other replies to his "List of Quaeries" showed "that these things were found in like manner in Barbary, in Egypt, in Guinea, and other parts of Africa: in Arabia, Syria, Persia, Malabar, China, and other Asiatic provinces: in Jamaica, Barbadoes, Virginia, New-England, Brasil,

Peru, and other parts of America" (*An Essay toward a Natural History of the Earth*, 1695, pp. 4–6). This information was a valuable contribution towards the knowledge of the regularity of the structure of the Earth's surface everywhere; though Woodward appears to have made no attempt to determine the precise stratigraphical order of that structure.

(3) PALAEONTOLOGY

ANTECEDENTS

Fossils were well known to the ancient Greek thinkers, and were regarded by them as the remains of plants and animals. During the Middle Ages, however, largely under the influence of the views of Theophrastus, of the Arabian philosopher Avicenna (980–1037), and the Schoolman Albertus Magnus (1193–1280), vogue was given to the view that fossils were not of organic origin, but were due to the moulding power of Nature, which playfully, as it were, shaped inorganic sports to resemble living things. This view prevailed during several centuries in spite of its repudiation by such thinkers as Leonardo da Vinci (1452–1519), Alexander ab Alexandro (1461–1523), and Hieronymus Fracastoro (1483–1553). When, in 1580, Bernard Palissy expressed views like those of Leonardo da Vinci, he was denounced as a heretic.

STENO

Even Steno, with all his anatomical knowledge, could not at first make up his mind whether the so-called *glossopetrae* (sharks' teeth) found in rocks were real teeth of dogfish (the anatomy of which he described in a book published in 1667) or merely mineral freaks. By 1669, however, he definitely expressed his conviction that fossils are the remains of once living things and that they might throw some light on the history of the formation of the Earth's crust. Considering fossils as a special class of "solids naturally contained within solids," Steno remarks that the fossilized cockle-shells are so like ordinary cockle-shells that there could be no doubt that they were once the parts of animals living in a fluid, "though there never had been seen any testaceous marine creatures." He distinguishes various stages of disintegration of cockle-shells, and points out that the "very pretty kind of marble called Nephiri is nothing else but a sediment of the sea full of all sorts of shells, where the substance of the shell being wasted, a stony substance is come into the place thereof." Steno upheld the view of an organic origin for other fossils. "What hath been said of shells, the same is to be said of other parts of animals, and of the animals themselves buried under ground, of which number are the teeth of sea-dogs, the teeth of the fish *aquila*, fishes' backbones, all sorts of whole fishes, skulls, horns, teeth, thigh-bones and other bones of terrestrial animals." Similarly with fossil plants. "What is said of animals and their parts, suiteth likewise with plants, whether they be digged out of earthern beds or lodged within stony substances." The length of time required to account for fossils appears to have presented no serious difficulty for Steno. In fact, he seems to be more concerned to explain why they have not disappeared altogether in the course of the centuries than to explain how all the changes could have taken place in the few thousand years since the Creation. He is quite content to identify the prehistoric fossils found in the Aretine fields with the remains of Hannibal's war elephants; and the Deluge of Noah is sufficient to wash away all his more serious palaeontological difficulties, by accounting for all sorts of marine fossils anywhere. However, the association of the Flood with fossil remains served the useful purpose of helping orthodox thinkers like Steno, Woodward, and others to recognize in fossils "the real spoils of once living animals" (Woodward).

FRACASTORO AND BRUNO

The view that the presence of shells on land could be accounted for by reference to Noah's Flood was widely maintained for a long time in spite of the contention put forward by Fracastoro (1483–1553) that the presence of shells in the depths of the strata which form the mountains could not really be explained by such a temporary inundation as the Deluge, which would only have scattered the shells over the surface of the Earth. Giordano Bruno (1548–1600) had actually denied that there had ever been a universal Flood, and had insisted that changes in the distribution of land and sea were ordinary natural occurrences. But all this made no impression on the Diluvialists.

HOOKE

Fracastoro's view was also that of Hooke, who argued that the Deluge did not last long enough "for the production and perfection of so many and so great and full-grown shells," and that "the quantity and thickness of the beds of sand with which they are many times found mixed, do argue that there must needs be a much longer time of the sea's residence above the same, than so short a space can afford" (*Posthumous Works*, p. 341). Hooke, it may be added, laid great stress on the significance of fossils as "monuments and hieroglyphick characters" which give a record of "transactions of the body of the Earth, which are infinitely more evident and certain tokens than anything of antiquity that can be fetched out of coins or medals, or any other way yet known, since the best of these ways may be counterfeited . . . but those characters [fossils] are not to be counterfeited by all the craft in the world. And tho' . . . it is very difficult . . . to raise a chronology out of them, and to state the intervals of the times wherein such or such catastrophes and mutations have happened; yet 'tis not impossible, but that much may be done even in that part of information also" (*Posthumous Works*, p. 411).

LHUYD

In the closing years of the seventeenth century a new hypothesis was proposed as a kind of compromise between the view which regarded all "figured stones" as miraculous sports of Nature and the view that they contained the actual remains of living organisms. The hypothesis in question was suggested by Edward Lhuyd (1660–1709), keeper of the Ashmolean, Oxford. It was formulated in a letter appended to his *Lithophylacium Britannicum*, or a treatise on British figured stones, published in 1698. The letter was addressed to John Ray, who included an English version of it (made by Lhuyd himself) in his *Physico-Theological Discourses* (in Discourse II, "Of the General Deluge"), from which the following statement of the hypothesis is taken. "I have, in short, imagined they might be partly owing to fish spawn received into the chinks and other *meatuses* of the Earth in the Water of the Deluge, and so be derived . . . amongst the shelves or layers of stone, Earth, etc., and have further thought it worth our inquiry, whether the exhalations which are raised out of the sea, and falling down in rains, fogs, etc., do water the Earth to the depth here required, may not from the *seminium*, or spawn of marine animals be so far impregnated with . . . *animalcula* (and also with separate and distinct parts of them) as to produce these marine bodies. . . . I imagined further that the like origin might be ascribed to the mineral leaves and branches, seeing we find that they are for the most part the leaves of ferns and such like plants . . . whose seeds may be easily allowed to be washed down by the rain into the depth here required" (4th ed., 1732, pp. 190 f.). This idea of seminal vapour to account for the presence of marine fossils in mountains, etc., found favour even in the eighteenth century.

(4) CRYSTALLOGRAPHY

HOOKE AND BARTHOLINUS

Hooke's *Micrographia* (1665) contains one of the earliest accounts of crystals. He observed the regularity with which the minute quartz crystals line the cavities of flint stones. According to Hooke these crystals are built up of spheroids. Shortly afterwards Erasmus Bartholinus (1625–98) published the results of his investigations into crystals (*Experimenta crystalli Islandici disdiaclastici*, Copenhagen, 1669), and drew attention to the double refraction and the rhomboidal cleavage of Iceland spar or crystals of calcite. He measured the angles formed by the facets of Iceland spar and estimated them to be 101° and 79°. He observed that of the two images which are seen on looking through Iceland spar one image changes its position when the spar is turned, whereas the other remains stationary; and that in looking through the spar in a certain direction only one image is visible. He showed, moreover, that the double image is not the result of reflection, but that one image is due to ordinary refraction, and the other is due to an unusual kind of refraction, which he could not explain. (This phenomenon was subsequently explained by Huygens as due to the spheroidal form of the particles composing the crystals. See Chapter XI.) Bartholinus also studied various other physical and chemical properties of Iceland spar. He discovered that, when rubbed with a cloth, it attracts light particles of straw, etc., just as amber does; and that when immersed in water it gradually loses its smoothness; that it bubbles when *aqua fortis* is applied to it; and that under the action of intense heat it changes into lime.

STENO

The same year in which Bartholinus' book appeared a more important study of crystals saw the light in Steno's *De solido intra solidum*, to which reference has already been made. For Steno crystals were, of course, a common kind of "solids naturally contained within solids." He devoted especial attention to quartz, pyrite, and diamonds. These, he insists, are not original substances dating from the time of the Creation, but later products. Moreover, unlike plants, they do not grow by inward additions through nourishment, but by accretions from outside. They are found in the fissures and crevices caused by the collapse of the strata constituting the Earth's crust. They are formed from various liquids in the same kind of way as salt, vitriol, and alum crystals coagulate in suitable solutions, into which they can be resolved again. Steno discovered this by means of experiments which he made while in Florence. (In

Nicolaus Steno

Illustr. 192

Thomas Burnet

Illustr. 193

John Woodward

1695 Leeuwenhoek observed with his microscope that different
kinds of crystals result from the solutions of different salts.) Steno
also made a careful study of the geometrical forms of crystals. He
found that rock crystals have a nucleus having the shape of a six-
sided prism, terminated at each end by a six-sided pyramid, produced by the accretion of layers of material to the sides of the
nucleus. Steno had no clear idea of the precise way in which crystals
grow out of fluids. He could only suggest some kind of magnetic
force to account for their crystallization. But, anyway, he knew that

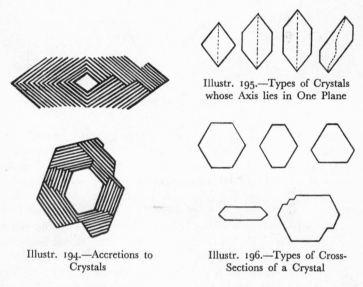

Illustr. 195.—Types of Crystals
whose Axis lies in One Plane

Illustr. 194.—Accretions to
Crystals

Illustr. 196.—Types of Cross-
Sections of a Crystal

owing to the uniformity in the formation of the accretions the faces
of a crystal are always parallel to the faces of its nucleus, and though
the crystal may change in size and shape, the angles between its
faces remain constant. Illustr. 194 shows how accretions to a crystal
take place without changing the angles, though the number and
length of the sides may change. Illustr. 195 represents some varieties
of crystals whose axis lies in one plane. In the first three diagrams
the axes of the component parts of the crystal form a straight line,
though the intermediate prism is absent in the first, short in the
second, longer in the third; in the fourth diagram the axes of the
component parts of the crystal do not form a straight line. Illustr. 196
shows several varieties of cross-sections parallel to the base of a
crystal. In the first four diagrams there are six sides, which are all
equal in the first, while only the opposite sides are equal in the

second and fourth, and the opposite sides are unequal in the third; in the fifth diagram the cross-section has twelve sides instead of six. Illustr. 197 represents certain angular bodies of iron pyrite which are enclosed by twelve planes. The first diagram shows the twelve planes spread out in a single plane, six being triangular and brilliant, and six pentagonal and striated; the second diagram shows the cross-section, while the last diagram shows the plane of the axis. Steno also gives diagrams to illustrate those angular bodies of iron pyrite which are bounded by thirty planes, of which six are pentagonal and brilliant, twelve are triangular and brilliant, six are

Illustr. 197.—Iron Pyrites enclosed by Twelve Planes

triangular and striated, and six are oblong quadrilaterals and brilliant. Possibly he was describing what was really a distorted crystal showing the cube, pentagonal dodecahedron and half the number of faces of a diakis-dodecahedron.

BOYLE

In the foreword to his translation of Steno's book, Oldenburg pointed out that to his knowledge both Boyle and Hooke had been carrying out similar researches some years before the publication of Steno's investigations. And Oldenburg added a brief summary of the views which Boyle had expressed to him, namely, "First, that he doth, upon several inducements, suppose the generality of transparent gems or precious stones to have been once liquid substances, and many of them, whilst they were either fluid, or at least soft, to have been imbraced with mineral tinctures, that concoagulated with them; whence he conceiveth that divers of the real qualities of gems (for he doubts, most ascribed to them are fabulous) may probably be derived. And as for opacous gems and other medical stones, as blood-stones, jaspers, magnets, emery, etc., he esteems them to have, for the most part, been earth (perhaps in some cases very much diluted and soft) impregnated with the more copious proportion of fine metallic or other mineral juyces or particles; all which were afterwards reduced into the forme of stone by the supervenience (or the exalted action) of some already in-existent petrescent liquor or petrifick spirit, which he supposeth may sometimes ascend in the forme of steams; from whence may be probably deduced not only divers of the medical vertues of such stones, but some of their other qualities, as colour, weight, etc., and also explained how it may happen what he . . . hath observed of stones of another kind, or marcasites, or even vegetable and perhaps animal substances that have been found inclosed in solid stones. For these substances may easily be conceived to have been lodged in the Earth whilst it was but mineral earth or mud, and afterwards to have been, as it were, cased up by the supervenient petrifick agents that pervaded it." Boyle published his book, *An Essay about the Origin and Virtues of Gems*, in 1672.

(See A. Geikie, *Founders of Geology*, 2nd ed., 1905; K. A. von Zittel, *History of Geology and Palaeontology*, 1901; F. D. Adams, *The Birth and Development of the Geological Sciences*, Baltimore and London, 1938; K. F. Mather and S. L. Mason, *A Source Book in Geology*, New York and London, 1939; F. D. Adams, "The Origin of Springs and Rivers—An Historical Review," *Fennia*, Vol. 50, No. 1, Helsingfors, 1928, and "Rainfall and Run-off," *Science*, Vol. LXVII, No. 1742, New York, 1928.)

CHAPTER XVII

GEOGRAPHY

I. EXPLORATION. II. CARTOGRAPHY. III. TREATISES

By a natural, and indeed necessary, division of labour, the principal sciences have, from the beginning of the modern period, pursued the path of specialization and abstraction. Geography, however, has resisted, and is still resisting, this tendency, preferring to maintain a more concrete and composite character. It is a synthetic or composite science, and draws to a considerable extent on the results obtained by the more specialized sciences of astronomy, meteorology, geology, and even the anthropological and social sciences. The geography of the sixteenth and seventeenth centuries was certainly a picturesque coat of many colours. In a work like the present one, in which all the sciences cultivated in the sixteenth and seventeenth centuries receive due attention, it is not necessary to deal with the data borrowed by geography from other sciences. It will be sufficient to deal with the more specific geographical problems and achievements of the two centuries under review. The present chapter is, accordingly, confined to three main topics, namely, geographical discovery or exploration, the progress in cartography or the construction of maps, and the geographical text-books and treatises produced during the period.

I. Geographical Exploration

Geographical exploration in the sixteenth and seventeenth centuries was mainly directed to developing the discoveries of the great pioneer explorers of the preceding period. The fifteenth century had seen the gradual progress of the Portuguese mariners down the west coast of Africa, culminating in the discovery of the sea route to India by Vasco da Gama in 1497–9. It had seen also the discovery of America by Columbus, while he was attempting to reach Asia, or to discover some legendary island, by sailing westward across the Atlantic (1492–1504). In the early years of the sixteenth century, while the Portuguese traders were pressing on to open up the far eastern sea routes as far as China and Japan, America was being explored piecemeal by European discoverers and conquerors.

First, the Florentine pilot Amerigo Vespucci, in the course of his two voyages (in 1499 and 1501), which are alone generally regarded as genuine, seems to have reached Brazil, thus anticipating Cabral's discovery of that country, and to have explored the east coast of South America from about 5 degrees to about 50 degrees South latitude. Meanwhile, exploratory voyages had been undertaken, with motives similar to those of Columbus, but in higher latitudes, by John Cabot of Bristol. In his voyage of 1496 Cabot struck land probably in the neighbourhood of what is now New-foundland, and this region was shortly afterwards explored by fishermen of several nationalities. From discoveries such as those of Vespucci and Cabot, it had become clear, by the early years of the sixteenth century, that a new continent had been discovered interrupting, at least partially, any Atlantic sea route to India. In the course of unsuccessful attempts to find an opening in this barrier, a series of Spanish expeditions explored the coast-line of the Gulf of Mexico, and, having rounded Florida, extended their survey from Yucatan to Chesapeake Bay before 1526. It was Spanish adventurers also, who first opened up the interior of the new continent in their greed for the spoil of its fabulous golden cities. Their expeditions radiated northward and southward from Mexico City, when this had been captured by Hernando Cortes in 1521, and the surrounding country had been occupied. To the north an expedition under Coronado in 1540 moved up the Pacific coast as far as the head of the Gulf of California, discovered the Grand Cañon of the Colorado river, and moved south-eastward across the Rio Grande and Pecos rivers, observing as they went the Indian tribes, and the herds of bison on which they subsisted, but failing to discover the gold and silver of which the expedition was in search. Another party, under de Soto, landing in Florida in 1539, explored what are now the southern United States, and, after many adventures in quest of gold, returned down the Mississippi. South of Mexico the Spaniards soon overran Central America as far as Panama, which formed the starting-point for their conquests in South America. Setting out from Panama in 1531, after a preliminary reconnaissance, Francisco Pizarro passed down the west coast of South America, exploring and pillaging the country as he went, and conquering it on behalf of Spain. By 1533 he had captured Cuzco in Peru, the Inca capital. Of subsequent expeditions radiating from Peru, that of Almagro crossed the snow-clad mountains into Chile, penetrating as far south as about latitude 37° South, while another, led by Pizarro's brother, Gonzalo, in 1540, crossed the Cordilleras to the head-waters of the Amazon, down which some of the party escaped to the sea, while the survivors returned to Quito, after suffering severe hardships in the tropical forests. Under Valdivia and Mendoza, Chile was explored as far south as the Magellan Strait, and the Spaniards crossed the Andes into what is now Argentina. In 1560 an expedition crossed from Lima, into the

Amazon basin, on a wild-goose chase in search of El Dorado, a "land of gold," then believed to exist somewhere between the Amazon and the Orinoco. The expedition became mutinous, and the survivors finally escaped down the Orinoco to the sea. Much of the northern part of South America had been already explored by Spaniards settled along the north coast, and also by adventurers from overseas (including Raleigh), who kept up the search for El Dorado till the close of the century. The discovery of the Plate river estuary, in 1515, marks the beginning of Spanish expansion into the south-east portion of South America, which led to the foundation of Buenos Aires in 1535, and of Asunción in 1537. By the middle of the sixteenth century communication had been established between the Plate estuary and Peru.

The first man to pass beyond the barrier of the New World and to reach the far eastern countries by a westward circumnavigation of the globe was Ferdinand Magellan, a Portuguese nobleman. He was born about 1480, and saw service in the East Indies, but he later transferred his allegiance to the Emperor Charles V, who was also King of Spain. At the Emperor's command, Magellan set out on a voyage of discovery on September 20, 1519, with a fleet of five old ships. After striking the South American coast the explorers followed it southward as far as Port St. Julian, where they remained for five months and encountered Patagonian natives. Here Magellan lost one of his ships and had trouble with his crews. Sailing southward again, he came on the strait which now bears his name, though the existence of such a breach in the American barrier to westward navigation may well have been known or surmised before the voyage. It required thirty-eight days to thread the 320 miles of the strait and to reach the Pacific Ocean, and meanwhile one of the ships deserted. Magellan coasted some way up the western side of South America, and then struck north-westward across the Pacific. The crews were reduced to great extremities through shortage of food and water during a voyage of nearly four months, which seems to have brought them finally to some island in the Paumotu Archipelago. Thence they sailed to the Ladrones, and on to the Philippines, where, however, Magellan was killed (April 27, 1521) while helping a native king in war. The ships finally reached the Moluccas, the goal of their journey, where the crews traded advantageously with the natives. Only one ship was fit for the return journey, and after rounding the Cape of Good Hope it entered St. Lucar on September 6, 1522. A considerable amount of exploration was carried out in the Pacific during the following century, New Guinea being discovered in 1526. A Spanish navigator, Andres de Urdaneta, in 1565 sailed eastward across the Pacific, following a high parallel of latitude so as to miss the trade winds, and thus making a direct connection between Spain's possessions in Asia and her American empire. Another expedition, under Alvaro de Mendana, sailed in 1567 from Lima in search of a continent rumoured to exist in the southern ocean. They found no continent, but came near enough to Australia to discover the Ellice and Solomon Islands. Sailing north and then east, they reached California, and thence coasted back to Lima. In 1578 Francis Drake, in the course of his circumnavigation of the world, was in the Pacific seeking, apparently, for the *Terra Australis* which was believed to occupy the whole Antarctic region of the Earth, and to be separated from South America only by Magellan's Strait. Drake seems to have sailed south beyond Cape Horn, and to have explored the islands forming the Cape. He also touched the north-west coast of America in latitude 43° North, which was beyond the Spanish sphere of exploration. The Spanish monopoly of the Pacific, thus challenged by Drake, was soon to decline as the Dutch rose to naval and colonial supremacy.

During the sixteenth century mariners began to search for a passage which would enable them to sail westward from Europe to the East Indies through North America instead of going through Magellan's Strait. As alternatives they searched for a "North-east Passage" by which ships might sail eastward to China along the north coast of Asia, and for a "North-west Passage" through which ships might sail to the East Indies round the north coast of America. These three projects had all ultimately to be abandoned, but they each led to a series of expeditions with important consequences to geographical discovery.

Ships of all the chief maritime nations explored the north Atlantic coast of America during the sixteenth century. The most noteworthy discoveries, however, were those made by the Frenchman Jacques Cartier in the course of three voyages undertaken in the years 1534-41. On the first of these voyages Cartier sailed to Newfoundland, passed through Belle Isle Strait, carefully examining the coasts of Newfoundland and Labrador as he went, and coasted round the Gulf of St. Lawrence. He searched Chaleur Bay for a passage, but did not enter the St. Lawrence river. On his second voyage, however, in 1535, he did go up the river to where Montreal now stands, but he failed to get farther on his third voyage or to discover a way through to the Pacific.

In the attempts to discover a North-east or a North-west Passage, it was English and Dutch mariners who played the leading parts. A series of attempts to reach China by sailing along the north coast of Asia began in 1553 with an expedition of three ships led by Sir

Hugh Willoughby and Richard Chancelor, and planned by John Cabot's son, Sebastian, under the auspices of the newly founded Muscovy Company of Merchant Venturers. Willoughby and two of the three ships were lost, but Chancelor sailed up the coast of Norway until "hee came at last to the place where hee found no night at all, but a continuall light and brightnesse of the Sunne shining clearly upon the huge and mightie Sea" (Hakluyt: *Principal Navigations*, Vol. II, p. 248). He landed on the coast of the White Sea, and returned home by way of Moscow. Three years later (1556) Stephen Burrough, the master of Chancelor's ship on the former expedition, pushed still further eastward and came to the Petchora river and Novaya Zemlya. The storms and ice which the explorers encountered gave them some idea of the hitherto unsuspected difficulties of Arctic navigation, which prevented the next expedition, under Pet and Jackman (1580), from sailing beyond Novaya Zemlya, though a few years later the mouth of the Ob river was reached. Several noteworthy voyages in quest of the North-east Passage were made by the Dutch pilot William Barents. In his first Arctic expedition (1594), Barents reached the northern cape of Novaya Zemlya. A second expedition in the following year penetrated beyond Vaigach Island some way into the Kara Sea. In his third and last expedition (1596) Barents discovered Bear Island and Spitzbergen, and tried to circumnavigate Novaya Zemlya, but was forced to winter there, and died on the return voyage in the following year. Attempts to reach the Far East by sailing across the Polar regions were made in the early years of the seventeenth century by Henry Hudson. Sailing in the spring of 1607, Hudson visited Greenland and Spitzbergen and passed the eightieth parallel, but was turned back by ice. The same fate befell his attempt, in the following year, to sail eastward between Spitzbergen and Novaya Zemlya. Hudson's later voyages were directed in search of a North-west Passage; and attempts to open a sea route eastward from Norway, or northward across the polar regions, were practically abandoned after a few further efforts.

The arguments for the existence of a North-west Passage were summed up (for what they were worth) in Sir Humphrey Gilbert's Discourse "to prove a Passage by the North-west to Cathaia, and the East Indies" (1576). Gilbert draws on the writings of ancient philosophers and recent geographers. He points out that, if America were joined to China, it would have been invaded by Chinese or Tartars, and he thinks that the (alleged) distribution of ocean currents points to the existence of a northern communication between the Atlantic and Pacific Oceans. Search was made for such a passage in three voyages undertaken by Martin Frobisher in the years 1576–8. In the first of these Frobisher, after touching Greenland, reached what is now Baffin Land, and sailed up the comparatively insignificant "Frobisher Bay," which he mistook for the strait which he sought. He brought home a specimen of gold ore, and his second voyage of 1577 was chiefly concerned with the collection of some two hundred tons of this mineral. The third voyage was undertaken with the object of establishing a colony to work the ore. The fleet ran into stormy weather, and failed in its main object, but Frobisher seems to have happened upon what is now Hudson Strait. The search for the North-west Passage was continued by John Davis in the years 1585–7. In his first voyage Davis coasted round South Greenland and crossed to what is now the Cumberland Peninsula in Baffin Land. He felt convinced that Cumberland Sound was the passage he was seeking. On his second voyage (1586) Davis revisited Greenland, exploring the south-west coast and striking some way inland, and he sailed on to Cumberland Sound and the Labrador coast before returning home. Davis' third voyage (1587) took him up the same coast of Greenland as far as latitude 72° 12′ North, and down the whole Labrador coast. In 1609 Hudson turned his attention to exploration in North America, when the state of the wind had interrupted a further voyage which he was making in search of the North-east Passage. He reached Nova Scotia, worked southward as far as South Carolina, and went some way up the Hudson river. Hudson's last voyage was begun in 1610. After calling at Greenland, he sailed into the passage now called after him, Hudson Strait, and down the east coast of Hudson Bay, where he wintered. Here, however, the crew mutinied and set Hudson adrift in a small boat with several companions; and his fate has never been known. The conviction that a passage had been found led, in 1612, to the establishment of a chartered company to develop it. This company sent out Thomas Button, who explored the west coast of Hudson Bay but could find no way through. In 1615 and 1616 expeditions were sent to Hudson Bay under Bylot, with Baffin as pilot. On the first voyage they looked for a passage north of Southampton Island; on the second they sailed to the north of what is now Baffin Bay, exploring the coasts on both sides. Baffin concluded that no North-west Passage was to be found, though actually Lancaster Sound, discovered on this voyage, offers the nearest approach to one. An expedition under Foxe and James in 1631 explored the west and south coasts of Hudson Bay, and penetrated Foxe Channel. As a result of all this exploration, a clear idea of the coastline of North America began to emerge, and hopes of a practicable North-west Passage suffered a corresponding decline.

378 HISTORY OF SCIENCE, TECHNOLOGY, AND PHILOSOPHY

During the seventeenth century the Pacific Ocean was more thoroughly explored, mainly by Dutch pilots, and many new islands were discovered. Most of the voyages of exploration were undertaken with the purpose of discovering the vast southern continent, or *Terra Australis*, of ancient tradition. Considerable stretches of the coast of Australia were traced, but the relation of this new land to the known continents and to the hypothetical southern continent long remained obscure. Among the leading seventeenth-century explorers of the South Pacific must be mentioned the Spaniards Quiros and Torres, who discovered the New Hebrides (1606), which Quiros thought was the southern continent, and claimed for Spain, while Torres went on to explore the south-west coast of New Guinea; also the Dutch navigators Schouten and Le Maire, who rounded Cape Horn as an alternative route to Magellan's Strait (1616); Willem Janszoon, who seems to have been the first to touch Australia, in the Gulf of Carpentaria; Hartogszoon, Houtman and their successors, who explored portions of the west and south-west coast of Australia (1616–30); Tasman, who sailed round Australia without sighting it, but discovered what are now Tasmania and New Zealand (1642–3); and the English buccaneer, William Dampier, who among other exploits landed in Australia and explored the islands to the east of New Guinea. As for the northern part of the Pacific, the ocean east of the Philippines and Japan was sailed by Quast and Tasman in 1639, while an expedition by Vries and Schaep reached Sakhalin and the Kurile Islands. From about the end of the seventeenth century Russian explorers began to play a part in the opening up of this area; and in the latter part of the eighteenth century the Pacific Ocean was the scene of the historic voyages of Captain James Cook, who proved that no southern continent, of anything like the extent depicted on the traditional maps, could exist.

While Portuguese and, later, Dutch navigators played the leading parts in exploring the coasts and islands around the Indian Ocean, the inland areas of southern Asia were chiefly opened up by the traders and travellers who, in the sixteenth and seventeenth centuries, visited these parts in ever increasing numbers. Among the pioneer travellers of the modern period was Ludovico di Varthema, who, starting out from Europe in 1502, followed a route whose principal stages were Cairo, Aleppo, Damascus, Medina, and Mecca (which he was the first European to visit), by sea to Aden and Ormuz, India, Ceylon, and the East Indies, with an excursion into Persia, and a return journey round the Cape of Good Hope. A voyage of somewhat similar scope was described by the Portuguese Duarte Barbosa in 1516, while Mendez Pinto claimed, some years

later, to have extended his travels to Siam, China, and Japan. Many
others followed in the track of these pioneers, particularly when
trade interests and Catholic missionary enterprise drew to the East
an increasing number of Europeans whose memoirs have in many
cases come down to us. Especially noteworthy were the travels of
Anthony Jenkinson, who sailed down the Volga from Moscow to the
Caspian and so to Bokhara, and later to Persia (1557–62); of Bento
de Goes, who made his way from Lahore through Peshawar, Kabul,
and the Pamirs to Su-chow, whence he established contact with
missionaries in China; of Antonio de Andrade, who was the first
European to strike through the Himalayas into Tibet; and of
Grueber and D'Orville, who marched through unknown country
from China direct to Lhasa, which they were probably the first
Europeans to visit. Siam, Burma, and Indo-China were mainly
opened up by Dutch traders in the seventeenth century, but information about these countries and about China was chiefly
forthcoming through the activities of Jesuit missionaries. The
progressive colonization of Siberia to the shores of the Pacific was
achieved by Russian traders and military expeditions in the first half
of the seventeenth century. In 1676 Nicolas Spafarik crossed Man-
churia from Russia to Peking, and in 1698 the French Jesuit Gerbillon crossed from Peking to Irkutsk.

The exploration of Africa continued, down to the end of the
eighteenth century, to be restricted to certain special regions lying
round the coast. Access to the interior of the continent was long
barred by deserts, unhealthy coastal regions, and hostile races. The
river system did not favour explorers, and there seemed little to
attract pioneers and traders. Abyssinia, however, became known to
Venetian and Portuguese traders in the fifteenth century, and its
relations to the surrounding country were opened up by a number
of missionary explorers in the sixteenth and seventeenth centuries. Of
these men, Pedro Paez, in 1613, reached the head of the Blue Nile
and solved the mystery of the Nile floods, while others investigated
the overland approaches to Abyssinia from north and south. Later,
in 1699, Poncet travelled down the Nile to Abyssinia from Cairo.
During the fifteenth century European traders penetrated the
north-west coastal districts of Africa and reached Timbuktu; this
area was explored by the Moorish Leo Africanus, and described
by him in his *Description of Africa*, of which a Latin version appeared
in the middle of the sixteenth century. During the following century
several English explorers sailed up the Gambia river, while the
French carried out similar expeditions up the Senegal river. The
Congo river was discovered late in the fifteenth century by the
Portuguese, who colonized near the mouth, and pressed southward

into Angola. The Congo district was explored and described by Capuchin missionaries during the seventeenth century. Similarly, in East Africa, the Portuguese occupied the coast between Mozambique and Mombasa in the early part of the sixteenth century, and later pressed up the Zambezi river in search of gold. The first European settlement at the Cape of Good Hope was that established by the Dutch in 1652; and by the end of the seventeenth century only the country immediately surrounding the Cape Colony itself had been explored.

French, English, and Spanish explorers all played their parts in the opening up of North America during the seventeenth century. Following up the previous discoveries of Cartier in the St. Lawrence river, Samuel de Champlain, an experienced French explorer, undertook three expeditions during the years 1608-16, after some earlier reconnaissances. On the first of these voyages he discovered the lake which now bears his name, Lake Champlain, south of what is now Montreal. On the second journey he went up the Ottawa river to Allumette Island in search of an hypothetical northern sea. On the last of his great expeditions (1615-16), Champlain went up the Ottawa river, westward past Lake Nipissing to Georgian Bay, on Lake Huron, across Ontario to Lake Ontario, which he rounded, and after an excursion to Lake Oneida he returned as he had gone. In 1634 Nicollet crossed Lake Huron into Lake Michigan, and so up the Fox river to the edge of the Mississippi basin. The Mississippi was reached, and Lake Superior explored, by Chouart and Radisson in 1659, and three years later they seem to have crossed Ontario to Hudson Bay. In the latter half of the seventeenth century French Jesuit missionaries played a leading part in elucidating the geography of North America. In 1672 Joliet and Father Marquette sailed down the Mississippi to where the Arkansas flows into it, and a few years later Father Hennepin, having reached the Mississippi by sailing down the Illinois river, sailed up it as far as where Minneapolis now stands, while in 1681 La Salle sailed down the Mississippi to its mouth, round about which the French subsequently colonized. Meanwhile ways were being opened up along the Saguenay and Ottawa rivers to Hudson Bay, which was thus linked by a chain of discoveries with the Gulf of Mexico. The exploration of the eastern seaboard of North America in the seventeenth century was chiefly the work of the English colonists and traders settled along the coast at intervals between Florida and New Brunswick. At first their westward expansion was hemmed in by the mountains lying some way back from the coast. Among expeditions across the watershed formed by these mountains may be mentioned those of Bland and Wood, who penetrated to the Roanoke river in Virginia (1650); of Lederer who, a few years later, explored Blue Ridge; of Batts and Fallam, who crossed the Ridge; and of Needham and Arthur who reached the Tennessee river. The Hudson's Bay Company was chartered in 1670 for purposes of trade and discovery in that part of the world. Under its auspices trading posts were established all round the bay, and a number of expeditions westward into the interior were launched in the eighteenth century. Reports of French and English exploring and trading activities in North America in the seventeenth century stimulated the Spaniards to renew their own penetration northward into California and New Mexico, and eastward into Texas. In South America the Spanish missionaries and traders during the seventeenth century continued their penetration of the country from the estuary of the Plate river, from the coast of Brazil, and westward from Peru. At the mouth of the Amazon there were also Portuguese, Dutch, and French settlements. A remarkable Portuguese expedition under Pedro Teixeira, setting out from the mouth of the Amazon in 1637, reached Quito in ten months, having conducted a careful survey of the Amazon and the Napo on the way. Of the missionaries who entered the Amazon basin from the west, perhaps the most distinguished was Samuel Fritz, who worked for thirty-seven years among the Indians in that area, and whose geographical discoveries were preserved in a map of remarkable accuracy published in 1691.

(See J. N. L. Baker: *A History of Geographical Discovery and Exploration*, London, 1931.)

II. CARTOGRAPHY

APIAN

The development of cartography in the sixteenth century owed something to the labours of Peter Apian and of Philip, his son. Their adopted name of *Apianus* was a Latin version of the family name of Bienewitz or Bennewitz. Peter Apian (1495–1552) was born at Leisnig in Saxony, and after studying at Leipzig and Vienna he became Professor of Mathematics at Ingolstadt in 1527, and remained there for the rest of his life. He was on friendly terms with the Emperor Charles V, who ennobled him and employed him on several diplomatic missions. Apian wrote on a wide range of scholarly and scientific topics. He designed a number of ingenious astronomical instruments for measuring celestial angles—mostly combinations of graduated scales and travelling sights on the usual lines of the time. He also made a systematic study of observations of comets, and he drew attention to the fact that the tails of these bodies always point away from the Sun. Apian's first important contribution to geography was the publication, in 1520, of a general map of the world, which took account of the newly discovered western lands (and seems, indeed, to have been the first printed map to apply the name "America" to them), but which still showed the north and south portions of the New World as islands with a channel between them. Apian's *Isagoge*, which followed in 1524, contains a number of elementary propositions on the construction and use of world maps, though without giving precise details of the projections used. Peter Apian's masterpiece, however, was his *Cosmographicus Liber* (1524; revised and corrected edition by Gemma Frisius, 1533). This book is brief and lucid, and is illustrated by numerous quaint figures. Some of these (illustrating devices for solving astronomical problems mechanically) have movable parts attached to the page by thread. At the outset of the book *geography* is distinguished from *cosmography* on the one hand, and from *chorography* on the other. Cosmography deals with the whole Universe, and divides the Earth up according to astronomical circles; geography gives, as it were, a portrait of the Earth as a whole, divided up by mountains, seas, and rivers; while chorography or topography deals with particular places by themselves, which are comparable to the individual features of a portrait. The Universe is next described, with the chief circles and zones of the Earth. Methods are explained for determining the latitude from the altitude of the pole, or from the meridian altitude of the Sun, and for determining difference of longitude from the difference in the observed times of occurrence of a given phase in a lunar eclipse as observed from the two stations whose difference of longitude is required, or from measurements of the angular distance of the Moon from suitable fixed stars. The second part of the book consists of a summary description of the known world, and contains a sort of gazetteer giving the longitudes and latitudes of important places, of which, however, the longitudes are naturally of comparatively little value. In the world maps appearing in the text, the equator and the parallels of latitude appear as straight lines, and the meridians, as portions of circles of gradually increasing curvature dividing the field into thirty-six strips having equal breadths at the equator. This projection held its place for about two hundred years.

Philip Apian (1531–89) held his father's professorship for some years after the latter's death, and was later at Tübingen; but his career was chequered by the religious strife of the age. He, too, wrote on a variety of scientific subjects, but his principal achievement was his survey of Bavaria. This was begun about 1554, and occupied about seven years, the results of the work becoming current through the *Baierische Land-Tafeln XXIII* (München, 1566, and Ingolstadt, 1568). These were soon recognized as marking an epoch in accurate topographical cartography.

(See *Abhandlungen der königl. Böhm. Gesellschaft der Wissenschaften*, Folge VI, Bd. 11 : S. Günther: *Peter und Philipp Apian*, Prag, 1882.)

MERCATOR

The important additions to geographical knowledge which were the fruits of the widespread explorations of the fifteenth and sixteenth centuries, rendered largely obsolete the traditional maps of the world, which continued to be based upon the ideas of Ptolemy of Alexandria. The reform of cartography in the sixteenth century owed very much to the achievements of Mercator and of Ortelius.

Gérard de Cremer, whose surname was Latinized to Mercator, was born in 1512 at Rupelmonde, in Flanders, the son of a shoe-maker. He was educated at the expense of a grand-uncle, who sent him to Louvain University, where he graduated. For a time Mercator devoted himself to the study of natural philosophy, but, in order to earn a living, he was obliged to open a workshop as a scientific instrument maker and map engraver. While learning the trade he took lessons in mathematics from Gemma Frisius, who was a Professor at Louvain, and was himself soon authorized to teach the subject to University students. Mercator's labours were interrupted in 1544 by his arrest on a charge, apparently unjustified, of holding Lutheran opinions. He was acquitted, but left Belgium in 1552 for Duisburg, on the Rhine, where he worked, taught, and shared in the public life of the place until overtaken by the illness which caused his death in 1594.

Mercator achieved excellence as an instrument maker, and he secured the patronage of the Emperor Charles V, though none of his handiwork seems to have survived. But he developed even greater talents in geography, in which he had always felt a great interest, and the maps which he drew and engraved were soon recognized to be the finest ones of his age, though these, again, in their original form, have almost all perished. Beginning with a map of Palestine in 1537, he next, in 1540, published a map of Flanders, based upon a laborious survey of the country which occupied him for three years; and later he prepared a map of Lorraine with similar care. His subsequent, more extensive, maps of Europe and of the world, for which a personal survey was impracticable, were based upon a critical collation of all the available information afforded by explorers instead of reliance upon the traditional authority of Ptolemy. Mercator's cartographical master-piece was undoubtedly his *Nova et aucta orbis terrae descriptio ad usum navigantium emendate accommodata* of 1569. This world-map extends from 80° North to 66° 30' South latitude, and measures 2 metres by 1·32 metres. It is constructed upon the projection which bears Mercator's name, and which represents probably his greatest con-tribution to geography. In this projection the equator appears as a straight line; the successive meridians are equally spaced parallel straight lines perpendicular to the equator; and the parallels of latitude are straight lines perpendicular to the meridians. The successive parallels on the map are more widely spaced towards the polar regions, so that in any region the degrees of latitude are exaggerated in the same proportion as the degrees of longitude. Such a map has, for navigation, the useful property that the course of a ship which constantly sails towards the same point of the compass appears as a straight line cutting the meridians on the map at the same angle as that which the ship's course makes with the meridians on the sphere. Mercator charts, however, did not establish them-selves until well into the seventeenth century. In the meantime the analytical theory of the projection had been elaborated by Edward Wright in his book, *Certaine Errors in Navigation* (1599). Besides inventing this important projection, Mercator improved upon the conical projection employed in the old maps. In this projection points on a zone of the sphere are transferred to the surface of a cone touching the sphere along the parallel of latitude passing through the midst of the zone. The cone being then unrolled, the parallels of latitude appear projected into circles whose common centre is at the vertex of the cone, and the meridians transform into radii of these circles. The map is distorted, however, owing to exaggeration in the length of the parallels of latitude near the north and south boundaries of the area mapped. Mercator refined on this projection by making the cone cut, and not merely touch, the sphere, in two suitably chosen parallels. The general map in Mercator's *Europae Descriptio* (1554) was constructed on this pro-jection; this map is also noteworthy as having diminished Ptolemy's exaggerated estimate of the extent of Europe in longitude eastward and westward. Mercator planned a grand series of cosmographical works, which, however, was never completed. The volumes of this series which appeared were an erudite *Chronologia* (1569) dating events from the Creation down to 1568 by reference to astronomical epochs; a revision of Agathodaemon's maps illustrating Ptolemy's *Geography*; and a Latin edition of this last-named classic in 1584. Mercator's contributions to cartography culminated in his *Atlas*—the familiar term is due to him—which he published in three parts

(1585, 1590, and 1595), containing 103 maps, and which was completed and edited by Hondius in 1606.

(See J. van Raemdonck: *Gérard Mercator, sa vie et ses œuvres*, St. Nicolas, 1869.)

ÖRTEL

About the middle of the sixteenth century collections of maps began to be made which were the precursors of the modern bound atlases. One of the pioneers in this direction, second only to Mercator in importance, and preceding him in publication, was Abraham Örtel (otherwise Wortels, etc.), generally known as Ortelius (1527–98). He was born at Antwerp, the son of a merchant, and started life as a map engraver. He travelled and corresponded widely, and made friends with Mercator, who doubtless confirmed his predilection for cartography. In the end, Ortelius became Geographer to the King of Spain. Ortelius' principal contribution to geography was his *Theatrum Orbis Terrarum* (Antuerpiae, 1570), which was a collection of seventy maps. An *Additamentum* containing seventeen more appeared in 1573, and there were a number of subsequent revised and enlarged editions. Where Ortelius' maps were not original, they were critically selected from the work of previous geographers (and often improved), and their source was acknowledged. Ortelius also produced in 1564 a map of the world which is often referred to in the history of geography.

(See *A. Ortelii Catalogus Cartographorum*, Bearbeitet von Leo Bagrow, Gotha, 1928, in *Petermanns Mitteilungen*: Ergänzungsheft 199.)

CLÜVER

Philip Clüver (1580–1622) came of the Danzig branch of an old German family. His early years were spent at the Court of Poland and the Imperial Court of Prague. He was sent to Leiden to study law, but his chief interest was in geography, and this preference was confirmed at Leiden by the influence of Joseph Scaliger. He abandoned law, and was cast off by his father. Thereafter he wandered through Europe for years, serving for a time against the Turks, and suffering imprisonment for his share in a political intrigue, but steadily gathering first-hand topographical information about a range of countries extending from Norway to Italy. The publication of his *Germania antiqua* in 1616 led to his obtaining a salaried post as Geographer to Leiden University, but he was soon back in Italy, collecting, by personal itineration, the necessary material for a projected work on the ancient geography and archaeology of that country. The over-exertion and hardships of this expedition were largely responsible for his premature death in 1622, and though he was able to publish the material relating to Sicily (*Sicilia antiqua*, Lugd. Batav., 1619), his great book on ancient Italian geography first appeared after his death (*Italia antiqua*, Lugd. Batav., 1624). Clüver early recognized that ancient history must be based upon a sound knowledge of ancient geography, and that this knowledge could not be obtained by merely studying literary authorities, but required a first-hand examination of the sites of ancient civilization. He made such examination wherever possible, and his conclusions brought him into conflict at many points with accepted archaeological authorities. His *Germania antiqua* is modelled on the work of Tacitus, which, indeed, he reproduces in full, before going on to deal more comprehensively with the climate and soil of the country, its ancient topography, and the ethnography, life, and beliefs of the primitive Germans. In treating of ancient Italy, Clüver could derive more assistance from previous scholarship; but he showed up many false Italian antiquities, rejected many legendary elements in early Roman history, and, advancing into the sphere of textual criticism, he was able to emend many classical passages relating to his subject. His account of the physical geography is full of personal reminiscences of the country which he had crossed and re-crossed. Clüver's pioneer work on German and Italian archaeology, however, exerted but little influence at the time of its publication, and he was best known to succeeding generations of geographers through his brief *Introductio in universam Geographiam, tam veterem quam novam* (Amstelodami, 1624), which was probably the basis of the private lectures which he gave on the subject. This book, too, was first published posthumously, but it went into many editions and translations, and remained an authority for over a century. The work is an illustration of the enduring tendency to regard European geography as a branch of classical scholarship rather than as a science. Of its six Books, the first deals with the mathematical geography of the globe, and the remaining Books, with the regional geography of western Europe (Book II), Germany, northern Europe and Italy (Book III), eastern Europe, including Greece and Scythia (Book IV), Asia (Book V), and Africa and America (Book VI). The first Book is written from the Ptolemaic standpoint, and ignores the claims of the Copernican system. The regional surveys of the several countries are concerned chiefly with the extent, nature, and products of the land, its topography, with especial regard to river systems, its ethnography, and ancient and modern political divisions.

(See *Geographische Abhandlungen*, herausgegeben von Dr. A. Penck, Wien, Bd. V, Heft 2; J. Partsch, *Philipp Clüver, der Begründer der historischen Länderkunde*, 1891.)

III. Treatises on Geography

The most important treatises on geography written in the sixteenth and seventeenth centuries were those written by Münster, Carpenter, and Varenius.

MÜNSTER

Sebastian Münster (1489–1552) was born at Nieder-Ingelheim on the Rhine between Mainz and Bingen. He was educated at Heidelberg University, and later, as a young Franciscan monk, he studied mathematics and cosmography under Conrad Pellikan and Johann Stöffler. He became a Protestant, and subsequently won distinction as Professor of Hebrew at Basel. In 1528 he outlined schemes for projected works on cosmography, and invited the co-operation of scholars. He proceeded to write a series of books on geography, including *Germaniae descriptio* (1530), *Mappa Europae* (1536), and *Rhaetia* (1538), while he collaborated in a *Novus Orbis* (1532) which contained accounts of the recent explorations of Columbus, Vespucci, and other navigators. He also edited the geographical works of Solinus, Mela, and Ptolemy (1538–40). Münster's masterpiece, however, was his *Cosmographia: Beschreibung aller Lender*, Basel, 1544, which was the first account of the world for popular readers to be produced on such a scale in the German language. The *Cosmographia*, in the original edition, consists of six books, prefaced with twenty-four double-page maps, and with two smaller maps in the text. The maps include the traditional map of the world according to Ptolemy, and another, for comparison with it, showing the recent discoveries, and the supposed North-west Passage. There are pictorial maps of the several European countries (Germany occupying a number of sections), and maps of India and the East, America and the Pacific, and Africa. The first book contains a *résumé* of Ptolemy's mathematical geography, brought up to date with some account of the use of the compass as an adjunct to surveying instruments. The supposed history of the chief races of the ancient world is traced from the settlement of Noah. The remaining books deal systematically with the countries of the world—their geography, natural products, and fauna; the origin, history, laws, and manners of the inhabitants; the chief industries, etc. Book II deals with the countries of western Europe; Book III with Germany, in far greater detail; Book IV with the Baltic countries, and with Greece and Turkey; Book V with Asia and the "new islands" (America); and Book VI with Africa. The last two books are naturally much less authentic than the earlier ones. The whole work is copiously illustrated with woodcuts depicting persons and places, picturesque episodes, and natural marvels. The material was derived from practically the whole available relevant literature, from the Bible onwards, and Münster seems also to have been assisted by more than one hundred and twenty different collaborators. The book is written in brilliant style, and, though often defective, uncritical, and pedantic, it was a great success. It went through forty German editions, and was translated into several European languages, an abridged version appearing in English in 1552. Much additional material, and fresh illustrations of high quality, were introduced into the later editions, though the information about America continued to be inferior to the rest.

Only comparatively few maps had appeared in Germany before 1540. Münster did much to popularize the use of maps, and himself originated not less than one hundred and forty-two. Their refinement was impaired by the crude printing of the time. Münster's world-maps were roughly elliptical in shape, as in the *Cosmographia* of Peter Apian, the equator being represented by the major axis of the ellipse, and the parallels of latitude by equally spaced straight lines parallel to this axis. The central meridian appears as a straight line, and the other meridians as circles of gradually increasing curvature. The northern and southern parts of the Earth suffer great distortion. In reproducing the Ptolemaic maps, Münster used the old conical projection, but for smaller areas he ignored the curvature of the Earth. Münster's maps are not always very consistent with one another, and, except for the regional maps of Germany and its surroundings, not at all accurate. This, of course, was largely due to the want of trustworthy data, but also partly to the uncritical methods of work characterizing that generation, and first ameliorated under the influence of Gérard Mercator.

(See *Abhandlungen* (*der philologisch-historischen Classe*) *der königlich Sächsischen Gesellschaft der Wissenschaften*, Leipzig, Bd. 18, 1899, No. 3; Viktor Hantzsch, *Sebastian Münster, Leben, Werk, wissenschaftliche Bedeutung*. There is also a descriptive review of this monograph, by C. R. Beazley, in *The Geographical Journal*, April 1901.)

CARPENTER

Some idea of the state of formal geographical studies in the first half of the seventeenth century may be obtained from a perusal of Nathanael Carpenter's *Geographie delineated forth in two Bookes, containing the Sphericall and Topicall parts thereof*, Oxford, 1st ed., 1625; 2nd ed., corrected, 1635. Nathanael Carpenter (1589–1628?) was a Fellow of Exeter College, Oxford, and a friend of Archbishop Ussher. He became known as a writer on divinity and philosophy, as well as on geography.

Carpenter treats geography in a formal and scholastic manner, and his book is full of references to old writers on the science. Every division of the subject, or class of facts, which arises for discussion is immediately split up by successive dichotomies into general and special, primary and secondary, natural and artificial, real and imaginary, and so forth. Geographical terms receive strict definition; thus a place is defined as "a superficiall space of the Terrrestriall Globe, fitted for habitation" (2nd ed., p. 2); a river is "a perpetuall course of water from a certaine head or fountaine running from an higher to a lower place on the earth" (p. 141), etc. Nevertheless, the book shows the influence of modern ideas and discoveries. Carpenter accepts, with some reserve, the diurnal rotation of the Earth, and he attributes it, following Gilbert, to the agency of magnetism; but he denies that the Earth has an annual revolution about the Sun, and he repeats the traditional Ptolemaic proofs that it is stationary at the centre of the universe.

Carpenter defines geography as "a science which teacheth the description of the whole Earth" (p. 1), and he divides it into "sphericall" and "topicall" parts, since the globe should be studied "first in regard of the *Mathematicall* lineaments and circles, whereof the Spheare is imagined to consist; out of which wee collect the figure, quantity, site, and due proportion of the Earth and its parts: Secondly, of the places *Historically* noted and designed out unto us, by certaine names, markes and characters" (p. 5). The work accordingly falls into two books. The principal topics dealt with in Book I are the definition and classification of the subject (ch. 1); gravitation, in determining which the centre of the Earth is "not an Attractive but a mere Respective point" to which earthy bodies move as near as they can, and towards which "two heavy bodies of the same figure and matter whether Equall or Unequall, will in equall time move an equall space" (ch. 2, p. 32); magnetism, in which Gilbert's account is followed, and the inconstancy of the magnetic variation not yet recognized (ch. 3); views on the motion and situation of the Earth, already alluded to (chs. 4 and 5); the divisions and graduation of the Earth's surface and of the celestial sphere (chs. 6, 9, and 10); globes and maps (ch. 7) measurements of the size of the Earth (ch. 8); determination of longitude and latitude, and calculation of distances on the Earth's surface between points of specified longitude and latitude (chs. 11 and 12). Book II teaches that the Earth is everywhere habitable, even at the poles, where the Sun supplies its heat for six months without interruption (ch. 1). The topography of a place is to be defined by the "adjuncts" which especially characterize that place, and which are its *magnitude, bounds, quality* (i.e. "natural temper and disposition" including heat or cold, wholesomeness, natural productions, etc.), *magnetic elements*, *"air,"* and *situation* (chs. 2 and 3). Chapter 4 deals with the elements of surveying and map-making, and chapters 5–8, with hydrography and navigation. Carpenter discusses the probability of there being a North-west Passage. He asks how the species of animals now found in America, which are similar to those in Asia, could have got thither, after the landing of the Ark, if such a Passage existed. But he suggests that there may originally have been a land communication, severed since "by the violence of the Water." Chapters 9–11 deal with "Pedography," the description of the dry land—with definitions of the various types of scenery—rivers, mountains, valleys, woods, "champian countries," islands, etc. Chapter 12 gives an account of famous inundations and earthquakes. The remaining chapters, 13–16, are concerned with the "civil affections" of land. Carpenter here seeks to correlate differences in the geographical situation and character of countries with the "complexions" and dispositions of the inhabitants, while allowing that these also depend, to some extent, upon education, "the exercise of many people in religious, or morall discipline." Most of the ideas in this part of the book seem to have been derived from Bodin's *Republic*.

VARENIUS

A more illuminating treatment of geography than Carpenter's is found in the *Geographia Generalis* of Bernhard Varen, or Varenius (1622–50), a German physician and geographer. Varenius' book was published at Amsterdam in the year of its author's death at the age of twenty-eight, and it remained a standard authority for more than a century. A corrected and enlarged edition of the work was brought out in 1672 by Newton, for the use of the students to whom he was lecturing upon geography at Cambridge. A further impression, with an appendix, was produced by Jurin in 1712. This was the basis of an English translation by Dugdale, published in 1733, in which, however, the arguments ·for the Copernican hypothesis were strengthened, and explanations in accordance with the Newtonian system were substituted for those which Varenius had based upon the philosophy of Descartes.

Varenius defines geography as "that part of mixed mathematics which explains the state of the Earth and of its parts depending on quantity, viz. its figure, place, magnitude, and motion, with the celestial appearances and other related properties." General geography is thus more than a bare description of countries; but it should exclude accounts of political constitutions. Human geography was included in a further scheme which Varenius drew up but did not live to elaborate. The principles upon which geographical knowledge is based are (1) purely mathematical propositions, (2) astronomical science, (3) experience and observation (and chiefly these, geography not being a demonstrative science). Varenius divides general geography into three branches—Absolute(concerned with the Earth in itself), Relative (concerned with appearances arising from the Earth's relation to the rest of the Universe), and Comparative (concerned with the relation of places to one another). The work correspondingly falls into three Books, subdivided into sections, chapters, and propositions. Section I is made up of the above *praecognita* on the science of geography, followed by a selection of useful propositions in elementary geometry and trigonometry, and by a comparison of the chief units of length used throughout the world. In Section II the following topics are treated: (i) The figure of the Earth, with the traditional proofs of its sphericity. (ii) The determination of the size of the Earth according to the several methods employed in ancient and mediaeval times, all depending upon the measurement of the difference in the altitudes of a heavenly body, or of the pole, as measured from two different stations, or else upon the measurement of the distance at which an object of known height just disappears below the horizon. (iii) the motion of the Earth and its place in the Universe: arguments in favour of the Copernican system. (iv) The composition of the Earth. Varenius holds that there are five simple substances composing all things—water, oil or sulphur, salt, earth, and "a certain spirit, which some call an acid, or which may be the Mercury of the chemists" (ch. 7). Following Descartes, he holds that these different elements have particles of different shapes and sizes, but are the same in substance. Salt is the element which binds particles together to form solid bodies. In Section III there is a broad survey of the chief divisions of the land. The continents (including *Terra Australis*) are defined by their boundaries, and the chief islands, peninsulas, and isthmuses are enumerated. Several chapters are devoted to mountains, with the methods of measuring their altitudes. Varenius supposes those mountains which contain sea-shells to be of recent date, and to have been gradually formed by rapid winds accumulating gravel into heaps which were subsequently solidified by rain. The chief mountains, ranges, peaks, promontories, volcanoes, mines, woods, and deserts of the world are summarily described. Section IV is devoted to hydrography, and surveys the principal oceans, seas, bays, and straits. A chapter is devoted to discussing whether the ocean is everywhere at the same level, which some doubted in view of the existence of ocean currents. Varenius thinks that bays and inlets may probably be depressed below the adjoining oceans. One reason, he thinks, why the Mediterranean and Red Seas were not artificially joined long since by a canal was the fear that the Red Sea might inundate Egypt with water flowing from it into the (supposedly more depressed) Mediterranean. As to the saltness of the sea, Aristotle had supposed that the rain absorbed saline exhalations from the air, and brought them down. Varenius holds either that the sea has been, by its nature, salt from its creation, or else that its waters derive salt from salt rocks situated on the ocean bed, or extract it from the underlying soil. If, as alleged, the sea is saltest towards the equator, this must be because the more rapid evaporation of (fresh) water from the sea in the torrid zone leaves proportionally more salt than in higher latitudes, where evaporation is less, and dilution with rain more, pronounced; also because salt water tastes the salter the hotter it is. Moreover the hotter water near the equator will dissolve and hold in solution greater quantities of salt. The reason why the ocean is not swelled indefinitely by the river water which it is constantly receiving, is that the excess of water returns in part to the heads of the rivers through subterranean channels, and is in part raised in vapours which later fall as rain upon the dry land. A general survey is given of ocean currents which, together with tides, are explained in terms of Descartes' hypothesis of a vortex surrounding the Earth. Lakes are classified according as they are (i) neither fed nor drained by rivers; (ii) drained but not fed; (iii) fed but not drained; (iv) both fed and drained by rivers. Lakes of the first type are maintained by rain, springs, melting ice or snow, or inundations; those of the second by springs; the third type loses its water by evaporation or infiltration into the surrounding soil; lakes of the fourth type may emit more or less water than they receive according as there are sources or sinks in their beds. Instances of all these types of lakes are given. Rivers are next discussed, their origin being assigned to rain or melting snow (causing overflowing lakes), or to springs. Aristotle had attributed springs to the generation of water from air in the bowels of the Earth; other writers to the collection of condensed vapours, or of rain, in an internal reservoir or "promptuary," from which all rivers were supplied. Varenius inclines to the belief that as much water is withdrawn from the sea as the rivers supply to it, the water so withdrawn losing its salinity by being strained through sand, etc. He thinks that many river beds are of human construction, and that we have no salt rivers simply because only fresh water was worth canalizing. There are, however, plenty of salt springs, and certain hot, cold, bituminous, petrifying, poisonous, and coloured springs, whose varieties and properties are here set forth. Section V describes the conditions under which areas covered by sea may become dry land, and *vice versa*, and indicates regions where such changes have occurred. Section VI deals with the phenomena of the atmosphere, which is supposed to be made up of various exhalations rising from the Earth. The section also contains a survey of the distribution of winds, first superseded by that of Halley in 1686; and there is a theory and table of atmospheric refraction, and instructions for making a graduated air-thermoscope for testing the heat of the atmosphere.

The second book of the *Geographia Generalis* deals with the various parts of mathematical geography, e.g. the use of the globes; the various circles and zones of the Earth, and methods of finding the latitude; the seasons; time; the construction of dials, etc. Book III deals with longitude, and its determination from the difference between the observed local time, and the predicted standard time, of some celestial signal (e.g. an eclipse). The work concludes with an account of methods for making globes and maps, and some hints about the construction, lading, and navigation of ships.

CHAPTER XVIII

THE BIOLOGICAL SCIENCES

I. BOTANY.   II. ZOOLOGY.   III. ANATOMY AND
PHYSIOLOGY.   IV. MICROSCOPIC BIOLOGY

THE revival of ancient learning, the voyages of discovery, and the invention of printing gave a new stimulus to the biological sciences as well as to the mathematical and physical sciences. During the centuries immediately preceding the Renaissance the study of plants and animals had been almost entirely subordinated to medicinal interests. The whole atmosphere of the Middle Ages was unfavourable to an interest in Nature for its own sake. The new contact with classical literature helped to revive and stimulate a purely naturalist interest, and a new generation of naturalists gradually came into existence with a genuine interest in biological phenomena for their own sake, independently of utilitarian aims. The numerous voyages made for the sake of discovery and trade also helped to encourage this tendency by the importation of many unfamiliar types of plants and animals. One manifestation of the new regard for biological studies may be found in the formation of botanical and zoological gardens, as well as collections of herbaria and anatomical specimens, which were characteristic of the new period. The rapid increase in the material of biological studies created the urgent need of some kind of systematic classification that would make it manageable and easier to survey. Hence the long and persistent occupation with the problem of systematic classification of plants and animals. Intimately connected with the work of classification was the task of elucidating such concepts as those of species, genus, etc. In the meantime, moreover, the invention of the microscope opened up a new world of biological research. Minute organisms and parts of organisms which had hitherto escaped observation on account of their small size could now be studied to good purpose. Lastly, the amazing success of the "mechanical philosophy" in the physical sciences exercised no small influence on biologists as well; and attempts were consequently made, not only by philosophical thinkers like Descartes, but also by more severely biological investigators like Borelli, to construct a kind of bio-mechanics, which treated living organisms, even human bodies, as mere automata or machines.

I. THE PROGRESS OF BOTANY

HERBALS

The progress of botany was particularly marked at the beginning of the modern period. It had been the custom to suppose that Theophrastus, Pliny, and Dioscorides had already exhausted the world of plants, and had said all there was to be said about them. This tacit assumption was rapidly abandoned when the newly awakened interest in Nature prompted people to make direct observation of the plants roundabout them. It was soon discovered that there were many varieties of plants which had not been known to the ancients, or at least had not been dealt with by them. Interest thus came to be focused on special groups of flora, which were fully described and well illustrated in the so-called *Herbals*. As the art of wood-cut illustration developed, the art of literary description improved likewise. Although this improvement in the art of botanical description and illustration was itself the outcome of closer observation, yet in its turn it helped to improve still further the art of close attention to details, with the result that classifications of flora became more accurate, and the kinship between plants was better appreciated. Among the investigators mainly responsible for this advance were Brunfels, Bock, and Fuchs, who did much to make it clear that different geographical regions have different flora, and that the plants known to Theophrastus, Pliny, and Dioscorides were consequently different from those to be found in central Europe.

BOTANICAL GARDENS

Already in ancient and mediaeval times the practice had arisen of cultivating medicinal plants in special gardens, instead of collecting them in places where they grew wild. Such gardens existed in Salerno and Venice in the fourteenth century. But they were entirely in the service of the art of healing. They were not botanical gardens in the strict sense. It was only about the middle of the sixteenth century that some of the universities took up the study of botany as a branch of science independent of the art of medicine, and then botanical gardens came into being as an essential means of teaching botany. The Universities of Padua and Pisa were the first to lay out such botanical gardens. The one at Pisa was provided at the expense of the Medicis, who also obtained for it plants and seeds from the East. In Venice a similar botanical garden was provided for by the generosity of the Cornaros and the Morosinis, merchant princes whose world-wide connections enabled them to secure a representative botanical stock. The example set by Italy naturally stimulated botanical interest in other countries as well. The result was that numerous botanical gardens came into being, already in the course of the sixteenth century, in various famous cities, such as Montpellier, Bern, Strasbourg, Antwerp, Nürnberg. Some of these gardens were attached to universities, others belonged to private people. It was in the course of the sixteenth century, too, that there came into vogue the practice of making herbaria by pressing plants and sticking them on paper.

CLUSIUS AND LOBELIUS

The greatest botanist at the beginning of the modern era was Clusius, or l'Eclus, of Antwerp (1525–1609). The Netherlands had attained to an important place in commerce and industry generally, and in horticulture more particularly. Clusius spent some years in Vienna, where he was in charge of the Imperial Gardens, and he also studied the natural history of Hungary. Eventually he was appointed Professor of Natural History at the University of Leiden. He made a scientific tour through France, Spain, and Portugal, and published, in 1576, an account of the rarer flora of the Peninsula. In 1583 he published a treatise on the rarer flora of eastern Europe in which he gathered the results of his researches in Austria and Hungary. In 1605 he published a description of the plants of the Levant and of India. His descriptions were always illustrated by excellent pictures. His enterprise could, of course, only be carried through with the help of other travellers and investigators. Of his co-workers the most eminent was Matthias de l'Obel, or Lobelius (1538–1616), whose name is commemorated in certain ornamental flowers (Lobelias). He was born in the Netherlands and ended his days in England, where he was in charge of the royal gardens under Queen Elizabeth and King James I. Lobelius showed a definite perception of the natural kinship of plants, and he recognized such natural groups as grasses, lilies, and orchids. But his adoption of the form of the leaf as the basis of division betrayed him into such erroneous classifications as putting ferns and certain monocotyledons into the same group.

MATTIOLI

While the botanists of central Europe busied themselves exploring the flora of their environment, the Italian botanists of the sixteenth century were mainly occupied with the explanation of the old treatises on botany. Soon, however, they noticed that Pliny and Dioscorides mentioned but a small number of the plants to be found in Italy. And then the botanists of Italy, especially of northern Italy, likewise turned their attention to the study of the local flora. Special attention was paid to the extraordinary wealth of plants in the calcareous formations of the southern Alps, such as Monte Baldo. Of the Italian botanists of the sixteenth century one of the most eminent was Pietro Andrea Mattioli (1501–77). He was the greatest commentator on the works of Dioscorides, and showed a remarkable sagacity in identifying the plants mentioned by ancient writers. But he was no mere bookworm. He was a keen observer and an enthusiastic collector who enriched the science of botany with the knowledge of numerous new varieties of plants. His *Commentaries on Dioscorides* (1544) exercised a wide influence.

BAUHIN

The new tendencies in botany reached their climax in the work of Bauhin, who introduced a natural classification of plants in place of the artificial alphabetical classification which had been customary hitherto. Kaspar Bauhin (1560–1624) was born at Basle, was a student of Fabricius, in Padua, for a time, and studied the flora of Germany, Italy, and France. He discovered many new varieties of plants. But he rendered even more important services to botany by carrying out an exhaustive diagnosis of the various kinds of plants, introducing the binomial nomenclature, classifying plants according to their resemblances, and disentangling the innumerable synonyms in use among botanists till then. The last point may be considered first. The revived interest in botany, as has already been pointed out, led to the discovery of a great many European and non-European plants hitherto unknown to botanists. The new plants, in fact, greatly exceeded in number the plants known to, and described by, the ancients. The naming of the new plants was not guided by any uniform or generally accepted principles. Sometimes old names were applied to new plants in a purely arbitrary fashion. Thus it came about that different writers often gave different names to the same plant, and the same name to different plants. There resulted a confusion of language which threatened to hinder all progress. It is to Bauhin's great credit that he ended this Babel of tongues by means of his thorough-going treatise on botanical synonyms published in 1623 (*Pinax theatri botanici*, Basel). In this work he dealt with all the class names used by various botanists for the approximately six thousand varieties of plants which were known to him, and thereby created the possibility of clearness and mutual intelligibility in botanical discussions. The book still holds an important place in the literature of botany after the lapse of more than three hundred years. Bauhin, however, did more than remedy the confusion caused by his predecessors and contemporaries. He set an example of the way in which plants should be named and described, and thereby prevented the future recurrence of similar confusion in botanical literature. He developed the art of describing plants very concisely and yet in such a manner that the diagnosis given made it possible to recognize the plants easily. Each description referred, though very briefly, to every part of the plant concerned. The shape and size of the plant, the ramification of its roots and stem, the form of its leaves, the character of its flowers, its fruits, and its seeds—all these were described concisely and aptly within about twenty lines. Moreover, he distinguished carefully between genera and species (classes and their sub-classes). Each species usually receives a binomial designation composed of the generic name and the specific determinant as, for example, *gramen caninum* (couch grass?), *lilium album* (white lily), *ranunculus montanus* (mountain crowfoot). The binomial nomenclature (system of class names) was subsequently completed by Linnaeus.

Bauhin's classification of plants according to similarities in the totality of their chief characteristics shows an implicit recognition of their natural kinship to a greater extent than was shown by the classification adopted by Lobelius, although his method of naming and co-ordinating the various groups of plants is not yet sufficiently clear and distinct. Like Lobelius, he begins with the grasses as the simplest kind of flowering plants. Next he deals with the liliaceous plants, then with the most important kinds of herbaceous plants, cryptogams, and finally with trees and shrubs. Like Lobelius, Bauhin failed to recognize the peculiar character of ferns. His classifications are, of course, erroneous sometimes, as, for instance, when he classes the phanerogamous (flowering) duckweed with mosses, or sponges with seaweeds. But such mistakes were not unnatural in view of the fact that the relation between phanerogamous and cryptogamous (flowerless) plants was not understood till much later, while the character of zoöphytes (plant animals) was not discovered till the eighteenth century, namely, by Trembley. Bauhin devoted forty years to his great treatise, and died in 1624, a year after its publication.

CESALPINI

In contrast with the above tendency towards a natural classification of plants, Italian botany tended towards an artificial classification, following more or less the *a priori* methods of division according to Aristotelian logic, and paying attention mainly to the nature of the fruits of the plants. The chief merit of this kind of classification was its convenience for various practical purposes, to which the more natural classification was not so well suited, though it was more sound scientifically. The most eminent Italian botanist of the time was Andrea Caesalpino or Cesalpini (1519–

1603), whose treatise *On Plants* was published in 1583. In this work the descriptions given of the various plants differ from those found in the usual herbals in two important respects. In the first place, Cesalpini did not restrict his description to an account of the general habits of a plant, but described its several parts in detail, paying special attention to its organs of pollination. In the second place, the descriptions are introduced by philosophical reflections upon the general nature of plants. In their main outlines these theoretical reflections, contained in the introduction to the first book of his treatise, are Aristotelian in tendency. Since plants are endowed with only that kind of soul which is necessary for nutrition, growth, and reproduction, they have much simpler organs than have animals, which are capable also of motion and sensation. The function of the vegetative or plant soul is to sustain the individual plant by means of nutrition, and to perpetuate the species by reproduction. Hence the two parts of a plant: the roots, wherewith nutriment (which was supposed to be already digested in the soil) is obtained; and the stem, which bears the fruit. The fruit was selected as the basis of his classification because its characters appeared more stable than those of the roots. As some of the lower plants, such as the lichen and the mushroom, appeared to have no organs of fertilization, Cesalpini assumed, with Aristotle, that these arise by spontaneous generation from decaying matter, and therefore all they need to do is to take in nutriment and grow. They mark the transition stage from inorganic nature to complete plants, just as there are transition stages between plants and animals.

Cesalpini exercised a great influence on the development of botany during the seventeenth and eighteenth centuries, and his point of view reached its culmination in the work of Linnaeus, who in all essentials completed the development of systematic botany as based on artificial classification.

JUNGIUS

The seventeenth century witnessed the beginnings of a scientific morphology of plants. The first steps in this direction were taken by Joachim Jungius or Jung (1587–1657), of Lübeck. He studied in Padua, and eventually settled in Hamburg as headmaster of a school. Jungius embraced the atomic philosophy of Democritus, and was a versatile and ardent advocate of free scientific inquiry. He published nothing during his lifetime. But when his writings appeared posthumously they exercised an immediate influence not only in Germany but also in England and Sweden, where Ray and Linnaeus respectively appreciated their value. Ray, in fact, had already read some of Jung's works in manuscript in 1660. The chief botanical treatise of Jungius (*Isagoge phytoscopica*, 1678) accomplished two things. In the first place, it created a scientific terminology for the adequate description of the parts and processes of plants. This terminology has proved its fitness by its survival, in part at least, to the present day—for instance, the expressions still in use for the different kinds of inflorescence, such as *spica* (a cluster of flowers growing direct from the stem), *panicula* (a loose cluster of flowers), *umbella* (a cluster of flowers arising from the same level of the stem), *corymbus* (a cluster from different levels of the stem), and many others, and the current definitions of these terms, are derived from Jungius. In the second place, Jungius first directed attention to the changes in form which stem leaves undergo as their distance from the ground increases. He also clearly distinguished and named the simple leaves, as well as some of the compound leaves which were frequently mistaken for branches. Jungius, moreover, described very fully the forms of flowers, although he was unacquainted with the nature of the sexuality of plants. Guided by the different forms of their flowers, he clearly distinguished such classes as the *compositae* (the daisy family), the *labiatae* (the dead-nettle family), and the *leguminosae* (the bean family). His clear exposition of the fundamental concepts of plant morphology helped also towards a better classification of plants. Such characteristics as scent, taste, colour, medicinal uses, and similar secondary attributes were dismissed by Jungius as unsuited for the scientific classification of plants; and he ridiculed the custom still current in his day of classifying plants into trees, shrubs, and herbs. His nomenclature follows mainly the binomial system introduced by Bauhin.

MORISON AND RAY

The work of Bauhin and Jungius was carried a stage farther by the two British botanists, Robert Morison (1620–83) and John Ray (1628–1705). Morison submitted Bauhin's treatise to a searching criticism, pointing out various errors in his system of classification. In 1672 he published a treatise on umbellifers (the parsley family). This appears to have been the first large monograph ever devoted to the detailed study of one group of plants. In this book umbelliferous plants are arranged in a series of subdivisions according to the character of their fruit. John Ray followed the example of Bauhin in attempting to gather all the botanical knowledge of his time in one comprehensive work, *Historia plantarum* (1684–1704), which deals with nineteen thousand plants, divided into one hundred and twenty-five sections or classes. The morphological portions of the work follow closely the lines pursued by Jungius. Ray's work is noteworthy for the fact that it was the first to enumerate the great natural groups, or orders, of plants. It begins with the imperfect plants, algae, mosses, ferns, and marine plants (including seaweeds and zoöphytes). Flowering plants are divided into monocotyledons and dicotyledons. Of the monocotyledons the grasses receive a very thorough treatment, and are systematically divided according to their total character. Palms, the lily family, and orchids are included among the monocotyledons. The *labiatae* (the dead-nettle family), the *leguminosae* (the bean family), and the *compositae* (the daisy family) had already been identified before Ray. But the *cruciferae* (the wallflower family), the *rubiaceae* (the madder family), the *asperifoliae* (the forget-me-not family) and various other families of plants were now assigned their places in the systematic classification of plants.

RIVINUS

Whereas Morison and Ray attached great importance to the character of the fruit as a basis of the classification of flowering plants, the German botanist Rivinus, otherwise Bachmann, 1652–1725, preferred to lay stress on the number and the connection of the petals. Rivinus also adopted the practice of including the name of the genus, or wider class, in the name of the sub-class, or species, adding a suitable specific adjective—a practice which was afterwards carried through systematically by Linnaeus.

TOURNEFORT

The greatest French botanist of this period was J. P. de Tournefort (1656–1708), Professor at the *Jardin des Plantes* (from 1683), and noted for his study of the flora of Greece, North Africa, and Asia Minor. Like Rivinus he based his classification of flowering plants on the character of the corolla. Accordingly he distinguished between plants with petals (petalous) and those without petals (apetalous); and petalous plants were further subdivided into those with one petal (monopetalous) and those with more than one (polypetalous). Among the monopetalous plants he included the *campanulaceae* (Canterbury bells, etc.) and the *labiatae* (the dead-nettle family), whose corolla consists of one piece; among the polypetalous plants he included the *cruciferae* (the wallflower family), the *rosaceae* (roses, etc.), the *papilionaceae* (gorse, clover, etc.). Combining these distinctions with others, such as the popular distinction between trees, shrubs, and herbs, Tournefort set up a system of twenty-two classes of plants. This artificial system dominated the botany of the earlier decades of the eighteenth century until it was supplanted by the classification made by Linnaeus. In one respect the work of Tournefort was reactionary, inasmuch as his classificatory system failed to give due recognition to certain comprehensive natural groups recognized by Ray, namely the cryptogams, the monocotyledons, and the dicotyledons.

II. THE PROGRESS OF ZOOLOGY

As in the case of botany so in the case of zoology, the voyages of discovery, etc., brought to light many new facts not mentioned in the classical treatises on the subject, and so stimulated a desire to observe and study the facts independently. The pioneers of the new zoology were Gesner and Aldrovandi.

GESNER

Conrad Gesner (1516–65) was a Swiss naturalist. He lived in Zürich, but somehow managed to keep in touch with scientific workers all over Europe. His work on zoology (*Historia animalium*, 1551–87) fills five folio volumes, contains a full, if unsystematic, account of all the animals known in his time, and thus supplied the material for the further development of zoology. His descriptions are definite and clear, and they are supplemented by numerous pictorial illustrations, some of which are original and many are effective. The new friendly attitude towards Nature is very marked in Gesner, who was interested in plants as well as in animals, and showed a love of mountains such as was quite unusual in his time.

ALDROVANDI

Italy had its counterpart to Gesner in Ulissi Aldrovandi (1522–1605). He was born in Bologna, where in 1567 he founded a botanical garden, of which he was the first director, to be succeeded by Cesalpini as the second director. Like Gesner, Aldrovandi also tried to produce an encyclopaedic work on zoology. He published a work in three volumes, dealing with birds, in 1599. And in 1602 he published another work treating of insects. His complete works fill thirteen volumes. Aldrovandi's account of animal life was not as comprehensive as Gesner's; but he paid more attention to anatomical considerations as a guide to classification, and thereby approached much nearer to a scientific zoology

WOTTON

In the year following the publication of Gesner's first volume, and many years before the appearance of Aldrovandi's treatises, an English zoologist attempted a more systematic classification of animals than either of them had achieved. This was Edward Wotton

(1492–1555), an Oxford physician and naturalist. In 1552 he published a Latin treatise *On the Differences of Animals*, in which he gave a general account of the animal organism and its parts, and a general survey of the animal kingdom, based on the principles of natural kinship, and following largely the Aristotelian classification of animals.

BELON AND RONDELET

The French naturalist Belon (1518–64) and the Italian Rondelet (1507–66) were commentators of classical zoology. Both sought to verify by personal observations the forms described by the ancients, and for this purpose they reinvestigated the fauna of the Mediterranean region. Their books on this subject were purely zoographical, for problems of a natural classification or of the affinities of the animals which they described were not attacked. Belon's book on the results of his Mediterranean survey was published in 1553, *A History of Fish* in 1551, and *A History of Birds* in 1553. Rondelet concentrated on a study of the marine forms of the Mediterranean, and published his work *Aquatic Animals* in 1554.

In his *History of Birds* Belon compared the skeleton of a bird with that of a man (Illustr. 198). Beyond this, however, neither he nor his fellow commentator-naturalist pursued the comparative method of study already used by Aristotle, nor did they attempt a classification based upon it. Instead, they followed mere convenience or popular tradition for their order of arrangement, as Pliny had done. Accordingly, Belon deals with the bat in his *History of Birds*; and such diverse forms as Crustacea, molluscs, whales, porpoises, and fish are described together in Rondelet's book on *Aquatic Animals*.

VESALIUS

Meanwhile the study of anatomy was also making some progress. Throughout the Middle Ages the progress of anatomical studies had been hindered by the prohibition or the dislike of dissection. In the absence of such direct observation of the structure of the human body, medical students and other biologists had to rely mainly on the authority of books, chiefly the books of Galen. Gradually, however, though slowly, opportunities for dissection came. Already in the thirteenth century the free-thinking Emperor Frederick II showed some interest in the study of anatomy, and permitted the dissection of human corpses. In the centuries which followed, such dissections were carried out with increasing frequency for medical and purely scientific ends. In the course of the sixteenth century the time arrived for putting the study of anatomy on a proper foundation of direct observation, in place of the mere

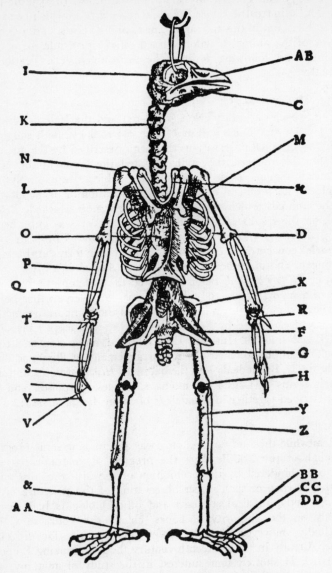

Illustr. 198.—Skeletons of Bird and Man Compared.

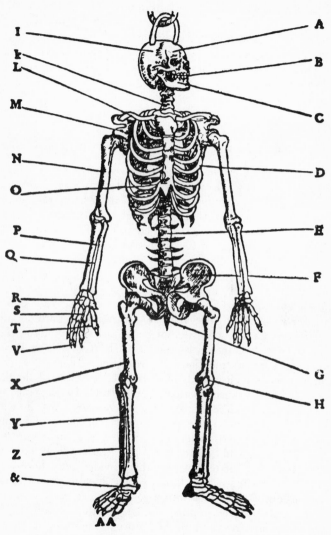

Corresponding Bones are indicated by the same letters

authority of Galen. The founder of this renewed scientific study of anatomy was the Belgian Vesalius (1514–64), whose work will be dealt with in the next section. His book *On the Structure of the Human Body*, published in 1543, was revolutionary. The customary fancies about the microcosm and the macrocosm, the futile search for analogies and connections between the parts of the human body and the heavenly bodies, or other parts of the cosmos, were passed over in utter silence in this great book. Instead, there is a clear matter-of-fact account of the actual structure of the human body and all its parts; and this account is illuminated from time to time by means of comparisons with corresponding parts of the lower animals.

RAY

The further progress of zoology followed more or less on the same lines as botany. New material for study was collected from far and wide, and carefully observed and described. Specialization developed to the extent that individual investigators sometimes contented themselves with the detailed study of some one class of animals. In this way, about the middle of the seventeenth century, separate works appeared on the fauna of Brazil and the East Indies. The period of collecting material was followed by a period of systematic classification, in the case of zoology as in that of botany. This parallelism is partly due to the fact that it was, to some extent at least, the same investigators who were interested in both botanical and zoological studies, and attempted the task of systematic classification in both domains. This is particularly true of John Ray, of whose work in botany mention has already been made.

John Ray made a close study of the fauna, as well as of the flora, of Great Britain, France, Germany, and Italy. In 1693 he published his *Synopsis methodica animalium quadrupedum*, etc., in which we meet with the first really systematic classification of animals. Ray begins with the Aristotelian classification of animals into those which have red blood (vertebrates) and those which have not (invertebrates). The vertebrates are then divided into those which breathe through lungs and those which breathe through gills (namely fishes). The former are later subdivided into viviparous and oviparous animals (reptiles, birds). Further subdivisions of viviparous animals are based on the nature of their teeth or of their toes. Thus, for instance, he distinguishes animals with hoofs (*ungulata*) from those with nails (*unguiculata*). The *ungulata* are subdivided into those having single, double, quadruple hoofs; while the *unguiculata* are subdivided into two-toed and five-toed, and so on. Ray, moreover, was the first to formulate a clear conception of the nature of a biological "species." In his *History of Plants* (1686) he laid it down that "forms which are different in species always retain their specific natures, and one species does not grow from the seed of another species." This conception of species was adopted by Linnaeus, who also took over a good part of Ray's system of zoological classification. It is noteworthy, however, that Ray himself did not regard the nature of species with the same rigidity as did most of the biologists of the eighteenth century. For, after making the above statement about species, Ray added: "Although this mark of unity of species is fairly constant, yet it is not invariable and infallible." Besides his services to systematic biology, Ray has to his credit that he realized the real character of fossils as petrified remains of extinct plants or animals.

III. THE PROGRESS OF ANATOMY AND PHYSIOLOGY

Even at the beginning of the modern period biologists did not confine their attention to the external features of living organisms, but sought to understand their internal economy and also their development. This tendency became more marked in the course of time, especially when the microscope disclosed to observation many hitherto unknown facts relating to the structure and function of various parts of plants and animals. Moreover, under the growing influence of the marked mechanistic character of the physical sciences of the time, biologists likewise attempted to explain the movements and activities of living organisms in accordance with the laws of mechanics. But the most important anatomical and physiological discoveries of the period were those connected with the circulation of the blood. For the adequate appreciation of these discoveries some knowledge is required of the ideas which they displaced.

During many centuries the anatomical and physiological views commonly accepted as authoritative were those of Galen (130–200), physician to the Emperor Marcus Aurelius. Even the revolutionaries at the beginning of the modern period could not free themselves entirely from Galen's influence, and so the change came about slowly and gradually. Now, Galen's views on the heart and the blood-vessels were briefly as follows. Blood is formed, and endowed with "natural spirits," in the liver, whence it flows through the veins to the various parts of the body, and returns again by the same veins to the liver—the movement being rather like a tidal ebb and flow. The right ventricle of the heart is a part of the venous system. Of the blood which enters it, after discharging its impurities into the lungs, the major portion returns to the liver, while the rest penetrates the porous wall (or septum) and enters the left ventricle, where it mingles with the air coming from the lungs, and is converted into a kind of more refined substance called "vital spirits." These vital spirits are conveyed by the arteries to various parts of the body, including the brain. The vital spirits which enter the brain are there refined into "animal spirits," which the nerves (conceived as hollow tubes) distribute all over the body. The uncertain, semi-material and semi-spiritual status of the various "spirits" made them a ready help to doctors in perplexity, and a positive hindrance to the advance of medical science.

The revolt from mere authority, and the revulsion from mere book-learning in favour of the objective study of facts, which characterized the dawn of the modern period, favoured a critical revision of Galenian views. The reforms were brought about chiefly by Vesalius, Servetus, Fabricius, and Harvey. The changes came about slowly and piecemeal, because the reformers themselves were so steeped in Galenian ideas that they could not relinquish them altogether; but the changes did come. The general distaste of the Middle Ages for a direct study of natural phenomena and the consequent tendency to rely on the authority of books were perhaps nowhere more marked than in the domain of anatomy and physiology. For in this domain religious or moral scruples and a certain sense of disgust co-operated in militating against the direct study of animal organisms, especially of human bodies. And so the authority of Aristotle and Galen reigned more or less supreme. This kind of thing, however, had to end sooner or later, if only because of the intimate relation of these studies with medicine and the successful treatment of the thousand ills that human flesh is heir to. So from the thirteenth century onwards there is observable a gradual return to the practice of dissecting human bodies. In the course of the fourteenth century such a direct study of human anatomy became more or less habitual in various medical schools in Italy. The fifteenth century produced one of the greatest anatomists of all times, namely, Leonardo da Vinci, whose 750 anatomical sketches afford clear evidence of his genius in this field of work. In 1489 he actually planned a treatise on the human body. But, unfortunately, the plan did not materialize, and his anatomical sketches were not published until the end of the nineteenth century and the beginning of the twentieth. Leonardo may have exercised some influence on the development of human anatomy even without the aid of publication. But to all intents and purposes it was Vesalius who revived the direct study of anatomy, initiated the revolt against mere authority in the realm of biological science, and

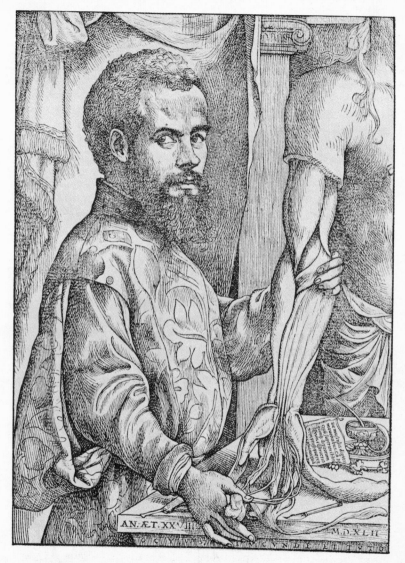

AN. ÆT. XXVIII

M.D.XLII

Andreas Vesalius

SECVNDA
MVSCVLO.
RVM TA
BVLA.

A Plate from Vesalius
(The Muscles of the Human Body)

introduced new methods and instruments for the effective pursuit of anatomical and physiological studies.

VESALIUS

Andreas Vesalius (1514-64) was born in Brussels, studied there, and also at the universities of Louvain, Paris, and Padua, in the last of which he was appointed teacher of anatomy in 1537. Instead of the then usual practice of leaving the demonstrations in anatomy to unskilled barber-surgeons, Vesalius himself laid bare before his students the parts of the human body. And, although Galen was the authoritative text-book used by him and his students, Vesalius did not hesitate to point out in the actual body under examination things which contradicted what Galen had written. In 1543, the year in which the revolutionary work of Copernicus saw the light, Vesalius published his great treatise, *On the Structure of the Human Body*. Of course, the book met with opposition. Vesalius was consequently less reluctant to leave Padua for Spain, where he acted as court physician to the Emperor Charles V, and later to his successor, Philip II. In course of time he tired of court life, and in 1563, in order to escape for awhile from the Spanish Court, he set out on a pilgrimage to Jerusalem, visiting Padua again on his way. On his return journey from Palestine he was taken ill, and was put ashore on one of the Ionian Islands, Zante, where he died soon afterwards.

The great treatise of Vesalius, *De humani corporis fabrica*, published in the same year as the work of Copernicus, was as epoch-making in its more limited sphere as was the astronomical work of Copernicus; and it was quicker in its effects, just because it was not so far-reaching in its disturbing influence on people's world-views. The great classic of human anatomy was not particularly revolutionary, in spite of the opposition which it encountered. The order of exposition was essentially traditional in character—first came an account of the bones, then of the muscles, of the blood-vessels, of the nerves, of the organs of the abdomen and of the thorax, and finally an account of the brain. The main ideas were also largely traditional—there are the Aristotelian views of the "cooking" of the food in the cavity of the abdomen, of respiration as cooling the blood, Galen's views of the rôles of the heart and of the liver in the vascular system, and so on. Perhaps the most original part of the book is the last chapter, in which he describes his method of vivisection. His methods and his instruments were new and epoch-making. They are still largely at the base of modern anatomical technique. But he did make many discoveries in the details of anatomy, and repudiated hundreds of old errors. Moreover, Vesalius took special care with his illustrations—a matter of peculiar importance in the study of anatomy and physiology. The plates were made under his direction by a gifted disciple of Titian, and they still elicit the admiration of all who see them. Among the numerous errors of Galen, which Vesalius corrected, one is of special interest for our present purpose. According to Galen, as has already been stated above, the septum or wall between the two ventricles of the heart is porous, so that some of the blood can percolate through it from the right to the left ventricle. This idea was definitely rejected by Vesalius in the following words: "It seems to me that the septum of the heart is as thick, dense and compact as is the rest of the heart. So I do not see how even the smallest particle can pass from the right to the left ventricle through the septum." Moreover, his sketch of the portal circulation shows such a close mutual approach of the minute terminals of the arteries and of the veins in the tissues of the body, and his account of the portal vein and the *vena cava* states so clearly that "the extreme ramifications of these veins inosculate with each other, and in many places appear to unite and be continuous," that one wonders how he failed to conjecture that the blood circulates. However, he did fail, and the next step towards the recognition of the circulation of the blood was taken by Servetus.

SERVETUS

Michael Servetus (1511–53) was a native of Aragon in Spain. He studied in Paris, where Vesalius was one of his fellow-students. His unitarian zeal brought him into conflict with the Church authorities, Protestant as well as Catholic. He escaped the net of the Inquisition only to fall into the toils of Calvin, who had him burned at the stake, together with nearly all the copies of his *Restitution of Christianity*. It was in this treatise that Servetus incidentally expounded the doctrine of the pulmonary or lesser circulation of the blood. The important passage reads as follows: "In order that we may understand how the blood is the very life, we must first learn the generation in substance of the vital spirit, which is composed of, and is nourished by, the inspired air and the very fine blood. The vital spirit has its origin in the left ventricle of the heart, the lungs especially helping towards its perfection; it is a thin spirit elaborated by the power of heat, is of a light colour, of a fiery potency. . . . It is generated through the commingling, in the lungs, of the inspired air with the elaborated fine blood communicated from the right ventricle to the left. This communication does not take place through the septum of the heart, as is generally believed, but a special device drives the fine blood from the right ventricle through a long passage in the lungs. There it is rendered

Michael Servetus

Illustr. 202

Hieronymus Fabricius

lighter in colour, and from the pulmonary artery is poured into the pulmonary vein. Here it is mixed with the inspired air, and by expiration is cleansed of its fumes. At length, completely mingled with the air, it is drawn in by the left ventricle during its dilation, and is fit to be vital spirit." As only two or three copies of Servetus' book escaped destruction, it is difficult to estimate the influence of the new views on the impermeability of the septum and of the circulation of the blood from the right side of the heart to the left through the lungs. Similar views were expressed, in 1559, by Realdus Columbus (1516–59) of Padua. The fact that Columbus made no reference to the heretical treatise of Servetus is no evidence that he was ignorant of it. It is probable enough that if Servetus had been less theologically minded, or if Calvin had been less fanatical, the systemic circulation of the blood, and all its attendant advances in physiology, might have come half a century or so earlier than they did.

FABRICIUS

Another important step towards the discovery of the full extent of the circulation of the blood was taken by Fabricius when he discovered the valves of the veins, though he did not fully appreciate their significance. Hieronymus Fabricius (1537–1619) was born in the Tuscan village, Aquapendente. For sixty-four years he taught at the University of Padua, and made many valuable contributions to biological science, notably to embryology and the mechanics of muscular action. In 1603 he published a treatise, *On the Valves of the Veins*, in which he described the thin little membranes on the inside of the veins opening towards the heart but closed in the opposite direction. He showed that if an arm is bandaged above the elbow, then the veins swell up, and the valves become prominent as "knots" or swellings. He explained this phenomenon by saying that the valves retard the flow of blood so that the tissues may have time to absorb the necessary nutrition; they also prevent extreme irregularities in the flow of the blood, which might otherwise all collect in one part of the body. The true function of the valves, as effecting the proper circulation of the blood, escaped him, because he still believed, with Galen, that the movement of the blood was a kind of ebb and flow, the veins conveying fresh blood from the liver to the tissues, and bringing back the stale blood from the tissues to the liver. The true explanation was discovered by a pupil of Fabricius, namely, Harvey.

HARVEY

William Harvey (1578–1657) was born at Folkstone, and educated in Cambridge. In 1597 he went to the University of Padua, where he studied medicine under Fabricius until 1602. It is worth noting that Galilei was teaching in Padua during Harvey's student years there. In 1602 Harvey settled in London as medical practitioner, and eventually counted Francis Bacon among his private patients. In 1607 Harvey was elected a Fellow of the Royal College of Physicians. Two years later he was appointed physician to St. Bartholomew's Hospital, and in 1615 lecturer in anatomy at the Royal College of Physicians. In 1616, the year in which Shakespeare died, Harvey gave his first course of College lectures, in which he already sketched the main outlines of his theory of the circulation of the blood, although his book, *On the Movement of the Heart and the Blood*, was not published until 1628. In 1632 he was appointed physician to King Charles I, and had his share of trouble during the subsequent Civil Wars, when his house was sacked, and his manuscripts, drawings, and anatomical collections were destroyed. In 1648, after the King's surrender, Harvey returned to London and lived in retirement. In 1651 he published his treatise *On the Generation of Animals*. Three years later he was offered the Presidency of the Royal College of Physicians, but declined it, though he bequeathed his fortune to the College. He was the acknowledged ornament of that institution, and a statue of him was erected in its hall during his lifetime.

In his Preface to the book *On the Movement of the Heart and the Blood* Harvey voices the spirit of the new age as represented by Vesalius and Galilei. "I profess," he says, "to learn and to teach anatomy, not from books, but from dissections; not from the positions of philosophers, but from the fabric of nature." He then proceeds to refute current errors relating to the heart, the arteries, the veins, and the blood, and to explain and establish his own view of the systemic circulation of the blood.

Harvey's most important points may be indicated briefly as follows. The heart is a hollow muscle, whose characteristic action consists of a jerky contraction (systole) followed by a passive dilation (diastole). The contraction expels from the heart the blood which has entered it during its dilation; and the regular repetition of these contractions keeps the blood moving in the blood-vessels. This was a mechanical explanation which soon exorcized the various "spirits" which used to be invoked to account for the motion of the blood. Again, the quantity of blood which the heart propels in the course of half an hour exceeds the whole of the blood contained in the entire body at any moment. This cannot be reasonably explained without supposing that the blood propelled from the heart returns to it in the course of a comparatively short time. And there is ample observational and experimental evidence to show that the blood moves incessantly in one continuous circulation. The various valves in the vascular system insure this movement in one direction. Experiments with ligatures and with incisions for blood-letting show that the blood in the arteries always flows in the direction away from the heart, while the blood in the veins always flows towards the heart, so that it is reasonable to assume a continuous circulation from the heart to the arteries, from the arteries to the veins, and from the veins back to the heart, and so on incessantly while life lasts.

The accompanying diagram (Illustr. 203) will help to make clear the circulation of all the blood in the human body.

The heart contains four chambers, namely, two auricles and two ventricles. As the left ventricle contracts, the blood in it is forced through the valves into the great artery called the *aorta*. From there it passes into smaller arteries, etc., until it enters the veins, and then passes through the great vein, called the *vena cava*, into the right auricle. When this auricle contracts, the blood in it is forced through the valves into the right ventricle, and passes through the pulmonary artery into the lung. From the lung the blood passes through the pulmonary vein into the left auricle, and thence into the left ventricle once more; and the whole circulatory process is repeated. Thus the whole of the blood contained in the body circulates in the direction shown: the valves, which open in this direction only, prevent the flow of the blood in the reverse direction. Such was Harvey's conception of the circulation of the blood.

There were gaps in Harvey's theory of the circulation of the blood; but most of them were filled in the course of the seventeenth century. Thus, for instance, Harvey did not know how exactly the terminals of the arteries are linked up with those of the veins; but in 1660 Malpighi observed the passage of the blood through the capillaries connecting the two sets of blood-vessels, and the discovery was subsequently confirmed and extended by Leeuwenhoek. Again, Harvey clung more or less to the old idea that blood was somehow manufactured by the liver out of consumed food, but he had no clear ideas on the subject. In 1651, Jean Pecquet showed how the chyle (a milky fluid) is conducted by the lacteals into the thoracic duct, and thence, through the junction of the jugular and subclavian veins at the root of the neck, into the blood-stream. About a year or two later Rudbeck of Upsala and Bartholin of Copenhagen discovered the lymphatics, a system of vessels like the lacteals but containing a colourless fluid (lymph) which they discharge into the veins. In 1659 Francis Glisson gave a detailed account of the anatomy of the liver, the stomach, and the intestines. In 1656 Thomas Wharton gave a careful account of the pancreas, the

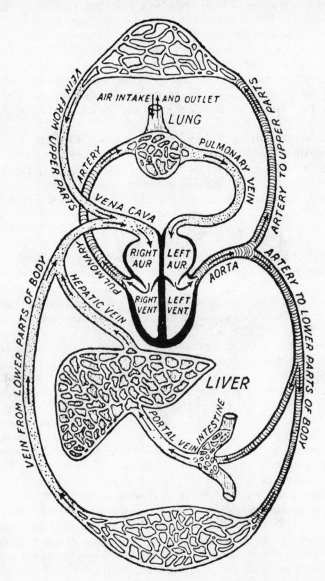

Illustr. 203.—Diagram to Illustrate the Circulation of the Blood (from C. Singer's *Discovery of the Circulation of the Blood*)

William Harvey

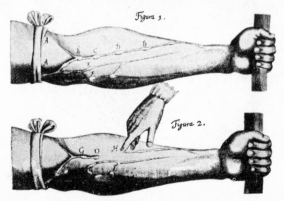

Veins of the Front of the Forearm
(An illustration in Harvey's *Exercitatio*)

Giovanni Alfonso Borelli

kidneys, the thyroids, and various other glands, refuted the view of Descartes that the pineal gland is the seat or organ of the soul, and insisted that it merely drains off the waste products of the brain. In 1664 Thomas Willis published an experimental study of the nerves, and demonstrated their influence on the heart and the lungs. All these discoveries helped, in one way or another, to throw new light on the theory of the circulation of the blood, and to add vastly to its range and significance. Lastly, whereas Harvey had no precise conception of the changes which the blood undergoes in the lungs, the chemical work of Boyle, Hooke, Lower, and Mayow (see Chapter XV) threw some light on the subject, though the complete explanation was not found till the time of Lavoisier.

Harvey, as has already been mentioned, wrote also on embryology. His treatise, *On the Generation of Animals*, is noteworthy for the doctrine that "all animals, even those that produce their young alive, including man himself, are evolved out of an egg" (or briefly, *Omnia ex ovo*). But although the book contains evidence of much patient observation and thought, yet it is mainly Aristotelian in character, and is on a very different footing from the treatise *On the Movement of the Heart and the Blood*. The culminating theory of this treatise, the circulation of all the blood through the vascular system by the pump-like action of the heart, marked a new epoch in the history of physiology by giving a lasting impetus and a new direction to the innumerable investigations connected with the economy of the body in health and in disease. Moreover, by attributing the movement of the blood to the merely muscular contraction of the heart, Harvey helped to free the biological sciences from the obscurantism which haunted them so long as quasi-spiritual categories, instead of physical and chemical categories, were used in the explanation of the phenomena of life. Harvey himself, it is true, never entirely emerged from the mystifying language of his contemporaries, and even regarded himself as a loyal Aristotelian, but he builded better than he knew.

BORELLI

Of those who, in the seventeenth century, attempted to explain the mechanics of the living organism, Borelli was the most important. Giovanni Alfondo Borelli (1608–79) was born at Naples, and studied at the University of Pisa, where Galilei was at one time a professor. Borelli was successively professor at Pisa and in Rome, and in 1657 he went to Florence, where he worked for ten years at the *Accademia del Cimento*. He then went to Messina, which, for political reasons, he had to leave in 1674. For a time he was in the service of ex-Queen Christina of Sweden in Rome, but ended his days in a monastery.

His treatise, *On the Movement of Animals*, was published in the year of his death (1679).

Borelli had felt the powerful influence of Galilei, and took for his model Galilei's work in the mathematico-physical sciences. So he undertook to investigate and to expound the movements of animals almost in the same way as if he had to do with levers and weights, etc. He begins his account with single muscles (for muscles are the main organs of animal movement), passes on to more and more complex organs and systems of organs, and ends with a synoptic account of an animal's entire mobility. Although the movements of human beings are Borelli's main interest, yet the movements of other animals also receive consideration. In the course of his investigation he deals fully not only with such human movements as walking, running, jumping, skating, lifting weights, etc., but also with the flight of birds, the swimming of fishes, and even the creeping and crawling of insects. As an example of Borelli's method we may take his account of the mechanics of lifting a weight, which is illustrated in the accompanying diagram (Illustr. 206). He showed that when muscles and bones co-operate, then the bones serve as levers, while the force exercised by the muscles acts on the shorter arm of the lever. Thus, for example, when the arm is in the position shown in the diagram, then the muscular force required to support the weight, R, will have the same proportion to the weight as the distance OK has to the distance OI. The force exercised by the biceps, CF, must therefore considerably exceed the pull of the weight at B. Borelli estimated that when the arm is held horizontally so as to support a weight of ten pounds on the fingers, then the total force exercised by all the muscles in the arm exceeds the weight many times. It is highly creditable to his insight and candour that, although he set out with the idea of explaining the movements of living organisms mechanically, he yet realized that the contraction and the swelling of the muscles, on which all such movements depend, cannot be purely mechanical, but involves

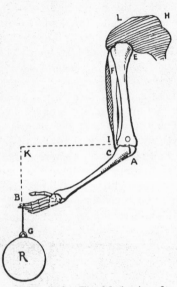

Illustr. 206.—The Mechanics of Muscular Action

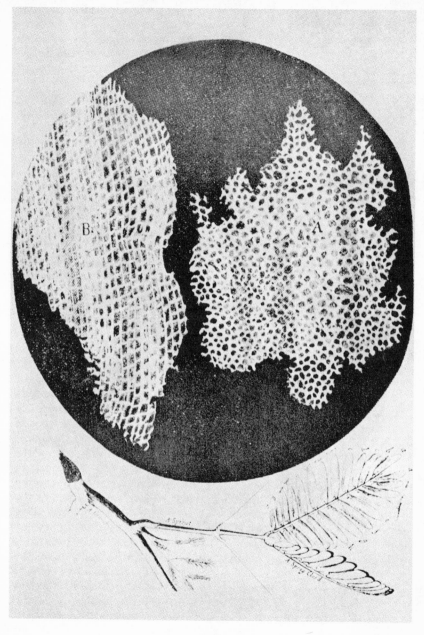

The Cellular Structure of Cork
(A Plate from Hooke's *Micrographia*)

Marcello Malpighi

Antonius Leeuwenhoek

Nehemiah Grew

also complex chemical processes. He held, namely, that neural stimulation had something to do with the contraction and swelling of the muscles, some kind of fermentation taking place there when the fluid coming from the nerves mingles with the blood contained in the muscles.

IV. THE PROGRESS OF MICROSCOPIC BIOLOGY

The range of biological knowledge was greatly extended in the course of the seventeenth century, through the use of the microscope, the story of which has already been briefly told above (see Chapter V). Organisms, and parts of organisms, that could not be observed adequately, if at all, with the naked eye, were now studied closely with the aid of simple and compound microscopes, were fully described, and effectively illustrated. The earliest biological observations with the help of the microscope appear to have been made, in 1610 or earlier, by Galilei, who thus examined the organs of motion and of sense in the smaller animals, and the compound eye of an insect. In 1625 Francisco Stelluti published an account of the anatomy of bees based on microscopic investigation. Harvey appears to have used some kind of magnifying glass for his study of the heart. Twice in the course of his treatise *On the Movement of the Heart and the Blood* (1628) he refers to the use of such lenses. One of these passages is well worth quoting, for it illustrates the enlargement of vision rendered possible by the new instrument. "I have observed that almost all animals have a heart—not only (as Aristotle says) the larger red-blooded creatures, but also the smaller pale-blooded crustacea and shell-fish, such as slugs, snails, mussels, shrimps, crabs, crayfish, and many others; nay, even in wasps, hornets, and flies I have, with the aid of magnifying glasses, myself seen, and made many others see, the heart pulsating at the upper part of what is called the tail" (*op. cit.*, Ch. IV). Hooke, Grew, and others made valuable microscopic studies of biological phenomena. But the most important microscopic biologists of the seventeenth century were Malpighi, Leeuwenhoek, and Swammerdam. Their work in this new and very important field of biology was not only the best in the seventeenth century, but remained unequalled till the nineteenth century.

MALPIGHI

Marcello Malpighi (1628–94) was born at Cavalcuore, near Bologna. In 1656 he was appointed professor of medicine at Pisa, where he became friendly with Borelli. From 1662 till 1666 Malpighi taught at Messina, and from 1666 till 1691 at Bologna. In the latter year he was appointed private physician to Pope Innocent XII, and so spent his last years in Rome. Malpighi's works consist chiefly of papers sent to, and published by, the Royal Society of London, which elected him a Fellow in 1668, and to which he presented his original drawings relating to the silkworm and the chick.

Malpighi took up the study of the lower organisms in the belief that it would throw light on the nature of the higher animals. In that belief he applied the comparative method wherever possible. It was his study of the lung of the frog that led him to the discovery that the lung is not, as used to be supposed, a homogeneous tissue in which the air and the blood mingle, but that it contains air cells, and that a membrane always separates the blood from the air so that they cannot come into immediate contact in the lungs. In 1660, while pursuing these investigations, Malpighi first saw the blood pass through the capillaries embedded in the lung of the frog and connecting the arteries with the veins. Later on he discovered capillaries also in other parts of the body. These important observations relating to the complete circulation of the blood were, of course, only possible through the use of the microscope; but they owed much also to the ingenuity of Malpighi, who first introduced the method of injecting water into the arteries, thus washing the blood from the vascular system and making the blood-vessels more visible.

Malpighi was the first to devote special attention to silkworms. Dissections made under the microscope showed him that these tiny animals have a complex organic structure, and that they breathe through a system of air-tubes, or extremely minute tubules, distributed all over their body. The observation of these tubules in silkworms prepared Malpighi's mind for his next discovery, which affords a striking illustration of his application of the comparative method and of the suggestiveness of analogies. The discovery relates to the subject of vegetable anatomy, to which Hooke had already made an important contribution by his microscopic observation of the cellular structure of the tissue of plants.

Strolling one day through a wood, Malpighi saw the broken branch of a tree, and his curiosity was aroused by some thread-like protrusions round about the fracture. Examining these threads with his pocket-lens, he observed their spiral form and their likeness to the air-tubules of silkworms. This discovery led him to the study of the comparative anatomy of plants, and to the formulation of many speculations and fancies concerning the common characteristics of all living things. One of these interesting conjectures concerned the respiration of living organisms. According to Malpighi, the size of the organs of respiration varies inversely with the grade of perfection of organisms. The less perfect organisms have the larger respiratory organs, while the more perfect organisms have the smaller organs of respiration. Thus plants are full of spiral air-tubules, insects are covered with numerous minute air-tubes, fishes have many gills, whereas man and the higher animals have but a pair of comparatively small lungs. With regard to the function of respiration, Malpighi suggested that respiration somehow promotes the fermentation of the alimental juices.

Of Malpighi's other microscopic researches mention may be made of his discovery of the pigmentary (now called Malpighian) layer of the skin between the surface skin and the true skin, his discovery of the papillae (or bud-like end-organs of taste) in the tongue, and his discovery of certain corpuscles (also called by his name) in the kidney and in the spleen.

Lastly, special mention must be made of Malpighi's contributions to the microscopic study of embryology. Following up the embryo-logical work of Fabricius (of Aquapendente) and Harvey, Malpighi made minute observations of the development of the chick in the egg. The results of these observations were fully described and illustrated by him in his papers *On the Formation of the Chick in the Egg* (1673) and *Observations on the Incubated Egg* (1689), which exercised considerable influence on the subsequent progress of embryology.

SWAMMERDAM

Jan Swammerdam (1637–82) excelled even Malpighi in the study of insect life. He was born at Amsterdam, where his father was a flourishing apothecary and a keen collector of zoological specimens and other curiosities. From his earliest days young Swammerdam took a keen interest in insect life, and in course of time he formed his own collection of some three thousand species of insects. He studied medicine at the University of Leiden, where he met De Graaf and Steno. For a time he stayed in France. In 1667 he took his medical degree, but he did not practise. Instead, he devoted himself to the study of minute anatomy with such self-sacrifice that he injured not only his sight but also his general health, so that he died young. He published very little during his lifetime. But long after his death his writings were collected and edited, with a Life, by Boerhaave, under the title of *The Bible of Nature* (1737).

Swammerdam showed extraordinary manipulative skill, and made a number of additions to the technique of minute anatomy. He made such tiny dissecting instruments—knives, scissors, lancets, scalpels—that he could only grind them with the aid of magnifying glasses. He drew fine glass tubes which were as thin as a bristle at one end, and he used them either to inflate the minute vessels of insects, etc., or to inject coloured liquids into them, so as to make them more easily visible. Sometimes he used melted wax for such injections. He also dissected under water, so that the parts dissected might be separated more readily. And he used oil of turpentine in order to dissolve and remove the fat which covered any parts he wanted to study. The result of his technical resourcefulness and his unsparing pains was that his descriptions and drawings of bees, mayflies, frogs, tadpoles, etc., surpassed any similar attempts made not only in his time but during many subsequent decades.

In the realm of biological theory Swammerdam has the merit of having opposed the idea of spontaneous generation, that is, the belief that some living things emerge out of lifeless matter. It was an old and widespread belief, quite natural so long as there was no microscope, that spontaneous generation of life could and did take place out of slime, mud, or putrefied matter. Even Harvey, notwithstanding his bold-sounding *Ex ovo omnia*, believed that some lower forms of life, notably certain kinds of insects, came into being by spontaneous generation from decaying matter by some kind of metamorphosis. Swammerdam rejected this view utterly. So did the Italian Redi (1618–76), who maintained that in all the cases which he had examined of the alleged spontaneous generation of insects from decaying matter he had discovered, by microscopic examination, that eggs had been deposited there by other insects of the same kind. And Swammerdam, in remarkable anticipation of subsequent discovery, urged that so far from decaying matter producing minute living organisms, it is such living organisms that produce decay in organic matter. He insisted that throughout Nature living things are born only of living things in the way expressed in Harvey's *Ex ovo omnia*—a maxim in the acceptance and application of which Swammerdam was more Harveian than Harvey himself had been.

LEEUWENHOEK

No one revelled so much in the sheer joy of microscopy as did Antony van Leeuwenhoek (1632–1723). He was born at Delft in Holland; he had no schooling worth mentioning, and was a shop assistant for a time. About 1660 he obtained a very modest municipal post in his native town, which left him sufficient leisure to pursue his great hobby. He was entirely self-taught, made his own lenses— in fact, hundreds of them—and with them he observed in a desultory fashion whatever aroused his curiosity. Like Malpighi, he sent numerous papers to the Royal Society of London, which elected him a Fellow in 1680, and to which he subsequently bequeathed twenty-six of his microscopes "as a mark of his gratitude, and acknowledgment of the great honour which he had received from the Royal Society." His chief works were published under the general title of *The Secrets of Nature* (*Arcana Naturae*, 4 vols., Delft, 1695–1719); a selection of them appeared in English under the title of *Microscopical Observations* (London, 1798).

Reference has already been made to Malpighi's and Leeuwenhoek's completion of Harvey's observations of the circulation of the blood. Leeuwenhoek was determined to see the whole circulation. After various attempts with other animals, he turned his microscope to the tail of the tadpole, in 1688, and this is his account of what he saw. "A sight presented itself more delightful than any mine eyes have ever beheld; for here I discovered more than fifty circulations of the blood in different places, while the animal lay quiet in the water, and I could bring it before my microscope at my wish. For I saw not only that in many places the blood was conveyed through exceedingly minute vessels from the middle of the tail toward the edges, but that each of the vessels had a curve or turning, and carried the blood back toward the middle of the tail, in order to be conveyed again to the heart. Hereby it plainly appeared to me that the blood-vessels which I now saw in the animal, and which bear the names of arteries and veins are in fact one and the same; that is to say, that they are properly termed arteries so long as they convey the blood to the furthest extremities of its vessels, and veins when they bring it back to the heart. And thus it appears that an artery and a vein are one and the same vessel prolonged or extended."

Of Leeuwenhoek's independent discoveries, one of the most important was that of unicellular organisms (now called Protozoa). He relates that he first observed the single-celled creatures in 1675 in some rain-water which had been standing a few days in a new earthen pot. They seemed to be about one ten-thousandth part the size of the water-fleas or water-lice which had been described by Swammerdam, and which are visible to the naked eye. Some of them appeared to consist of five, six, seven, or eight clear globules without any visible film to hold them together. When they moved they put forward two little horns. The part between the horns looked flat, though the rest of the body was roundish, sharpening a little towards the end, where they had a tail [stalk] nearly four times the length of the whole body and of the thickness of a spider-web (as seen through the microscope), and having a globule at its end. Some of these tiny animals (or "living atoms," as he calls them) seemed to be less than one-twenty-fifth part the size of a globule of blood.

Leeuwenhoek's comparison of the size of Protozoa with that of a globule of blood is significant. For, notwithstanding the rival claims made on behalf of Malpighi and Swammerdam, it was probably Leeuwenhoek who first clearly observed and definitely made known the existence of red blood corpuscles. He was also the first to point out that these red corpuscles are circular in the case of human and mammalian blood, but oval in the case of fishes and frogs.

Six years after his discovery of protozoa Leeuwenhoek discovered even more minute forms of life than these "living atoms," namely, bacteria. In 1683 he described his discovery as follows. Looking through a magnifying glass, he saw between his teeth a little white matter as thick as wetted flour. He mixed it with pure rain-water, and to his surprise perceived many small living animals moving about. They had various shapes, sizes, and movements. Some were long and nimble; some were shorter and spun about like a top; others were circular or oval, moved about like swarms of gnats, and seemed so small that many thousands of them might exist in the space occupied by a grain of sand.

Brief mention must be made of some of Leeuwenhoek's many other discoveries. He discovered that aphides (plant-lice) are generated without fertilization, the young ones emerging from the body of the unfertilized female. He showed that the scarlet dye-stuff called cochineal is derived from insects (cochineal insects), not from berries, as used to be supposed. He discovered rotifers, and observed that they turn into dry dust when the water containing them evaporates, but that they revive when they are put into water again. He also observed that the heart muscles are branched, yet, like the voluntary muscles, are striped. And he investigated spermatozoa, the structure of the eye-lens, the structure of bones, yeast-cells, etc.

Leeuwenhoek was first and last a great microscopic observer. He took little or no interest in mere theory. Possibly he felt no great capacity for comprehensive theories, and so fought shy of them. But it is to his credit that on the question of spontaneous generation he sided with Redi and Swammerdam, and definitely rejected its claims to rest on any accurately observed evidence.

GREW AND CAMERARIUS

Before closing this brief account of the microscopic biologists of the seventeenth century it is necessary to say something about the progress of vegetable anatomy, and especially about the work of Grew and Camerarius in this field of research. As has already been mentioned above, Hooke was the first to describe the cellular structure of plants, in his *Micrographia*, 1665 (see Illustr. 207). He estimated that 1 cubic inch of cork must contain about 1,200,000,000 cells. He also made microscopic investigations into the structure of the stinging nettle, of moss, of a leaf fungus, etc. Hooke, however, did not pursue the matter very far, as his interest lay in other directions—indeed, in too many directions. More important services in this field of research were rendered by Malpighi, whose work has already been described above. But the most important discoveries in connection with the anatomy and sexuality of plants were made by Grew and Camerarius.

Nehemiah Grew (1641–1712) studied medicine at first in Cambridge and then in Leiden, where he obtained the degree of M.D. in 1671. Thereupon he set up as a medical practitioner in London, became a Fellow of the Royal Society and eventually its Secretary (1677). His complete *Anatomy of Plants* was published in 1682, but part of it had already appeared in 1671. Like Malpighi, to whom he expressed his indebtedness for the discovery of air-tubules, etc., in plants, Grew was devoted to the comparative method and the exploitation of analogies between plants and animals, but, unlike Malpighi and more like his Dutch contemporaries, Grew was rather addicted to theological digressions. He described his microscopic observations of the anatomy of plants with great detail, pictured them with the utmost care, and did much to make people realize the peculiar organic structure of vegetable tissue. Among other things, he observed the pores in the upper surface of leaves, and thereupon suggested that leaves are the organs of respiration of plants. But his most remarkable discovery was that of the sexuality of plants, whose flowers he regarded as their sexual organs. He described the stamens (or "attire") of flowers as the male organs, the pollen as their seeds, and the pistils as the female organs. And all plants were regarded by him as hermaphrodites, that is, as uniting the characters of both sexes. In this he was, of course, mistaken. The subject of the sexuality of plants was dealt with more fully and experimentally by Camerarius.

Rudolf Jakob Camerarius (1665–1721) was born in Tübingen, Germany, where in 1688 he became professor of botany and director of the botanical gardens. His researches are described in his *Letter on the Sex of Plants* (1694). (A German translation of the Latin original was published, in 1899, in Ostwald's *Klassiker*, No. 105.) Having observed that a fruit-bearing mulberry-tree near which there was no pollen-bearing tree produced only empty, sterile seed-vessels, he decided to investigate the subject experimentally. He chose for this purpose such common plants as dog's mercury, having flowers of different sexes. Planting some of its ripe seeds in soil, he saw that they produced two kinds of plants, which, though similar in many ways yet differed in this respect, namely, that some of them had only stamens but no seeds or fruit, while the others bore fruit but did not have any stamens. When he isolated the fruit-bearing plants from the pollen-producing plants, then seed-vessels still appeared on the former, but they were sterile. He next experimented with plants in which both stamens and pistils grow on the same plant, such as maize and *ricinus* (the tropical plant from which castor-oil is derived). He found that when their stigmata were removed before the anthers were fully developed then the seed-vessels were always empty and sterile. He concluded, accordingly, that the anthers are male organs having pollen as the fertilizing seeds, and that the ovary and the style function as female organs. Even Camerarius, however, thought only of self-pollination, and had no idea of cross-pollination.

(See W. A. Locy, *Biology and Its Makers*, 3rd ed., 1928, and *The Growth of Biology*, New York, 1925; E. Nordenskiöld, *The History of Biology*, 1929; J. von Sachs, *History of Botany, 1530–1860*, Oxford, 1890; C. Singer, *The Evolution of Anatomy*, London, 1925, and *A Short History of Biology*, Oxford, 1931; C. Dobell, *Antony van Leeuwenhoek and his "Little Animals,"* London, 1932; Agnes Arber, *Herbals*, 2nd editn., Cambridge, 1938; C. E. Raven, *John Ray, Naturalist: His Life and Works*, Cambridge, 1942; F. J. Cole, *A History of Comparative Anatomy*, London, 1944; C. Singer and C. Rabin, *A Prelude to Modern Science*, Cambridge, 1946 (a study of the *Tabulae Anatomicae Sex* of Vesalius); on Harvey, see H. P. Bayon in *Annals of Science*, 1938 and 1939, Vols. III and IV.)

CHAPTER XIX

MEDICINE

MEDICINE AND SCIENCE

Medicine (including surgery) is essentially a practical art. It is the art of curing, mitigating, and preventing disease. Modern medicine is intimately connected with the biological sciences (especially anatomy and physiology), with chemistry, and physics. But the medicine of the sixteenth and seventeenth centuries was not yet modern, and benefited very little, if at all, from the advances made in biology, chemistry, and physics during those great centuries, in which the chief foundations of future medicine were laid. An account of these advances has already been given in previous chapters. Obviously the anatomical work of Vesalius, Harvey's discovery of the ciruclation of the blood, Lower's success in carrying out the operation of blood transfusion, Boyle's, Hooke's, Lower's and Mayow's work on the function of air in animal economy, and Leeuwenhoek's and Kircher's bacteriological discoveries, had most important bearings on the practice of medicine, surgery, and hygiene. But the medical practitioners and their patients were held fast in the shackles of earlier traditions, and did not take kindly to the new-fangled discoveries of science. Even the great Harvey's practice "fell mightily" after the publication of his discovery of the circulation of the blood. Presumably his patients lost confidence in him when he appeared in the rôle of an innovator, although Harvey himself was old-fashioned enough to believe in witches even after the Belgian doctor Johannes Wierus had clearly exposed the folly and cruelty of witch hunting and witch burning (*De Praestigiis Daemonum*, 1563). Even exceptionally competent practitioners like Thomas Sydenham paid little or no attention to the biological discoveries of the time, owing perhaps to the superabundance of fanciful hypotheses and the difficulty of sifting the grain from the chaff. Still, some medical advances were made in the course of the sixteenth and seventeenth centuries, even if their value was largely relative to the medical backwardness of the times.

THE MEDICAL HERITAGE

Sickness, and indeed trouble of any kind, is apt to make people credulous. In their desperation even otherwise critical people are prone to try anything; and the majority of people are not critical even now. In this way it came about that during long centuries all sorts of remedies were tried; and since people rarely distinguish between recovery *after* a certain treatment, recovery *because* of it, and recovery *in spite of* it, a very extensive, unofficial collection of alleged remedies accumulated in the course of the ages. It was an amazing collection. Even the official London Pharmacopoeia of 1618 included such delectable medicaments as bile, blood, claws, cock's comb, feathers, fur, hair, perspiration, saliva, scorpion, snake's skin, spider web, and wood-lice! Blood-letting was resorted to on all sorts of occasions. And astrology and magic were the intimate associates of medicine. These were by no means unmitigated evils. For the restriction of, say, blood-letting to such times as when the Sun was in certain signs of the zodiac may have saved people from this dangerous operation in the same kind of way as the restriction of hours for the sale of alcohol is alleged to save them from drunkenness, etc.; and the belief in the remedial powers of contact with kings and saints, pontiffs and "personalities," at least saved some people from trying the orthodox medicines, a sample of which has been enumerated above.

Moreover, there was little or no organization of medical practitioners. Almost anybody could practise medicine. Trained doctors were mostly employed only at Court, by the nobility, and other wealthy people. The masses, if they resorted to "professional" help at all, went to the apothecary, who was often an ordinary grocer or spice-merchant. Surgical operations were usually carried out by common barbers, some of whom were certainly skilful. In England an attempt was made in 1509 to restrict the right of medical practice to such as passed a qualifying examination and received a licence to practise. But unlicensed people were allowed to treat simple diseases long afterwards. When, thanks to the exertions of Thomas Linacre, the Royal College of Physicians was founded in London, the Charter given to it by Henry VIII described the deplorable state of affairs prevalent at the time. "Before this period," the Charter says, "a great multitude of ignorant persons, of whom the greater part had no insight into physic, nor in any other kind of learning; some could not even read the letter on the book, so far forth, that common artificers, as smiths, weavers, and women, boldly and accustomably took upon them great cures, to the high displeasure of God, great infamy of the faculty, and the grievous hurt, damage and destruction of many of the King's liege people." But many of the more learned medical practitioners appear to have done quite as much harm as did these illiterate practitioners. Paracelsus, one of the great doctors of the period, tells us that the best thing he could say about the famous physicians of his time was, not that they did much good, but that they did the least harm. For, he adds, some poison their patients with mercury, and

Theophrastus Bombast Paracelsus

The Title-Page of the First London Pharmacopoeia

others purge or bleed them to death. There are some who have learned so much that their learning has driven out all their common sense, and there are others who care a great deal more for their own profit than for the health of their patients (*Paragranum*, IV, p. 216, ed. 1658).

Of the theories current among the learned medical men of the period the most usual were the Greek doctrine of the four elementary qualities (hot, cold, dry, and moist) and the associated doctrine of the four "humours," or bodily juices (blood, phlegm, black bile, and yellow bile). Health was believed to depend on a proper proportion of the four; disease was supposed to result from their disproportion. Blood-letting was accordingly often resorted to as a means of restoring the proper balance among the "humours," though recourse was also had to special diet and the administration of special herbs and other medicaments which were believed to be capable of redressing the balance of the humours concerned. Another Greek theory was that of the "vital spirits." Each part of the body was alleged to have its specific "vital spirits," which had to be regulated somehow in case of illness. Paracelsus and van Helmont substituted *archei* for "vital spirits"; but that was a mere change of name of the old illusory doctrine. Then there were various astrological beliefs widely accepted and acted on by learned doctors. Man was regarded as a small model of the Universe, and the several parts of the human body were believed to be correlated with corresponding celestial bodies. Diagrams of "Zodiac man," purporting to indicate the connection between the various parts of the human body with the corresponding constellations, or signs of the zodiac, were in common use among learned doctors in order to determine the best season for administering certain remedies. For example, blood-letting was not practised when the Sun was in the constellation of the Bull, the Twins, the Lion, the Virgin, or of Capricorn; and so with other kinds of treatment. The association of astrology with medicine in the seventeenth century is still attested by the name of the familiar kind of catarrh called "influenza." The name was given by Italian doctors, in the seventeenth century, because they believed it was due to "the influence" of the stars. Paracelsus, it is true, denounced the association of astrology with medicine, and proclaimed that the stars control nothing in us. But he only substituted for it his own equally delusive fancy when he added that the Archeus, not the stars, controls man's destiny (*Paramirum*, 1529, Cap. II, and *De Tartaro—Opera*, ed. 1658, Vol. I, pp. 7, 528, and elsewhere).

One result of less doubtful value of the doctrine of humours was probably uroscopy, that is, the examination of a patient's urine in order to diagnose his illness and to prescribe for it. This mode of diagnosis was so widespread during a period of several centuries that the urinary flask served as the doctor's "sign," much as three

Illustr. 213.—Uroscopy

balls still serve as the "sign" of an English pawnbroker. Illustr. 213 shows a doctor's surgery with its large assortment of urinary flasks, and the urinary ritual. Uroscopy was denounced by Paracelsus; but it has survived nevertheless, and still forms a prominent part in the ritual of the medical officers of insurance companies.

Considering the general state of medicine in the sixteenth and seventeenth centuries, and even long afterwards, it is not surprising to find such adverse criticisms of it as those of Paracelsus, John Woodward (*The State of Physick*, 1718), and others. As a rule, however, the critics were little, if at all, better than were other doctors among their contemporaries. Paracelsus wanted to set himself up as a kind of arch-doctor. "You men of Montpellier, and Cologne, and Vienna, you Germans, men of the Danube and Rhine, and the Maritime Islands, Athenians, Greeks, Arabs, and Israelites . . . you shall follow me. . . . I am to be the monarch" (*Paragranum*, 1531, Preface; *Opera*, ed. 1658, Vol. I, p. 183). A medical Hitler born before his time, his aggressive, pretentious language made one of his Christian names (Bombastus) synonymous with all that is conceited, inflated, and pompous (bombastic). Woodward naïvely used fossil shells as ingredients in the medicines he gave to his patients in order to prove that fossil shells and sea-shells "have the same *vires* [virtues] and effects in Medicine when inwardly administered to Animal Bodies" (*The Natural History of the Earth*, Part I, ed. 1723, p. 24). Nor is it surprising to find such gibes associated with medical practitioners as that expressed in the following rhymes about John Coakley Lettsom, a prosperous London doctor of the eighteenth century:

> When any sick to me apply,
> I physics, bleeds, and sweats 'em;
> If, after that, they choose to die,
> Why, verily! I Lettsom.
>
> (See J. J. Abraham, *Lettsom*, 1933, p. 478.)

The general unsatisfactoriness of the state of medicine in the sixteenth and seventeenth centuries is sufficiently attested by a few data furnished by Sir William Petty (1623–87) relating to the principal hospitals in London and Paris. They are contained in the second of his *Essays in Political Arithmetic, Concerning the People, Housing, Hospitals, etc., of London and Paris* (1682).

"It appears that A.D. 1678 there entered into the Hospital of La Charité 2,647 souls, of which there died there within the said year 338, which is above an eighth part of the said 2,647; and that in the same year there entered into L'Hôtel Dieu 21,491, and that there died out of that number 5,630, which is above one quarter, so as about half the said 5,630, being 2,815, seem to have died for want of as good usage and accommodation as might have been had at La Charité.

"Moreover, in the same year 1679 there entered into La Charité 3,118, of which there died 452, which is above a seventh part, and in the same year there entered into L'Hôtel Dieu 28,635, of which there died 8,397; and in both the said years 1678 and 1679 (being very different in their degrees of mortality) there entered into L'Hôtel Dieu 28,635 and 21,491—in all 50,126, the medium whereof is 25,063; and there died out of the same in the said two years, 5,630 and 8,397—in all 14,027, the medium whereof is 7,013.

"There entered in the said years into La Charité 2,647 and 3,118, in all 5,765, the medium whereof is 2,882, whereof there died 338 and 452, in all 790, the medium whereof is 395.

"Now, if there died out of L'Hôtel Dieu 7,013 per annum, and the proportion of those that died out of L'Hôtel Dieu is double to those that died out of La Charité (as by the above numbers it appears to be near thereabouts), then it follows that half the said numbers of 7,013, being 3,506, did not die by natural necessity, but by the evil administration of that hospital.

"This conclusion seemed at the first sight very strange, and rather to be some mistake or chance than a solid and real truth; but considering the same matter as it appeared at London, we were more reconciled to the belief of it, viz. :—

"In the Hospital of St. Bartholomew in London, there was sent out and cured in the year 1685, 1,764 persons, and there died out of the said hospital 252. Moreover, there were sent out and cured out of St. Thomas's Hospital 1,523, and buried 209—that is to say, there were cured in both hospitals 3,287, and buried out of both hospitals 461, and consequently cured and buried 3,748, of which number the 461 buried is less than an eighth part; whereas at La Charité the part that died was more than an eighth part; which shows that out of the most poor and wretched hospitals of London there died fewer in proportion than out of the best in Paris.

"Furthermore, it hath been above shown that there died out of La Charité at a medium 395 per annum, and 141 out of Les Incurables, making in all 536; and that out of St. Bartholomew's and St. Thomas's Hospitals, London, there died at a medium but 461, of which Les Incurables are part; which shows that although there be more people in London than in Paris, yet there went at London not so many people to hospitals as there did at Paris, although the poorest hospitals at London were better than the best at Paris; which shows that the poorest people at London have better accommodation in their own houses than the best hospital of Paris affordeth."

The ablest men in the medical profession, if they had a strong scientific bent, turned their chief attention to subjects other than medicine, such as biology (Harvey, for instance), physics (Gilbert), geology (Agricola, Lister, and Woodward, e.g.), or psychology and philosophy (Locke), or demography (Petty). Apparently medicine offered them little attraction as a field for scientific research, as distinguished from empirical and traditional routine. There were some exceptions, of course. Thomas Sydenham was perhaps the chief of these exceptions. He and some others like him tried to build the foundations of a rational, scientific medicine by close observation and description of specific ailments; and Sanctorius even introduced some quantitative methods by the use of the clinical thermometer, the pulsimeter, and the weighing machine. These were exceptional men. Their work will be dealt with presently. Unfortunately, their influence on their contemporaries appears to have been negligible. Nevertheless, in the history of any subject the advances made are the most important things to chronicle, even if the extent of their practical neglect must not be passed over in silence. And the sixteenth and seventeenth centuries did witness a number of improvements in medicine and surgery, even if they are not comparable with the advances made in astronomy, mathematics, physics, or even in the biological sciences.

The advances made in medicine in the course of the two centuries with which we are concerned here may be summarized under four principal heads, namely, (1) the use of scientific instruments in connection with medicine; (2) improvements in the general methods of treatment; (3) the introduction of new medicaments; and (4) improvements in the methods of studying diseases. The subjects just enumerated are not entirely separable, but they may be described separately nevertheless.

SCIENTIFIC INSTRUMENTS IN MEDICINE

The advances of modern science, as has already been shown repeatedly in the preceding chapters, were intimately bound up with the application of quantitative methods and the use of scientific instruments for the measurement of various physical quantities. The progress of medicine similarly depended on the adoption of quantitative methods and the use of suitable scientific instruments. The seventeenth century witnessed important beginnings in both directions. The scientific instruments in question did not have to be invented by medical men. They were there already, even if they were still imperfect, and had only to be adopted or adapted for medical use. They were the thermometer, the pendulum, and the balance. It is significant that their medical use was mainly due to Sanctorius (1561–1636), a medical friend of Galilei. Until his time, and even long afterwards so far as general practice was concerned, medical diagnosis was purely qualitative. The state of a patient was described as "feverish," and if it changed he would be less feverish or more feverish; but there was no reliable way of indicating these states and changes by reference to an objective standard of measurement. Again, although the pulse-beat was known to vary considerably, these variations were usually described qualitatively and rather fancifully, not by reference to an objectively measured unit of time. Similarly, although it was commonly known that the skin gave off volatile substances from the body, and the condition of health or disease was believed to be in some way connected with these "invisible perspirations," no attempt had been made to measure them in any way until Sanctorius took the matter in hand.

As has already been indicated in Chapter V, the first clinical

thermometer was made by Sanctorius. Illustr. 214 shows its serpentine shape and the manner of its use. The upper, globular end was put into the mouth of the patient, the lower end of the tube was put into a vessel of water. The tube was graduated, by means of glass beads, at arbitrary intervals between fixed points which appear to have been determined respectively by the application of snow and of the flame of a candle to the bulb of the thermometer. It was a crude instrument, no doubt, but it was a promising beginning, and by means of it Sanctorius discovered the approximate degree of heat of the human body in health and the fluctuations of temperature during illness (*Commentaria in artem medicinalem Galeni*, 1612).

Illustr. 214.—Sanctorius'
Clinical Thermometer

That the pulse-beat might be treated as a symptom of health or of illness was believed in ancient times already, and Nicholas de Cusa attempted to measure the rate of the pulse-beat by means of a water-clock. Such measurement was difficult and unreliable. Sanctorius either introduced, or extended, the use of the pulsimeter (*pulsilogium*) for the more accurate determination of the rate of the pulse-beat. The pulsimeter consisted of a leaden bob attached to a long thread, the length of which could be adjusted gradually until the rate of oscillation of the pendulum thus formed coincided with the patient's pulse-beat. The relative lengths of thread thus afforded a basis of comparison and measurement of different rates of pulse-beat. To facilitate such measurement, a scale was attached to the pulsimeter so that the length of the pendulum, after it had been adjusted to synchronize with the pulse-beat, could be read off at a glance. Illustr. 215 shows two forms of pulsimeter, the principle being the same in both.

The use of the pulsimeter rested, of course, on the observation
that the rate of oscillation of a pendulum varies with its length.
The exact relation between the two was established by Galilei, who
discovered experimentally that the period of oscillation varies as
the square root of the length of the pendulum, so that, for example,
when the length of a pendulum is increased fourfold its period of
oscillation is doubled, when the length is increased ninefold its

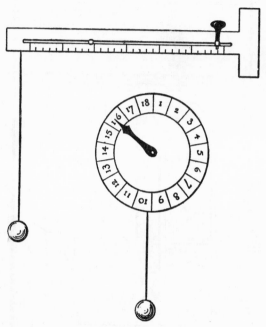

Illustr. 215.—Two Types of Pulsimeter

period of oscillation is trebled, and so on. The pulsimeter was
certainly an improvement on the water-clock, but was rather
arbitrary and somewhat deceptive because it had no reference to a
standard unit of time. This was remedied towards the end of the
seventeenth century. In 1690 John Foyer used a seconds pendulum
for measuring the rate of pulse-beat. By means of it he also estimated
the correlation between the rate of pulse-beat and the rate of
breathing.

The most important contributions which Sanctorius made to the
quantitative study of the body and its functions were those which
he published in his *Ars de statica medicina* (Venice, 1614; English
translation by John Quincy, London, 1712). In it Sanctorius

formulated, as he said, "the experience of thirty years," during a great part of which his life was "in the balance." Having constructed a large balance with a chair in one of the scales (see Illustr. 216), he spent a great deal of time in this weighing-chair with a table near him, and carefully recorded variations in his weight under all

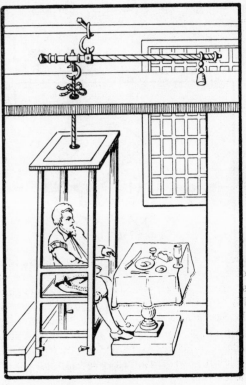

Illustr. 216.—Sanctorius' Weighing-Chair

sorts of conditions—before and after meals, when waking or sleeping, during activity and when at rest, when in a state of calm and when in a state of emotional excitement, etc. His conclusions are given in a series of about five hundred aphorisms arranged under the following headings: Insensible Perspiration, Air and Water, Meat and Drink, Sleep and Watching, Exercise and Rest, Affections of the Mind and Venery. The most general result at which he arrived was that the maintenance of health depends upon a proper balance of intake and output on the part of our bodily economy. But some of his detailed results are worth quoting. "Insensible perspiration

alone discharges much more than all the servile Evacuations
together. Insensible Perspiration is either made by the Pores of the
Body, which is all over perspirable, and covered with a Skin like a
Net; or it is performed by Respiration through the Mouth, which
usually, in the Space of one Day, amounts to about the Quantity
of half a Pound, as may plainly be made to appear by breathing
upon a Glass. If eight Pounds of Meat and Drink are taken in
one Day, the Quantity that usually goes off by insensible Perspiration in that Time is five Pounds" (Section I, Aphorisms 4-6). "With
seven Hours sleep the Body insensibly perspires, and without any
Trouble, twice as much as when awake" (Section III, Aphorism 2).
His contempt for the medicine of his time is betrayed in his remark
apropos of the plague, "Very few of the Wealthier people are cured
by Medicines, but a great many of the poorer Sort recover without
them" (Section I, Aphorism 139).

The only other instrument of the period that need be mentioned
here is the *speculum auris*. A speculum, or reflector, of some sort for
the better inspection of certain parts of the body appears to have
been in use in early times, certainly in the second century A.D.
But a speculum for the special examination of the ear seems to have
been first invented by Fabriz von Hilden in 1600.

IMPROVED TREATMENT

Some of the improvements in medical treatment related to the
prevention of contagion and infection. The existence of infectious
diseases was, of course, known already to the ancients, and the
Bible (notably the Book of Leviticus) contains some instructions
relating to the diagnosis of leprosy and the isolation of lepers. There
are also indications in the Bible and elsewhere of some association
between pestilence and flies and mice. During many centuries the
practice of isolation, according to the prescriptions in the Book of
Leviticus, was carried on more or less. But, although epidemics of
many kinds were common and devastating, there was little or no
understanding of their nature or of how to deal with them. From
the fourteenth century onwards, however, increasingly drastic steps
were taken in the direction of isolation and prevention. In 1377
the city of Ragusa took steps to prevent the entry of plague-stricken
people by isolating all suspected victims in a place outside the city
for a period of forty days (*quarantina*, which thus came to be used
in the general sense of isolation of those suspected of disease). In
1533 plague ordinances were issued in Paris ordering the notification
and isolation of all people suffering from plague, prohibiting the
transport of infected goods, and insisting on the cleansing of roads
and gutters, and the evacuation of all houses in which people had

Illustr. 217.—Overall to Protect
from Infection

*(Copyright of the Wellcome Historical
Medical Museum)*

died of the plague. The example of Paris was followed by London during the Great Plague in 1665. These measures no doubt helped to prevent the results from being even more appalling than they actually were. Anyway, the recognition that infection could be carried by things as well as by persons induced seventeenth-century doctors to wear overalls and to cover even their heads and faces in special gear when visiting cases of infectious disease. Illustr. 217 shows such an outfit. The strangest thing about it is the long nose covering. It was stuffed with aromatic substances. The idea that aromatic substances might help to ward off plague was the result of the popular association of plague with polluted air or miasma. In the fifteenth century, if not earlier, doctors and others used to carry about with them 'amber apples," composed of amber and aromatic drugs, which they smelled all the time they were near cases of plague or other infectious diseases. Sweet herbs and other aromatic substances long enjoyed popular and even professional favour in spite of their notorious failure to prevent infection. But the practice of wearing special overalls when dealing with infectious cases was a real improvement.

A number of improvements were also made in connection with surgical operations and the treatment of wounds generally. In 1514 Giovanni da Vigo introduced the practice of ligaturing arteries (instead of using red-hot irons) to prevent haemorrhage. The practice was extended in 1545 by Ambroise Paré, the famous surgeon, and in 1674 Morel, a French surgeon, invented the method of compressing the main artery by means of a tourniquet. In 1646 Marco Aurelio Severino introduced the use of snow and ice as a local (freezing) anaesthetic for operations. In 1536 Paré, thanks to a chance discovery, found a new and better treatment of gunshot wounds. Such wounds were regarded as poisoned by the gunpowder, and were usually treated by the agonizing method of pouring boiling elder oil into them. Thanks to a shortage of elder oil, Paré tried successfully a simple ointment made of attar of roses, turpentine, and yolk of egg. In 1616 Cesare Magati advocated a simple and better treatment of wounds generally, urging more particularly that their healing is delayed by a too frequent change of bandages. And in 1696 Augustin Bellosta taught the need of protecting wounds from infecting impurities contained in the air, and advocated the application of alcohol to wounds so as to prevent their festering.

Among other advances in remedial treatment the following were the most noteworthy. From 1550 onwards Hollerius and other oculists regularly prescribed spectacles for short-sighted people. Hydropathic treatment was advocated in 1547 by Georges Bernard Penot, of Toulouse. Massage was applied by Paré in 1575, especially for the bedridden. In 1650 Francis Glisson recommended massage and gymnastic exercises for the cure of rickets. In 1700 Hendryk van Deventer advocated the treatment of such troubles as rickets, atrophied muscles, contracted tendons, and crooked legs by means of bandages and mechanical apparatus. Artificial respiration in cases of asphyxiation appears to have been introduced, by Johann Schenck von Grafenberg, in 1584.

The sixteenth and seventeenth centuries also saw the beginning of artificial inventions intended to replace to some extent various parts of the body lost or injured by accident or disease. An artificial hand was first designed and made (of iron) in 1505, by a German knight, Götz von Berlichingen, who had lost his right hand in battle. (The "iron hand" is still in favour among German jingoes.) In 1575 Paré made artificial eyes of gold and silver; in 1617 Fabricius advocated the use of artificial eyes made of glass. Artificial ears were designed in the same year as artificial eyes (1575), by Caspar Tagliacozza. In 1640 Marcus Banzer succeeded in replacing a damaged ear-drum by an artificial one, which he described in his *De auditione laesa.*

However paradoxical it may seem, one of the greatest improvements made in connection with the treatment of patients consisted in giving them less treatment than had been customary. Medical practitioners had rather got into the habit of prescribing complicated medicines, in the belief perhaps that the more numerous the ingredients the more likely was it that one of them would prove to be the right one. The danger with such "gun-shot" remedies was that much harm might be done by the wrong ingredients. The danger was fully appreciated by some of the more critical doctors, notably by Thomas Sydenham, whose policy it was to "wait and see," and to interfere as little as possible by means of drugs. This policy and the corresponding theory had been brought home to him by extensive bedside experience, and by his critical attitude towards the traditional nostrums. He saw in many of the phases of a disease the efforts of the bodily organism itself to get rid of its disorder; and he believed that the best thing the doctor could do was to keep the ring, as it were, and give the body every chance of exercising its native curative powers, which might only be hindered by the administration of drugs, by bleeding, etc. "A disease," he writes, ". . . is nothing more than an effort of Nature, who strives with might and main to restore the health of the patient by the elimination of the morbific matter" (*Works*, ed. by R. A. Latham, London, 1848–50, Vol. I, p. 29); and elsewhere he praises Hippocrates because "he required no more of art than to assist nature when she languished, and to check her when her efforts were too violent . . . for this sagacious observer found that nature alone terminates distempers, and works a cure with the assistance of a few simple medicines, and sometimes even without any medicines at all." In another passage Sydenham prescribes a diet of whey as a cure for rheumatism, and adds characteristically: "Should any one despise this method for its simplicity, I would let him know, that only weak minds scorn things for being plain and simple" (*Works*, ed. Latham, Vol. II, p. 26).

In the same spirit he commended fresh air in sick rooms, and small beer for his patients, realizing that the plain water of seventeenth-century London was a dangerous beverage. Sydenham's ideas spread beyond England. On the Continent of Europe they were embraced with enthusiasm by Georg Ernst Stahl, and advocated by him in a form which showed a marked leaning towards psychiatry.

NEW MEDICAMENTS

The sixteenth and seventeenth centuries witnessed the introduction, or at least the wider adoption, of a considerable number of new medicines. The names by which these were described, and the secrecy and mystery in which prescriptions were frequently wrapped, as well as the lack of adequate sources of information, make it rather uncertain in some cases what was the precise character of certain medicines, and whether they were really new discoveries, or merely rediscoveries, or only a continuation of already existing practices. The main facts, however, may be summarized as follows.

Paracelsus, whose contributions to chemistry have already been dealt with in Chapter XV, is usually credited with the introduction of several new drugs. The external application of mercury in cases of "love pestilence" (syphilis) appears to have been known at least as early as 1494, but Paracelsus helped towards a wider adoption of this treatment from 1526 onwards; and, in 1540, Peter Andreas Matthiolus prescribed mercury also for internal use in cases of syphilis. About the same time (1526) Paracelsus also prescribed medicines containing preparations of antimony, copper, iron, lead, and milk of sulphur. He appears also to have used some preparation of opium. But there is no ground for crediting him with any of the many other preparations commonly attributed to him.

Illustr. 218.—Antimony Cup

Thanks partly to the influence of Paracelsus and partly to that of Algaroth († 1603), preparations of antimony were popular remedies in the sixteenth and seventeenth centuries, and antimony cups (or emetic cups) had a considerable vogue. These cups were made of antimony. When wine was left in them for some time, the tartar in the wine apparently combined with the oxide on the cup so as to form a tartar emetic. Illustr. 218 shows such a cup with the boastful German inscription: "Thou art a wonder of Nature and all men's certain cure." In any case, tartar emetic (potassium antimony tartrate), which seems to have been introduced in 1631 by Adrian van Mynsicht, was the most important medicine obtained from antimony, though the Paris Faculty of Physicians banned the use of antimonial remedies in 1566, and the ban continued for a whole century.

The medicinal use of iron appears to have originated in astrological considerations. Iron was associated with Mars, the martial god of "blood and iron." Salts of iron were accordingly prescribed for the anaemic and the weak; and they are still in use as a tonic.

In the seventeenth century Sydenham and Willis made extensive use of iron in their medicines, because they found that good results followed, though they did not pretend to understand its action. The original reasons for the medicinal use of silver and gold were on a par with those for the use of iron. Silver was associated with the silvery Moon, and the Moon with the brain; so preparations of silver were prescribed in the sixteenth century, and earlier, for cases of epilepsy and melancholia. Similarly, gold was associated with the golden Sun, and therefore with life. The alchemists sold "potable gold" throughout Europe as a cure for every evil under the Sun, and as an elixir for the prolongation of life. Even reputable doctors like Glauber, Lemery, and Kenelm Digby prepared the elixir. Some of the golden elixirs sold to the public actually contained no gold at all; and it is not difficult to surmise where the gold went to.

Of the remaining medicaments introduced or revived in the sixteenth century the following are the most noteworthy. Belladonna was used by Conrad Gesner in 1540 to relieve pain. The external use of arsenic appears to have been revived by Gabriele Fallopia in 1550. Moxa was introduced into Europe from the East, for use in cauterization, by Prosper Albinus in 1580. In the same year Fabio Columna used valerian for epilepsy; and Rembertus Dodonaeus used nasturtium as a remedy for scurvy, and tomatoes for various medicinal purposes. The use of calomel in medicine appears to have been revived by Joseph de Chesne (Quercetanus) in 1595; it seems to have been known to the Alexandrians and the Arabs.

The early decades of the seventeenth century witnessed the earliest use of Chinese gamboge (a yellow gum resin) as a drastic aperient, and the medicinal use of ammonia, both by Raymond Minderer, in 1610. Arnica was first prescribed in 1613, by Jacob Theodor Tabernaemontanus, as a remedy for haemorrhoidal colic. Copaiba oil or balsam was first recommended by Father Acugua in 1638. The most successful of the new medicaments, the powder obtained from the bark of the "fever tree" (cinchona) from Loxa in Ecuador, was introduced into Europe about 1633 and proved invaluable in the treatment of malaria. It was confused with the powder (an inferior febrifuge) obtained from another tree, the Peruvian balsam or *quina-quina*, and hence the name quinine was applied to cinchona. The history of this drug has been greatly confused, but the errors and confusions have now been resolved and the romantic story of the cure of the Countess of Chinchon by cinchona proved a mere fable by the scholarly researches of the late A. W. Haggis (*Bulletin of the History of Medicine*, 1941, Vol. X, pp. 417–59 and 568–92). The Jesuits took it up and used it extensively, so that it became known also as "Jesuits' bark" or "Jesuits' powder." In England and France the remedy became popular through Robert Talbor, an assistant to a Cambridge apothecary. Talbor published a book on fevers (*Pyretologia*) in 1672, in which he advocated this remedy, which he treated as a secret. Coming to London, he cured Charles II and various nobles. He was knighted, and appointed a royal physician. Going to France, he cured the Dauphin, and sold his formula to Louis XIV. Talbor's final success was in curing the Queen of Spain. He died in London about 1681, and his formula was published soon afterwards. It prescribed a mixture of cinchona with some rose leaves, water, lemon juice, and some juice of persil [parsley].

Illustr. 219.—Glauber as Apothecary's "Sign"

One of the most famous purveyors of medicine about the middle of the seventeenth century was Glauber, whose contributions to chemistry have already been described in Chapter XV. His "wonderful salt" (sodium sulphate), first made in 1648, came to be known as "Glauber's Salt," and is still on the market as a favourite aperient. Glauber devoted much of his time to the preparation of various other medicines, notably a preparation of ammonium sulphate, which he offered as a panacea. He also sold one of his secret remedies to Louis XIV. At one time Glauber's reputation appears to have been so great that some apothecaries used a wooden image of him for a "sign" outside their shops. Illustr. 219 reproduces one of these "idols" of the apothecary of those days. In England Glauber's salt had a strong rival in Epsom salt, which Nehemiah Grew (1641–1712) extracted from certain spring waters at Epsom, in Surrey, and made popular through his treatise on Epsom waters.

For a short time after its meteoric appearance in Europe, cinchona was under a cloud in consequence of its abuse by people who ignored questions of proper dosage. Other fever remedies were accordingly looked for and experimented with. In 1650 Sylvius introduced potassium chloride as a febrifuge, and used it extensively; and in 1697 Johann Christian Jacobi used a solution of white arsenic and potash in water to cure intermittent fever.

The only other noteworthy medicaments introduced in the seventeenth century are: ipecacuanha, which Le Gras appears to have used, in 1672, against dysentery; cascara, which was first used medicinally by Stisser in 1690; peppermint, which was first described by John Ray; and musk-scented yarrow, which was first recommended by Stahl, and is still used as a cordial in the form of a liqueur known as *Iva* in the Engadine. Tea, of which Europe first heard in 1588 (Giovanni Pietro Maffei, *Hist. indic. libri. XVI*) was prescribed in 1684 by a Dutch doctor, Bentekoe, as a kind of panacea, or even as an elixir to prolong life; and this pleasant drug still cheers the heart of the British empire at all events. Boyle prepared ether by the action of sulphuric acid on alcohol. Newton wrote about ether in 1700 (*Phil. Trans.*). In 1718 Friedrich Hoffmann made a preparation consisting of one part ether to three parts spirit of wine, and this preparation became famous under the name of "Hoffmann's Drops."

SPECIALISED STUDY OF DISEASES

At the beginning of the modern period the prevailing tendency as a whole was to simplify unduly the human body and its ailments. Under the influence of the very tenuous theory of the four humours, and similar fancies, remedial treatment usually sought to readjust the proportion of the humours, etc., in the body as a whole, and was thus largely side-tracked from paying close attention to the specific character of the various diseases and their specific requirements. In the course of the sixteenth and seventeenth centuries, however, important changes came about in this respect. The marked empiricism of the pioneers in the physical sciences gradually infected the more intelligent doctors. The empirical attitude, and its antagonism towards speculative adventures, is perhaps seen at its best in Thomas Sydenham. But it shows itself before his time already in the more careful observation and detailed description of individual diseases to be met with in the medical literature of the sixteenth century.

The beginning of this specialization in medicine is associated with Girolamo Fracastoro (1478-1553), a fellow-student of Copernicus at the University of Padua. In 1501 he made a special study of spotted typhus. In 1530 he published a long poem on "love-pestilence" or the "Gallic disease." He called the book *Syphilis*, in playful allusion to the mythological Sipylus, the son of Niobe; and *syphilis* the disease has been called ever since. The poetic and fanciful form of the book helped its circulation; and the important facts were in it—a correct description of the disease, its cause, and its cure. This work was followed up, in 1546, by a more substantial treatise on contagious diseases, *De Contagionibus*. In it the author for the first time in history clearly distinguishes three specific ways in which certain diseases are communicated from one person to another, namely (a) by contagion, that is by direct contact; (b) by infection through intermediaries, or fomites, such as garments holding contagious effluvia; and (c) by infection at a distance. He also suggested, in explanation of infection, a rudimentary germ theory of disease. For he maintained that the disease is caused and carried by certain *seminaria*, seeds which propagate their own kind. Fracastoro's views were greatly strengthened when Athanasius Kircher, in 1671, published his account of the microscopic organisms which he said he observed in the blood of plague victims. Incidentally, the treatise deals with typhus fever, and shows that phthisis is contagious. Instead of lumping together all kinds of fevers, Fracastoro carefully distinguished its main varieties.

Syphilis, though by another name, engaged the attention of Ulrich von Hutten already in 1517. He recommended guaiac gum for its treatment. Guaiacum had been imported from America into Spain in 1508; but its use proved fatal so often that it was soon abandoned in favour of mercury. In 1534 syphilis was described again by Jean Fernel. In 1540 Ambroise Paré dealt with its inheritability.

The first account of whooping cough (*Quinta*) was given in 1578 by Guillaume de Baillou, who witnessed an epidemic of this illness in Paris about that time.

In 1583 Georg Bartisch published the first account of the diseases of the eye, and described various new instruments and operations for their treatment.

Giovanni di Acosta, in 1590, gave the first description of mountain sickness, which he regarded as the result of the rarity of the air in the higher regions.

In 1600 Fabriz von Hilden described the structure and function of the outer ear. He also invented a special instrument, *speculum auris*, for its examination. In the same year Hieronymus Fabricius ab Aquapendente published a treatise, *De larynge vocis organo*, giving the first full account of the larynx as vocal organ.

Special studies of individual diseases, or of parts of the body and correlated ailments, increased considerably in the course of the seventeenth century. Little more than a bare enumeration of them is possible in a work of this kind.

Intermittent fever was dealt with by Ludovico Mercato in *Opera medica*, 1608. Diphtheria was described by Villa Real in 1611. In 1620 Van Helmont described the chemistry of digestion. He regarded it as essentially a process of fermentation, in which the gall with its alkaline properties neutralizes the acidity of the digested food. This view of the process of digestion was further elaborated by Sylvius, who published an account of it in 1663. In 1644 Van Helmont published a detailed study of the properties of urine. In the interval, namely in 1630, Samuel Hafenreffer brought out a detailed study of various skin diseases (*Nosodochium in quo cutis affectus tractatae*). Skin diseases were again dealt with by Jean Roilau in 1648, and by Thomas Willis in 1670.

Francis Glisson gave an account of rickets in 1650, and recommended its treatment by means of massage, gymnastic exercises, and the use of supports. In 1654 he also published a study of the anatomy of the liver. The first special study of apoplexy and the associated condition of the brain was published by Johann Jacob Wepfer in 1658. A fuller account of the brain was given by Thomas Willis in 1667. In 1660 Conrad Victor Schneider dealt with the subject of common colds, and brought to light the function of the mucous membrane in relation to the mucus discharge.

Richard Lower's treatise on the heart (1669) has already been dealt with in Chapter XV. In 1670 Thomas Willis published an account of diabetes, its cause and cure. Athanasius Kircher's account of microscopic organisms in the blood of those afflicted with the plague (1671) has already been referred to.

The first account of special diseases associated with various trades was given, in 1680, by Bernardius Ramazzini (*De morbis artificum diatribe*).

The year 1683 witnessed the publication of Thomas Sydenham's accounts of gout, St. Vitus' dance, and hysteria; Edward Tyson's study of tape-worms (*Phil. Trans.*); and Guichard Joseph de Verney's treatise on the ear. The abnormal pelvis and its treatment formed the subject of a study by Hendryk van Deventer in 1685. Bonomo and Cestoni gave an account of itch, in 1686. Consumption was dealt with, in 1689, by Richard Morton, who maintained that it always develops from tubercles. Morton also published a study of pernicious fever in 1697. He attributed it to the exhalations from swamps, and recommended Peruvian bark as a cure for it. Yellow fever was first described by Ferreyra da Rosa in 1694.

Mental diseases were dealt with by Georg Ernst Stahl in 1692. In 1698 he also described the maladies of the portal vein (which conducts venous blood to the liver). Finally, the closing year of the seventeenth century saw the publication of Lorenzo Torraneo's account of the various types and stages of gonorrhoea.

FAMOUS DOCTORS

The sixteenth and seventeenth centuries produced a considerable number of famous doctors. Here is a list of twenty-one of the most famous of them, arranged in chronological order: Girolamo Fracastoro (1483–1553), Paracelsus (1493–1541), Agricola (1494–1555), Ambroise Paré (1510–90), Andreas Vesalius (1514–64), Hieronymus Fabricius (1537–1619), William Gilbert (1540–1603), Sanctorius (1561–1636), Jan Baptista van Helmont (1577–1644), William Harvey (1578–1657), Johann Rudolf Glauber (1604–68), Giovanni Alphonso Borelli (1608–79), William Petty (1623–87), Thomas Sydenham (1624–89), Marcello Malpighi (1628–94), Richard Lower (1631–91), John Locke (1632–1704), Martin Lister (1638–1712), John Mayow (1640–79), Georg Ernst Stahl (1660–1734), and John Woodward (1665–1728). The great majority of these famous doctors, however, were not famous *as doctors*, but as pioneers in other fields of research, namely, in physics, chemistry, geology, biology, psychology, or philosophy. This fact will explain partly why histories of medicine when dealing with this period are usually unsatisfactory, diluting a few drops of medicine in a too liberal quantity of what is not really pertinent. It also explains why most of these famous doctors are dealt with in other chapters of this volume. Gilbert's work is described in Chapter XIII ; Paracelsus, van Helmont, Glauber, Lower, and Mayow are dealt with mainly in Chapter XV; Agricola, Lister, and Woodward in Chapters XVI and XXII; Vesalius, Fabricius, Harvey, Borelli, and Malpighi in Chapter XVIII; Petty in Chapter XXV; Locke in Chapters XXIV and XXVI. So it only remains to give some account of the life. of Fracastoro, Paré, Sanctorius, and Thomas Sydenham, their contributions to medicine having already been indicated in the preceding pages of the present chapter.

Hieronymus Fracastorius (or Girolamo Fracastoro) was born at Verona in 1483. He studied at the University of Padua, where Copernicus was among his fellow-students. A typical humanist, he studied literature, law, science, and philosophy, as well as medicine. When on his round of visits to his patients he used to carry a volume of Plutarch to beguile his time; he wrote on the art of poetry and on various poetic themes; and, as has already been pointed out, he even garnished syphilis with poetic fancies, and

HIERONYMI FRACASTORII.

Illustr. 220

dealt with it in poetic form in his treatise of 1530. His most important work was his *De Contagionibus*, which was published in 1546, and of the contents of which some account has already been given earlier in this chapter. His literary activities gave him considerable celebrity among his contemporaries, and brought him many honours from secular and ecclesiastical princes. He also received many offers of Court appointments. But his attachment to his country house near Verona, his love of books and of retirement, induced him to decline all such invitations, with the exception of the post of medical officer to the Council of Trent, to which he was appointed by Pope Paul III, and which he held but for a short time. He died at the age of seventy from a stroke of apoplexy. In 1555, two years after his death, a monument was erected to his memory at Verona.

Ambroise Paré was born in 1510 at Bourg-Hersent, near Laval, in Maine. For a time he was apprenticed to a barber, but eventually found his way to Paris, where he worked at the Hôtel-Dieu, and learned the art of surgery. When, in 1536, war broke out between Francis I and Charles V, Paré was appointed regimental surgeon, and was with the army of Marshal Montejan when the fortress of Villanie was captured. It was while dressing the wounded at this fortress that Paré ran short of elder oil, and made his discovery about the nature and treatment of gunshot wounds, to which reference has already been made. He tells us that after applying his ointment, consisting of attar of roses, turpentine, and yolk of egg, merely because he had no more elder oil, "I could hardly sleep for continually thinking about the wounded men whose wounds I had not been able to cauterize. I expected to find them all dead next morning. . . . I rose early to visit them. Greatly to my surprise, I found that those whom I had treated with the ointment had very little pain . . . no inflammation, no swelling, and they had passed a comfortable night. The others, whose wounds had been treated with boiling elder oil, were in high fever, their wounds were inflamed, swollen, and very painful. I decided, accordingly, never again to cauterize so cruelly the unfortunate wounded." He realized that, contrary to the then accepted views, gunshot wounds are not poisoned by the gunpowder. In 1538, after the peace of Nice, Paré returned to Paris, married, and settled down to practise. Some more war experience came to him after a few years. But he was back in Paris again in 1544, and in 1545 he published a classical treatise on the treatment of gunshot wounds. During the next five years he made a thorough study of the anatomical teaching of Vesalius. In 1552 war brought him a great opportunity for the application of his own ideas about surgery. He was convinced that ligature was better than cauterization for stopping haemorrhage, and he acted accordingly. In 1553 he was taken prisoner at Hesdin, but he gained his freedom through his skilful surgery. And in the next year he received the signal honour of being appointed surgeon-in-chief at the College Saint-Come in Paris. A son of the people, and no scholar, he was ever ready to learn, even from old housewives, and in this way came to adopt such remedies, for instance, as the treatment of burns and scalds by means of raw onions, chopped and sprinkled with a little salt. The modesty of this great doctor and surgeon forms a pleasing contrast with the bombastic attitude of Paracelsus. His favourite saying was *Je le pensai, Dieu le guarist*. Paré's simple faith in the healing power of God saved him from experimental excesses in the same way as did Sydenham's faith in the healing power of nature. Paré lived to the age of eighty years.

Sanctorius Sanctorius (or Santorio Santorio) was born in 1561, and was a fellow-student of Galilei at the University of Padua, where he obtained a degree in medicine in the year 1582. He came under the influence of Galilei's scientific outlook, and attempted to apply to the study of medicine the same kind of quantitative methods which Galilei applied to physics. Of the fruits of this discipleship some account has already been given earlier in this chapter, in the section dealing with the clinical thermometer, the pulsimeter, and the weighing-chair. In 1587 he accepted the offer of a medical post in Poland, where he built up a considerable practice and gained a great reputation. In 1611 he returned to Italy, and filled the chair of medicine at his old university of Padua. He resigned this post in 1629, and went to Venice, where he carried on medical practice as a private doctor. Besides introducing the clinical thermometer, etc., Sanctorius also invented a new kind of instrument (trocar) for operations of tracheotomy, a new instrument for removing stones from the bladder, and a special kind of couch to enable an invalid to have a bath without exertion. He died in 1636.

Thomas Sydenham was born, in 1624, at Wynford Eagle, in Dorset. He was of Puritan stock, and his four brothers were officers in Cromwell's army during the Civil War. In 1642 he entered Magdalen Hall, Oxford, but soon left to do military service. He returned to Oxford in 1646, and entered Wadham College in 1647. In 1648, the year in which Dr. Wilkins (one of the first secretaries of the Royal Society in 1662) became Warden of Wadham, Sydenham was made Bachelor of Medicine by order of the Chancellor of the University, and was elected a Fellow of All Souls College, of which he became Senior Bursar in 1649. In 1651 he accepted a commission in a cavalry regiment, and left Oxford, but returned soon, and stayed there till 1665, when he married and went to London as a medical practitioner. For a time he seems to have been toying with the idea of a political career, but eventually

Sanctorius Sanctorius

Ambroise Paré

Thomas Sydenham

Illustr. 224

Francis Glisson

Illustr. 225

Thomas Willis

settled on medicine, and went for an extra period of study to
Montpellier, returning to London in 1661. Two years later he
obtained the Licentiate of the Royal College of Physicians. In some
ways Sydenham was rather like Paré. Both had army experience;
neither had much learning, or much respect for mere bookishness;
and both were empiricists who attached much more weight to facts
of observation than to abstract theories. Sydenham's friendship with
Robert Boyle, the founder of empirical chemistry, who at one time
accompanied him on his medical visits, was probably significant.
Their common empiricism made them kindred spirits. Sydenham,
moreover, was a very independent spirit, and not greatly impressed
by high-sounding phrases or theories. "It is my nature," he con-
fesses, "to think where others read; to ask less whether the world
agrees with me than whether I agree with the truth" (*Treatise on
the Gout*, 1683, Dedication, Latham's tr., Vol. II, p. 122). Like
Newton, he disliked far-reaching hypotheses, and fought shy of the
medical theorists of his day. "All that has been written," he says,
"has been hypothesis; the unbridled wantonness of fanciful art.
Indeed, the very phenomena of those diseases, which their histories
are bound to describe, are forgeries of the same mill: all are hypothetical. Hence even their practice squares with the hypothetical
postulate, and not with the facts of nature" (*Venereal Disease*, Ep. II;
Works, ed. Latham, Vol. II, p. 32). The first requisite for the
improvement of medicine, he insisted, "depends upon getting as
genuine and natural a description, or history, of all diseases as can
be procured." And Sydenham contributed his share to this by his
careful, detailed descriptions of fevers and gout, measles and
scarlatina, bronchopneumonia and pleuropneumonitis, chorea,
dysentery, and hysteria. In his methods of cure he proceeded
cautiously and critically, not relying on custom or tradition but on
empirical verification. And, as has already been remarked, when
he was not sure about the right medicine he preferred to give none,
but to wait and see how the patient progressed, giving just a little
help here and there, with simple diet, fresh air, refreshing small
beer, suitable exercise, etc., so as to maintain the patient's strength
while nature completed the cure. Unpretentious and straight-
forward, a crusader against hocus-pocus in medicine, and a pioneer
of critical, scientific method in the study and cure of human ills,
Sydenham endeared himself to his generation and to after generations. And after his death, in 1689, the voice of the people canonized
him as the English Hippocrates.

(See F. H. Garrison, *Introduction to the History of Medicine*, 1917;
C. Singer, *A Short History of Medicine*, 1928; S. G. B. Stubbs and
E. W. Bligh, *Sixty Centuries of Health and Physick*, 1931; A. C. Wootton,
Chronicles of Pharmacy, 1910; D. J. Guthrie, *A History of Medicine*,
London, 1945.)

CHAPTER XX

TECHNOLOGY

I. SCIENCE AND TECHNOLOGY.   II. AGRICULTURE. III. TEXTILE PROBLEMS

I. SCIENCE AND TECHNOLOGY

THE primary aim of science is the discovery of the nature and laws of things and events, so that we may understand and explain them. Such a knowledge of things and events always has the higher utility of enriching human life with new interests and helping intelligent people to take their orientation in the great world in which they live their brief life. Man, however, must live before he can know; he must make use of a great many things before he understands them. Food, shelter, clothes, etc., are necessary long before there can be any insight into them. The efforts directed to the satisfaction of such basic human needs follow the groping methods of trial and error, and are prompted by the pressure of instinct and impulse rather than guided by scientific knowledge. Even when the necessaries of life have been sufficiently secured to make leisure and the pursuit of disinterested knowledge possible, other practical needs arise, and their satisfaction is sought sometimes with the help of knowledge already acquired, sometimes mainly by the older method of trial and error. Moreover, man's creative instinct constantly impels him to make things, whether useful or not. Art is one expression of this tendency, invention is another; perhaps science itself is but another expression of this creative tendency, though it consists in the creation of ideas rather than in the making of things useful or ornamental. Anyway, the invention of things and processes, on the one hand, and the discovery of their nature and laws on the other hand, are activities which may be pursued more or less independently, and have been so pursued in the earlier history of civilization, though, with the growth of knowledge, they tend to become closely interlinked.

The foregoing reflections may help to elucidate the somewhat intricate relations between science and technology. Science, or pure science (as it is sometimes called), is concerned with the discovery of truth; technology is concerned with the invention of new things and processes, or the improvement of old ones. They are intimately connected certainly, and especially so at the present time. But their relation is often misunderstood and historically misrepresented, so it is advisable to be clear about it. Technology is frequently described as merely "applied science." This identification rather suggests that one begins with the scientific knowledge of certain phenomena and then proceeds to apply it for some practical end. This kind of thing does happen sometimes, but not often; certainly not always. In the history of civilization advances in practical invention undoubtedly preceded progress in the theoretical knowledge of the phenomena concerned. And even in the earlier centuries of the modern period, though scientific progress has sometimes prompted practical applications, yet more often pre-existing technical methods have supplied the data for scientific discoveries; and perhaps most frequently technical inventions and improvements were made without any help from pure science.

A few examples may be given here by way of illustration of the statements just made concerning the varied relations between technology and science. The important arts of agriculture, building, mining, the manufacture of glass and porcelain, and the textile industries received extremely little, if any, aid from science till the end of the eighteenth century. In certain other cases, indeed, science learned from existing technical methods rather than taught them —as when Galilei and Torricelli, for instance, were led to their barometric discoveries by the practice of engineers who built water-pumps; or when Harvey relied partly on the kind of ligatures made by contemporary surgeons, when he formulated his theory of the circulation of the blood; or when Hall learned the significance of the rate of cooling of a fused substance from the method practised in the manufacture of glass. Above all, the progress of science depended in large measure on the invention of suitable scientific instruments. On the other hand, there certainly were cases, even in the early centuries of the modern period, in which technical inventions were the direct outcome of the deliberate application of scientific knowledge. Thus, for example, a knowledge of electricity enabled Franklin to invent the lightning conductor (1750), and Reizen and Salva to invent systems of spark telegraphs (in 1794 and 1798 respectively). Similarly, a knowledge of chemistry enabled Marggraf to prepare sugar from beetroots (1747); Hutton to manufacture sal ammoniac (? 1765); Leblanc to prepare soda from salt and sulphur (1775); or Berthollet to use chlorine for bleaching. And in the same way mathematicians invented calculating machines under the guidance of pure mathematics.

The pioneers of modern science certainly wished and expected the relations between science and technology to be most intimate. The notion of knowledge for its own sake had no glamour for them. In fact, it was their great expectation that the new science, unlike the old book-learning, would be of great practical use; that the new knowledge would confer power, and enable mankind to become master of the forces of Nature. Bacon was at least as keen on fruit-bearing as on light-giving experiments; Galilei made experiments on the strength of building materials; and all the early scientific academies busied themselves with useful inventions. The Paris Academy of Sciences actually published twenty volumes giving full, illustrated accounts of matters pertaining to the useful arts (*Descriptions des arts et métiers*, 1761–81); and, largely through the influence of the Academy, the year 1795 witnessed the foundation, in Paris, of the first museum of science and technology, namely, the "Conservatoire des Arts et Métiers." Some men of science, moreover, rendered invaluable services to the improvement of the useful arts and industries of their country. Desmarest, the geologist and Inspector-General of Manufactures, was a notable example of this tendency, and many reports on the making of cheese, cloth, paper, etc., stand to his credit.

The main aim of the technical improvements and inventions of the sixteenth and seventeenth centuries, as of preceding and of subsequent centuries, was to produce some mechanical means of reducing human labour or of dispensing with it. Aristotle already had looked forward to the invention of automatic machines as the means of ending human slavery. This hope and faith also inspired the efforts of the pioneers of modern science, and survived long afterwards. It was only occasionally that the men displaced by the machines tended to shake this optimism. And it has been reserved for the present generation to witness how uncontrolled over-mechanization may embarrass mankind by excessive richness of production, and hand over desperately impoverished masses to the ruthless tyranny of unscrupulous demagogues. But, at the time with which we are concerned here, all this was undreamed of. The world, awakened from its mediaeval dreams, was feeling young, energetic, and hopeful. The pioneers of the new kind of worldly knowledge believed in the possibility of harnessing the forces of Nature to the chariot of human progress by means of science and art. They valued knowing as an aid to doing, science as an aid to technics.

It is therefore entirely in keeping with the spirit of the period with which this volume deals that an account should be given here of the technology of the time, and not to confine the story to pure science. The task presents serious difficulties. The chief difficulty is that of describing complicated inventions in a really intelligible manner without devoting to the subject an amount of space altogether disproportionate to the rest of the volume. The only satisfactory way of studying these things is by going through one of the famous science museums under competent guidance. However, since a beginning must be made sometime, it is attempted here, in the hope that the little knowledge communicated will not prove dangerous, but rather whet the reader's appetite for more.

Another difficulty is that of the suitable arrangement of the material to be presented here. It might seem best to follow approximately the order of the basic needs which technical inventions and improvements were intended to satisfy—food, clothing, housing, health, transport, etc. But this is not altogether a feasible arrangement for the present volume. The fundamental tools and operations known till the end of the eighteenth century originated in antiquity, and the additions made during the early centuries of the modern period are not of equal importance in the several divisions just suggested. Moreover, there would be a good deal of inevitable mix-up. Under the provision of food, for instance, one would have to deal with agriculture, the chemistry of beet-sugar, and the steam-engine for converting bones into jelly. And some people would probably be shocked to find a section on medicine under technology. The chapter on medicine has therefore been placed to follow the chapter on the biological sciences. The invention and improvement of scientific instruments have likewise been dealt with in a previous chapter. The remaining technological topics will be treated here in the following order: agriculture, textile problems, building problems, mining and metallurgy, glass-making, mechanical engineering, the steam engine, and mechanical calculators.

II. Agricultural Improvements and Inventions

Agriculture is probably the oldest of human industries. For that very reason, perhaps, it was for long centuries the victim of sheer custom and superstition, unaided by scientific study. The practical Romans made indeed considerable progress in the art on empirical lines; but their achievements were forgotten or neglected during the Middle Ages, and the modern period found agriculture in a rather primitive condition. The sixteenth and seventeenth centuries witnessed a considerable measure of progress in European agriculture. The progress was mainly empirical, by the method of trial and error. But agricultural processes were improved, new implements were invented, and the foundations of a scientific study of agricultural phenomena were laid by the close observation and record of agricultural experiments and results.

Seventeenth-century agriculture was still characterized by a certain rigidity in the customary divisions and treatment of land. The division into arable land, meadows, pastures and waste-lands, was treated as permanent, and very few people considered the possibility of a periodical or occasional interchange. The arable land, moreover, was cultivated in such a way that a third, or even a half, of it was unproductive each year. In the two-field system one half of the arable land was planted while the other half was left fallow, the order being reversed in alternate years. In the superior three-field system, rye, wheat, and winter barley would be planted in one-third of the arable land; oats, summer barley, dredge, and some beans, peas, and vetches in another part; and the remaining third of the arable land would lie fallow, though it would be ploughed two or three times in the course of the year so as to clean it and prepare it for the next year's crop. This rather wasteful method was gradually displaced in England in the course of the eighteenth century by the so-called Norfolk system. This consisted of a four-course rotation of crops, namely, clover, wheat, turnips, barley, without letting any of the arable land lie fallow. Similar systems of crop-rotation appear to have been introduced in the Netherlands, and perhaps elsewhere, in the sixteenth century, but it was only in the eighteenth century that this kind of rotation was extensively adopted in the form of the Norfolk system. The adoption of this system in England depended on the cultivation of clover and turnips there. The introduction of these and other exotic plants (cabbage, carrots, parsnips, hops, etc.) into England was the work of such pioneers as Sir Richard Weston (1591–1652) and more especially Charles (nicknamed "Turnip") Townshend (1674–1738).

The Norfolk system was based upon certain beliefs derived from observation, though not yet understood scientifically. It was believed, namely, that clover somehow prepared the soil for wheat, because wheat had been observed to grow better on land previously cropped with clover. Similarly, and in the same sort of empirical manner, wheat was believed to prepare the ground for turnips, turnips for barley, and barley for clover. The scientific understanding of these things was reserved for the nineteenth century. In the same empirical way Townshend re-discovered the advantage of marling light soils like those of Norfolk. And the ideas obtained empirically in this domain found expression in the following popular rhymes:

> "He who marls sand
> May buy his land;
>
> He that marls moss
> Suffers no loss;
>
> He that marls clay
> Throws all away."

Another practical discovery was that made by Jethro Tull (1674–
1741), who observed that pulverizing the soil without manuring it
may be better than manuring it without pulverizing it. Such
pulverization of the soil allowed air, dew, and rain to reach more

Illustr. 226.—A Plough of the Sixteenth Century

effectively the roots of the plants, and increased the nutriment for
their lateral growths. But it is not clear how far Tull understood
these things.

With regard to agricultural implements, the sixteenth and seventeenth centuries have to their credit the invention of some new
ones and the improvement of old ones. The ploughs used up to the
sixteenth century were massive machines which required a team
of from six to eight oxen each. Sometime in the sixteenth century,

Illustr. 227.—The Norfolk Plough

however, a lighter plough that could be drawn by two horses was
invented in the Netherlands, and was thence introduced into
England, especially into Norfolk and Suffolk, in the course of the
sixteenth and seventeenth centuries (Illustr. 227). An imaginative
engineer of the sixteenth century even conceived the idea of a

Figura Trigesimatertia.

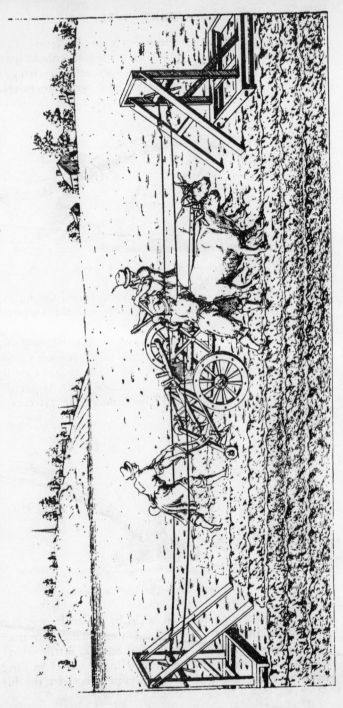

Illustr. 228.—Besson's Three-Shared Plough

three-furrow plough to be worked by a couple of oxen with the aid of ropes and pulleys. A picture of such a three-shared plough is given in J. Besson's *Théâtre des Instruments Mathématiques et Méchaniques* (Lyons, 1579), and is reproduced here (Illustr. 228). The picture may be pretty, but, like so many of the mechanical sketches of the period (see Chapter XXII, pp. 536 ff.), was not practical, as the capstans and ropes had to be moved and reversed at the end of each furrow, and the furrows could not be long enough to make it worth while. A more practical horse-drawn two-furrow plough was invented in the seventeenth century (see Illustr. 229).

From improvements in ploughing we may turn to improvements in sowing. Until the seventeenth century the only two methods of

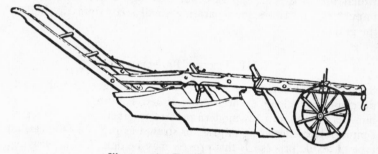

Illustr. 229.—Two-Furrow Plough
(Reproduced by permission of Messrs. J. C. and T. Yates)

seed-sowing practised in Europe were those of broadcasting and dibbling. Grain and small seeds generally used to be broadcast by hand, the seeds being scattered more or less uniformly over the whole area under cultivation. Larger seeds, like beans and potatoes, were dibbled, that is, holes were made in the soil in parallel rows and at certain intervals in each row, and one or more seeds were put into each hole. Broadcasting not only involved a great waste in the quantity of seeds used and in the amount of hand-labour required, but it also prevented the effective cultivation of the soil after it had been sown. In 1600 Sir Hugh Plat (in the *Setting of Corne*) recommended a method of dibbling wheat. The idea, he explained, was suggested to him by a curious accident. A "silly wench" accidentally dropped grains of wheat into some holes dibbled for other seeds, and the result was that uncommonly fine wheat plants sprang up in these places. Plat accordingly invented a board having iron dibblers fixed to it to facilitate the rapid dibbling of corn by hands. Of far greater importance was Jethro Tull's invention of the horse-drill in the eighteenth century.

We turn next to the last of the agricultural operations, namely that of threshing the sheaves of corn. This operation was, until the eighteenth century, carried out by means of a hand-flail, an implement which is still in use for small quantities of corn. The sheaves were put down on the threshing-floor and beaten with the flail so that the straw could be removed. The grain was thus left mixed with chaff, and the chaff was then removed from the grain either by means of a natural breeze or by means of an artificial draught produced with a fan. In 1636 Sir John Christopher van Berg patented a threshing machine; but the first really practical thresher did not make its appearance till the eighteenth century, when a Scottish engineer, Andrew Meikle, invented a threshing machine which also carried an apparatus for blowing away chaff and other impurities, and sieves for separating small seeds from the bulk of the grain.

III. TEXTILE PROBLEMS

Spinning and weaving are ancient crafts. Their invention and early development belong to prehistoric times. Knitting, on the other hand, is a comparatively modern process, originating in the fifteenth century. The interlacing of grass or straw was probably the earliest type of textile process. If this process may be described as weaving, as it well may be, then weaving is older than spinning. But the weaving of cotton, flax, silk, and wool could not be carried on without first spinning these raw materials. We may therefore begin this brief account of textile inventions with an outline of the history of spinning.

SPINNING

The earliest known implement used for spinning a continuous thread from short fibres was a wooden hand-spindle. It resembled a knitting needle, was from nine to fifteen inches long, and was rounded and tapered at each end. A notch at one end caught the yarn during the process of twisting. Round the middle of the spindle there was a wharve, or whorl, consisting of a disc of clay or stone or wood. This gave the spindle a certain amount of steadiness, and also provided a rest for the thumb when the spindle was rotated. Short fibres were first placed parallel to each other so as to form so-called carded rolls. Some of the fibres were then twisted and attached to the spindle, and the spindle was rotated (by being rolled by the hand against the thigh, or by being twirled between the fingers and the thumb of the right hand), and the fibres were drawn out by the hands in the form of a more or less uniform yarn, which was wound round the spindle. This simple kind of spindle was the sole spinning implement until comparatively recent times. Various improvements were, however, gradually introduced, though their dates and mode of origin are very uncertain. In the course of the fourteenth century, or earlier, an arrangement was introduced by which a belt passed round a large wheel and about a groove made in the whorl of the spindle, which was placed horizontally in a suitable frame. This arrangement was subsequently known in England as the bobbing-wheel, and was still in use in the early part of the nineteenth century. About the middle of the sixteenth century another improvement is said to have been made by Johann Jürgen of Brunswick. By cranking the axle of the wheel and connecting it with a treadle, the spindle could be rotated with the foot, this leaving the operator's hands free to manipulate the fibres. Another improvement of uncertain date was the so-called flyer, for twisting the yarn before winding it on a spool. There is a drawing of it by Leonardo da Vinci (*circa* 1490). Such an apparatus was in general use in the sixteenth century, and was known as the Saxony Wheel. It made possible continuous spinning. In the course of the seventeenth century an improved form of the Saxony Wheel came into use containing two spindles and two spools, the operator manipulating one thread with the right hand, and the other with the left.

WEAVING

The ancient Egyptians made considerable progress in the art of weaving, and invented a loom at least as early as the twelfth century B.C. In this loom the warp threads were suspended vertically from a horizontal beam. Alternate warp threads were attached by loops to a rod (or heddle), and could thus be moved forward together to allow of the passage of the weft threads. The other warp threads could be similarly moved backwards for the weft threads to pass in the reverse direction. The required tension in the warp threads was secured by hanging weights at their ends. Lease-rods were used to separate the even from the odd warp threads. The weft thread was wound on a reel which could be passed across the space opened out by the heddle. A kind of comb was used to bring the weft threads close together so as to make the woven fabric compact. This loom was first introduced into Europe about the fourth century A.D., and, with slight improvements, remained in general use until the early part of the eighteenth century. The chief improvements till then were these. The loom was mounted horizontally, treadles were invented for operating the heddles, and a batten was used to move the weft threads into

Illustr. 230.—Chinese Looms. *Above*, Plain Loom; *below*, Draw Loom

position. The heddles had been transformed into light wooden
frames strung with cords at right angles to the threads in the loom,
the cords having eyes through which the warp threads passed.
Pressure on the treadle drew one heddle down and raised the other

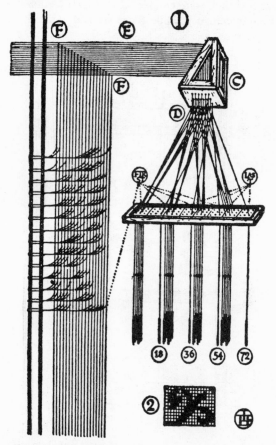

Illustr. 231.—Draw Loom of the Seventeenth Century

heddle, thus opening a passage for the weft thread. This simple
loom was well adapted for weaving plain fabrics. By adding more
heddles it could also be made to weave simple patterns into the
fabric. More elaborate patterns could only be made on a draw-
loom, which appears to have been invented in China some time
between the ninth and the third century B.C. In the draw-loom
each warp thread was controlled by a separate leash, and the
arrangement was such that the operator could raise simultaneously

all the threads that had to be raised for a single passage of the reel or shuttle. The movement of the warp threads was controlled by pulley cords fixed horizontally. Attached to these horizontal pulley cords were vertical cords, and as many of these as had to be raised at one time were connected to a heavy guide cord (which prevented entanglement), while those vertical cords that had to be

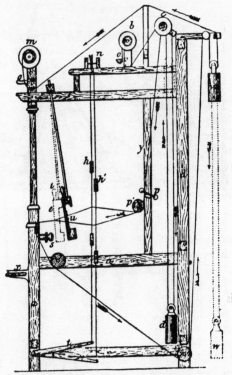

Illustr. 232.—An Early Ribbon Loom

raised next time were connected to another guide cord. The vertical cords were drawn forward and downward by the weaver's assistant, and this movement raised the leashes, opened the warp, and so enabled the weaver to pass the shuttle. The manipulation of the guide cords involved a considerable expenditure of energy, and so led to various mechanical improvements long before the draw-loom became automatic. The most important improvements, however, were not made till the eighteenth century.

Something must also be said here about the ribbon-loom, though its history is rather obscure. The ribbon-loom seems to have been invented in Holland about 1621, and came into use in England, Germany, and Switzerland in the course of the seventeenth century. The ribbon-loom could weave a number of ribbons simultaneously. It was provided with a number of reels (or small warp beams) corresponding to the number of ribbons to be woven; and it had a corresponding number of cloth beams, on which the several ribbons were wound as they were woven. The ribbon-loom became substantially automatic by 1765.

A few words may be added here about the fulling of woven cloth. The old process of fulling consisted in treading the cloth in vats. This method continued until late in the Middle Ages. A fulling mill operated by water power appears to have been devised as early as the twelfth century. But the earliest extant picture of a fulling mill appeared in 1607, namely, in Zonca's treatise on mills and machines. The fulling mill there depicted was a comparatively simple machine in which a water-wheel turned a shaft, which was fitted with cams for lifting two heavy wooden hammers. The motion of the cams released the hammers, which thereupon struck the cloth in the vats. The fulling mill saved much labour, and so promoted an improvement in the finishing of the woven cloth by fulling, instead of sending it straight from the loom to the market. Incidentally, the fulling mill also served as the first washing machine, for, when there was no cloth to full, the mill was employed to do the village washing. (See the Illustration on p. 464.)

KNITTING

Knitting is in some ways a more sophisticated process than weaving. In weaving, a number of separate threads are interlaced at right angles to each other in a manner essentially like the plaiting of grass or straw. It is a comparatively simple and obvious method of producing a fabric. But in knitting the fabric is produced by the continuous interlooping of a single thread—a process much less obvious and more ingenious than weaving. One need not therefore be surprised at the comparatively late origin of the art of knitting. Knitted goods—such as woollen caps and woollen or silk stockings— did not come into vogue until the end of the fifteenth century, but were in great demand soon afterwards. Before that time stockings used to be made of cloth. They were inevitably ugly and uncomfortable, as compared with knitted stockings. It seems, therefore, reasonable to assume that the extensive use of knitted stockings did not lag far behind the time of the invention of the art of knitting. At first, of course, knitting was done by hand; but with the rapid increase in the demand for knitted articles attempts were naturally made to invent mechanical aids. It is interesting to note, however,

Illustr. 233.—The Fulling Mill

that whereas spinning and weaving have long since ceased to be
domestic occupations or pastimes in industrial countries, hand
knitting has not yet been ousted by the machine, but still enjoys
great and growing favour as a genteel occupation among many
domesticated women and even among some men.

The first knitting machine, the so-called "stocking frame," appears
to have been invented, in England, in 1589. The inventor was the

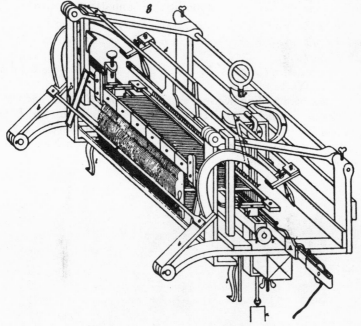

Illustr. 234.—An Early Stocking Frame

Rev. William Lee, curate of Culverton, near Nottingham. He failed
to get a patent of monopoly from Queen Elizabeth or King James I,
and migrated to France, where he settled at Rouen. But his stocking
frame was soon used extensively also in England, especially by the
Spitalfields silk workers in London and by craftsmen in Leicester
and Nottingham.

Lee's stocking frame was a treadle-worked machine having a
separate needle for each loop. At first it could only turn out flat
webs which had to be sewn together at the edges so as to provide
seamed hose. In time, however, Lee discovered a way of producing
shaped articles with his frame by throwing certain hooks of the
frame out of action (the equivalent of dropping stitches) at certain

stages in the process. The stocking frame, even in its earliest form, knitted ten to fifteen times as fast as the unaided hand, and could be manipulated by a child of twelve.

The stocking frame was, of course, not completely automatic, but depended on a human operator both for power and for the co-ordination of the movements of its several parts. Nevertheless, it was the basis of all subsequent inventions in the field of knitting and lace-making machinery. The stocking frame had, however, to wait till the eighteenth century for its most important improvements.

(On Agriculture, see N. S. B. Gras, *History of Agriculture in Europe and America*, 1926; R. E. Protheroe, *English Farming, Past and Present*, 4th ed., 1932.

On Textiles, etc., see A. P. Usher, *A History of Mechanical Inventions*, New York, 1929.

On Mechanical Engineering, see T. Ewbank, *Hydraulic and Other Machines for Raising Water*, New York, 1842; R. S. Kirby and P. G. Laurson, *Early Years of Modern Civil Engineering*, Yale, 1932.

The relevant *Catalogues of the Science Museum*, South Kensington, London, will be found helpful.)

CHAPTER XXI

TECHNOLOGY

IV. BUILDING PROBLEMS

A. THE STRENGTH OF BUILDING MATERIALS

DA VINCI

Leonardo da Vinci is known, from surviving manuscript notes of his, to have carried out experimental investigations on the behaviour of materials under stress. He was probably the first to advance beyond the merely rule-of-thumb treatment of structural problems adopted by ancient and mediaeval builders. Several such problems are discussed by Leonardo in the volumes of notes known as "MS. A" and *Codex Atlanticus* (see Ivor B. Hart: *The Mechanical Investigations of Leonardo da Vinci*, 1925). They concern the strength of the pillar and the beam.

Leonardo recognized that the load which can be supported by an upright pillar consisting of a compact bundle of shafts is many times greater than the total of the loads which each of several shafts could support separately. To verify this he suggested an experiment in which the weight under which an upright piece of iron wire, loaded above and fastened below, begins to bend, is compared with the successive loads under which two, four, etc., similar wires, bound together, begin to bend. He seems to have concluded from his experiments that the carrying power of a pillar of given height was proportional to the cube of its diameter. Leonardo considered the carrying power of pillars of given section to vary inversely as their heights. He attempted the problem (which was first treated mathematically by Euler in 1757, but still presents difficulties) of ascertaining how the carrying power varies when both the height and the diameter of a pillar are varied. He experimentally compared also the carrying powers of a beam consisting of a single balk, and of a beam composed of a bundle of such balks lashed together. He found the carrying power in one instance proportional to the number of balks, from which it appears that the balks cannot have been securely fastened together. He correctly ascertained, however, that the carrying capacity of a beam of given section varied inversely as its span, and he investigated how the load required to produce a deflection having a given proportion of the span varied with the span. Leonardo's results did not always agree with the modern formulae, but the crudity of the methods at his disposal and the unfinished nature of his notes must be borne in mind.

GALILEI

Galilei's contributions to the science of strength of materials were a theory of cohesion and a series of fundamental propositions on the strength of beams which first brought the subject to the notice of scholars.

Galilei's results are set forth in his *Discourses Concerning Two New Sciences* (1638). That the inquiries of the book were partly suggested by observations in the Venetian Arsenal and by conversation with craftsmen is admitted in the discourses of the chief speakers.

The precautions required in launching a big ship to prevent its breaking under its own weight, but unnecessary for an exactly similar vessel, built of the same material but of smaller size, drew attention to the importance of the *scale* of a structure as a factor determining its strength. This factor seems to have been allowed for by builders from ancient times in the methods employed by them in handling heavy columns, etc. Starting from current ideas, Galilei went on to inquire into the nature and the measurement of the resistance of materials to fracture.

The tenacity of solids is attributed partly to resistance to the formation of a vacuum through the separation of the component particles (as illustrated by the resistance to separation of two polished surfaces in contact), and partly to the presence of a viscous substance binding the particles together. An experiment is described for measuring the limiting resistance to the production of a vacuum in water by noting the force required to withdraw a piston from a closed water-filled cylinder. That this resistance could be overcome by sufficient tension was suggested by the fact, known to workmen, that a suction pump would not work when the water sank below a certain level in the sump (the well or depression from which the suction pipe of a pump draws). "Up to this time," says Sagredo, "I had been so thoughtless that, although I knew a rope, or a rod of wood, or of iron, if sufficiently long, would break by its own weight when held by the upper end, it never occurred to me that the same thing would happen, only much more easily, to a column of water."

The limiting height of the water column is given as 18 cubits. From the load under which a certain brass wire broke, it was calculated that it would break under the dead weight of 4,800 cubits of its own length; and since brass is about nine times as heavy as water, "the breaking strength of any brass rod, in so far as it depends upon the vacuum, is equal to the weight of two

cubits of this same rod." The relatively immense residual strength
of the rod was accordingly attributed to the action of a viscous
substance (*Discourses*, pp. 14 ff. in Crew and Salvio's translation),
though this might be only the accumulated effect of minute vacua
between the ultimate particles of the solid.

The second day of the *Discourses* is chiefly devoted to considering
the resistance to fracture of a beam fixed horizontally (e.g. in a wall)
at one end, and loaded with weights vertically suspended from it
at the other end. How this resistance varies according to the length,
thickness, and cross-section of the beam are the problems first considered. In treating them Galilei had to construct his own termi-

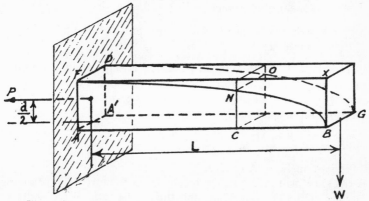

Illustr. 235.—Resistance to Fracture of a Beam Fixed Horizontally
at one End

nology, which is not very clear, e.g. he does not distinguish precisely
the bending-moment on the beam from the moment of the resistance
thereby brought into play, or from the resisting forces themselves.
His proofs are geometrical.

Galilei assumes, in his propositions on beams, that the base of
fracture AFDA′ (Illustr. 235) is under tensile stress only, and he
ignores the equivalent compressive stress necessary to keep the beam
at rest. He further wrongly assumes that this tensile stress is uniformly distributed over the base and equivalent to a resultant force
P through its centre. And he takes no account of any deformation
of the beam under its load, treating the fibres of the strained beam
as inextensible. These errors, however, do not affect the validity of
his determinations of the *ratios* of the strengths of beams of similar
sections, since, in these, the arm of the moment of resistance is
always the same fraction of the depth of the beam section.

Several of his propositions are reproduced here; and the following notation is used in the analytical outlines of the proofs given below:

L = span of beam;

d = depth or diameter of beam;

W = load;

P = the "resistance," or force across base of fracture AFDA′ (supposed to act horizontally through the centre of the base) evoked by the bending moment;

T = the force which, applied longitudinally through the centre of the base, would produce failure in direct tension;

B = bending moment = W × L;

M = moment of resistance = $P \times \dfrac{d}{2}$;

$M_{max.}$ = maximum moment of resistance to which the beam can be subjected.

Proposition I.—The solid prism ABXF is kept in equilibrium by the weight W, and the force P. (The weight of the beam is neglected.) These forces balance by producing equal moments about AA′, so that, in symbols:

$$B = M, \text{ i.e. } W \times L = P \times \frac{d}{2}; \quad \therefore \frac{W}{P} = \frac{d}{2L}$$

Proposition II.—"Any given ruler or prism whose width exceeds its thickness will offer greater resistance to fracture when standing on edge than when lying flat, and this in the ratio of the width to the thickness"—and Proposition III—dealing with the bending moment due to the weight of the beam itself, proved proportional to the square of the length, are really corollaries to Proposition I.

Proposition IV.—"In prisms and cylinders of equal length, but of unequal thickness, the [limiting moment of] resistance to fracture increases in the same ratio as the cube of the thickness of the base." For a cylinder of diameter d, on the point of failure:

$$P = T \propto \text{area of base} \propto d^2; \quad M_{max.} = P \times \frac{d}{2}$$

$$\therefore M_{max.} \propto d^3$$

This result is extended in Proposition V to prove that "Prisms and cylinders which differ in both length and thickness, offer resistances to fracture" (i.e. can support at their ends loads) "which are directly proportional to the cubes of the diameters of their bases and inversely proportional to their lengths."

$$M \propto d^3 \text{ (from IV)}; \quad B = W \times L; \quad \therefore \text{ when } M = B, W \propto \frac{d^3}{L}$$

Proposition VI states that, in similar cylinders and prisms fixed horizontally at one end, and supporting only their own weights, the actual resisting forces evoked at their bases of fracture are proportional to the limiting resistances raised to the power one and a half.

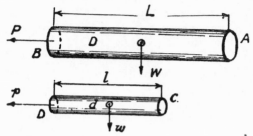

Illustr. 236.—Resistance to Fracture of Cylinders

In each cylinder M = B, i.e. $P \times \dfrac{D}{2} = W \times \dfrac{L}{2}$, or $\dfrac{P}{W} = \dfrac{L}{D}$

Similarly, $\dfrac{p}{w} = \dfrac{l}{d}$

But owing to the similarity of the cylinders $\dfrac{l}{d} = \dfrac{L}{D}$

$$\therefore \frac{P}{p} = \frac{W}{w} = \frac{D^3}{d^3}$$

But ratio of limiting strengths of bases $\dfrac{T}{t}$ (say) $= \dfrac{D^2}{d^2}$

$$\therefore \frac{P}{p} = \left(\frac{T}{t}\right)^{\frac{3}{2}}$$

Proposition VII.—"Among heavy prisms and cylinders of similar figure, there is one and only one which, under the stress of its own weight, lies just on the limit between breaking and not breaking: so that every larger one is unable to carry the load of its own weight, and breaks; while every smaller one is able to withstand some additional force tending to break it."

$$B = W \times \frac{L}{2} \propto (d^2 \times L) \times \frac{L}{2} \propto d^2 L^2$$

But, in similar prisms, $L \propto d$; $\therefore B \propto d^4$

But $M_{max.} \propto d^3$ (Proposition IV); $\therefore \dfrac{B}{M_{max.}} \propto d$

$\therefore$ B can equal $M_{max.}$ only at one value of d

This proposition showed that similar beams were not all of the same strength, as seems to have been supposed. The relation between length and diameter in cylindrical beams fixed at one end, and just able to support their own weights, is given in Proposition VIII: "Given a cylinder or prism of the greatest length consistent with its not breaking under its own weight; and having given a greater length, to find the diameter of another cylinder or prism of this greater length which shall be the only and largest one capable of withstanding its own weight." The condition was shown to be satisfied when the diameters of the cylinders varied as the squares of their lengths.

For each cylinder, Weight $\propto Ld^2$; $\quad B \propto Ld^2 \times \dfrac{L}{2} \propto L^2d^2$

Also $M_{max.} \propto d^3$; $\quad \therefore B = M_{max.}$ if $d^3 \propto L^2d^2$, i.e. if $d \propto L^2$

From these propositions is concluded "the impossibility of increasing the size of structures to vast dimensions either in art or in nature" (Crew, p. 130). Giant fish and big ships can exist safely at sea, it is stated, only because the water deprives them of their weight.

Beams supported at two points and loaded at an intermediate point are next considered, and it is shown that, under such conditions, a beam of uniform section is stronger near its supports than midway between them. Hence some of the material could be cut away near the supports. This led to the problem of finding the shape of a beam in which, for a given loading, the maximum stress should be the same at all cross-sections. The shape of such a "beam of uniform strength" was determined by Galilei for the particular case of a rectangular beam of uniform breadth fixed at one end and loaded at the free end (cantilever), the weight of the beam being neglected. For a given load, the moment of resistance at the section CNO (Illustr. 235) is proportional to the area of the beam section CNO and also to half the depth CN of the section, and hence to the square of CN. But the bending moment is proportional to CB. Hence, to obtain equal strength at all sections, the square of CN must be proportional to CB, and therefore the beam should have a parabolic profile BNF, which involves cutting away one-third of the material. Galilei describes (Crew, p. 148) how to draw a parabola by projecting a round brass ball along the surface of a metallic mirror held nearly upright, the ball tracing out a parabolic line on the mirror.

The second "Day," or Part, of the *Discourses* concludes with an investigation of the strength of hollow cylinders treated as beams.

It is shown that "in the case of two cylinders, one hollow, the other solid, but having equal volumes and equal lengths, their resistances" (moments of Resistance) "are to each other in the ratio of their diameters."

(Moment of resistance) $\propto$ (sectional area) $\times$ (diameter of section. Sectional areas are the same for both cylinders ($=$ Vol./Length), therefore moments are as diameters.

But Galilei underestimated the relative strength of the hollow cylinder. For let A be the area of section of each cylinder in the above proposition, and let

$\qquad$ D $=$ external diameter of hollow cylinder;
$\qquad$ d $=$ internal diameter of hollow cylinder;
$\qquad$ $\varDelta$ $=$ diameter of solid cylinder of equal volume.

The modulus being defined as the moment of resistance divided by the stress produced in the outer layer of fibres, we have:

	True Modulus	*Galilean Modulus*
Hollow	$\dfrac{AD}{8}\left(1 + \dfrac{d^2}{D^2}\right)$	$\dfrac{AD}{2}$
Solid	$\dfrac{A\varDelta}{8}$	$\dfrac{A\varDelta}{2}$
Ratio	$\dfrac{D}{\varDelta}\left(1 + \dfrac{d^2}{D^2}\right)$	$\dfrac{D}{\varDelta}$

WURTZ

The earliest record of experimental tests of the physical truth of Galilei's results on the strength of beams is found in correspondence between P. Wurtz, a Swede, and the French architect, François Blondel, published in *Mém. de l'Acad. Roy. des Sciences depuis* 1666 *jusqu'à* 1699 (Vol. V, p. 477). (For the history of this correspondence and the ensuing controversy, see Introduction to P. S. Girard: *Traité analytique de la Résistance des Solides*, etc., Paris, 1798). Blondel claimed in a letter of 1657 that Galilei's beam of uniform strength should have had an elliptic and not a parabolic profile, and Wurtz, in reply, stated that he had dealt with the problem in his *Gallileus Promotus* of 1649. The same amendment of Galilei's result was suggested by A. Marchetti, of Pisa, in his *Galilileus Ampliatus*, on the resistance of solids, published in 1669. Jealousy between Marchetti and G. Grandi, over a professorship, prompted Grandi to write a comprehensive geometrical treatise on the resistance of solids, included in his *Riposta Apologetica*, 1712, and to accuse Marchetti of plagiarism. But Galilei's hypothesis of non-extensible fibres was not corrected; nor was the experimental validity of his results tested by these Italian writers.

The problem of the strength of materials was, however, taken up in France by Edmé Mariotte (one of the founders of the French Academy) in connection with his works in hydraulics, a subject then in demand for its applications to ornamental water-works. The second Discourse of Part V of his *Traité du Mouvement des eaux*, English translation by Desaguliers, London, 1718, treats of the resistance of solids and of the strength of pipes to conduct water.

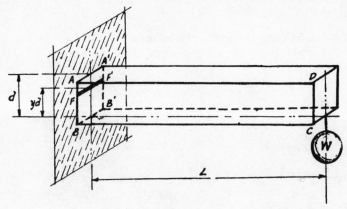

Illustr. 237.—Resistance to Fracture of Beams

In Galilei's theory $W \times L = T \times \dfrac{d}{2}$ or $W = \tfrac{1}{2}\dfrac{Td}{L}$, where T was the ultimate strength, or resistance to direct tension of the section ABB′A′, and W the breaking load of the beam.

Mariotte, however, made actual tests on beams, which showed that the above equation should be written $W = K \cdot \dfrac{Td}{L}$, where K was not $\tfrac{1}{2}$ as Galilei had supposed, but more like $\tfrac{1}{3}$ or $\tfrac{1}{4}$, and, with better data as to tensile strengths, he would have found it smaller still. Mariotte explained the discrepancy by supposing that the fibres could be variously extended by different loads, by amounts proportional to the loads, but that there was a degree of extension which they could not bear without breaking. The essential steps in Mariotte's obscurely expressed theoretical explanation of these experimental results were as follows (Illustr. 237):

Divide the fracture-base ABB'A' into n equal horizontal strips. The force on each strip is due to some portion of the load W. Consider the top strip AA', distant d from BB' (about which the beam is supposed to hinge). Let the extension at this top strip for which breakage occurs be due to a portion w of the total load W at C. Then the extension at the strip FF' (at a vertical distance above BB' of yd, where y is less than 1) for which breakage occurs would be produced by a load yw acting at C (since the moment about BB' of a given resistance acting at FF' is only y times that of the same resistance acting at AA'). But when the extension at AA' has reached breaking-point, the extension at FF' has reached only y times its breaking value, and the load at C required to produce this extension at FF' is y^2w. The load producing breakage is thus given by: $W = \Sigma y^2 w = w \cdot \Sigma y^2$.

For the mth strip from the bottom, $y = \dfrac{m}{n}$, and

$$W = w \cdot \Sigma \left(\frac{m}{n}\right)^2 = \frac{w}{n^2} \cdot \Sigma m^2 = \frac{w \cdot n(n+1)(2n+1)}{6n^2}$$
$$= \frac{nw}{3}\left(1 + \frac{1}{n}\right)\left(1 + \frac{1}{2n}\right) \qquad (A)$$

The total force P across the base of fracture is the sum of all the elements of force p across the n strips.

Equating moments about BB' we have, for the strip FF'

$$p \cdot yd = wy^2 \cdot L; \quad \therefore p = \frac{wL}{d} \cdot y = \frac{wL}{d} \cdot \frac{m}{n}$$

$$P = \Sigma(p) = \frac{wL}{dn} \cdot \Sigma(m) = \frac{wL}{dn} \cdot \frac{n(n+1)}{2} = \frac{nw}{2} \cdot \frac{L}{d}\left(1 + \frac{1}{n}\right) \quad (B)$$

Combining equations (A) and (B), and assuming n so large that $\dfrac{1}{2n}$ can be neglected, we have $\dfrac{W}{P} = \dfrac{2}{3} \cdot \dfrac{d}{L}$. But assuming p to be directly proportional to y, the average value of p is only half the maximum. Hence when the extreme fibre at AA' is extended to breaking point, P is only half the absolute resistance T of the beam to pure tension. Hence $W = \dfrac{1}{3} \cdot \dfrac{Td}{L}$, while in Galilei's result it had been $\dfrac{1}{2} \cdot \dfrac{Td}{L}$. This tended to confirm Mariotte's results already mentioned.

Comparison may now be made of the moment of resistance M, in a rectangular beam of section $b \times d$ under extreme fibre stress f, with the ultimate tensile strength T of that section, under various hypotheses as to the distribution of stress over the base of fracture (Illustr. 173).

Mariotte's experimental result that $M = \frac{1}{4} \cdot Td$ or $\frac{1}{3}Td$ must have

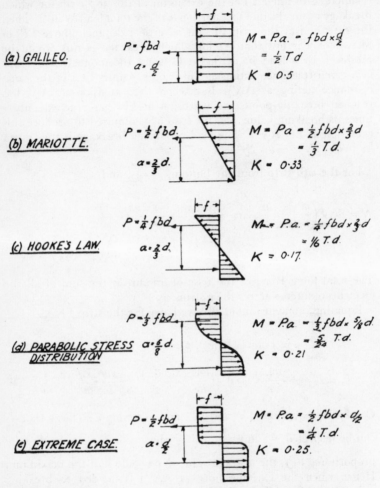

Illustr. 238.—Comparison of Estimates of Moment of Resistance on Various Hypotheses

been based upon assuming a wrong value of T. His beams were cylindrical rods fitted into horizontal sockets, while his tensile strengths were derived from experiments on cylinders of the same diameters as the beams, but with dumb-bell ends to which the loads were fixed by rope. This mode of fixing must have entailed some bending of the specimens, and the results would lead Mariotte to underestimate their tensile strengths. Mariotte was content with the agreement between theory and experiment which he had obtained, and he did not pursue the problem. But he had inklings of a more accurate theory, for he noticed that the bending of a beam under a load involved compression of the lower fibres as well as extension of the upper ones. "You may conceive," he wrote, "that for half the thickness the parts are pressed together, those near the outside more than those near the middle: and that for the other half of the thickness the parts are extended." But he does not appear to have noticed that, on this hypothesis, $M = \frac{1}{6}Td$.

Mariotte demonstrated that even brittle materials extend under load, and he measured the extension ($\frac{4}{5}$ line) of a glass rod 4 feet long and $\frac{1}{4}$ line thick, noting that upon being unloaded the rod returned to its original length.

Mariotte's ideas on the properties of beams were supported by Leibniz as against those of Galilei. Leibniz (*Demonstrationes novae de Resistentia solidorum, Act. Erud.*, July, 1684) was of opinion that the fibres were extensible and that "their resistance is in proportion to their extension," thus supposing Hooke's Law to apply to the individual fibres—an hypothesis which came to be called the Mariotte-Leibniz theory.

HOOKE

In England, following experiments, like those of Galilei, on the tenacity of metal wires, the Royal Society in February 1664 determined "to try the strength of several kinds of wood, as to bending, toughness, etc.", and placed Hooke in charge of the experiments (T. Birch, *History of the Royal Society*, Vol. I, pp. 384, 405). Sir William Petty and Lord Brouncker participated in the work. But no details as to the method and conclusions are given except that "in similar pieces, the proportion of the breaking weight is according to the basis of the wood broken." Inconclusive discussions on compressibility and "springiness" are reported in later volumes of Birch (II, p. 316, and III, p. 109).

B. Structural Mechanics

BEFORE THE SEVENTEENTH CENTURY

In ancient Eastern and Greek architecture little attempt was made to proportion the diameter of columns to their height and load. Under the later Roman Empire it was sought to economize on the material of pillars, but Vitruvius shows no knowledge of scientific principles of construction. Mediaeval builders appear to have treated structural problems by rule-of-thumb methods handed on in an unwritten tradition restricted to members of the craft. Indubitably much was learnt from the collapse of unstable or overloaded buildings. While no explicit theory or rules have survived it has been shown by Gwilt (*Encyclopaedia of Architecture*, 1881, p. 407) that in the ground-plans of mediaeval buildings the total cross-section of the supports of any part of the building bore to the total area of that part a ratio which was fairly constant at any particular period, but which steadily decreased (from a quarter to an eighth) as time went on. Early buildings were almost certainly based upon drawings. Only a few mediaeval drawings have survived; for the parchment and wood employed would mostly be cleaned for re-use, so that surviving examples are rare. Architectural drawings in ink on paper, in orthographic projection, appeared in the fourteenth century. Elaborate drawings begin in the sixteenth and seventeenth centuries, but they were not always followed very faithfully.

PALLADIO

The classical revival in architecture which followed the Gothic period was characterized by diligent study and imitation of antique proportions. In the sixteenth century there appeared many books illustrating classical models for the guidance of scholarly architects. The most influential of these books was *The Architecture of Andrea Palladio* (1518–80), published in 1570, of which several English translations appeared, the best being by I. Ware in 1738. The four books of this work were respectively devoted to:

(1) Materials; the Orders; etc.;
(2) Ancient Greek and Roman houses, and designs by the author;
(3) Ways, Bridges, Piazzas, Basilicae, and Xisti;
(4) Ancient Roman and other Temples.

The book is mainly based on that of Vitruvius, but includes accounts of some recently constructed trussed timber bridges, without, however, giving any clear mechanical explanations of their construction. Palladio gives rules for determining the proper thickness of the abutments of masonry arches according to their span. The abutments have to stand horizontal thrusts from the arches which they support. The Gothic architects had minimized such thrusts by using pointed arches, and they knew how to balance the horizontal thrust of one arch against that of the adjacent arch. But they do not appear to have formulated any theory. Palladio stated that the abutments should not be thinner than the fifth part, and need not be thicker than the fourth part, of the span of the arch; but his rule was defective through failing to allow for the effect of the *rise* of the arch in conditioning its horizontal thrust. He also assumed, mistakenly, that a semi-circular arch exerted no horizontal thrusts on its abutments; but his authority continued unquestioned even long after Hooke, Wren, and Gregory had established more satisfactory theories of the arch.

DERAND

A graphical construction for the abutment appropriate to any arch, a construction widely accepted in the seventeenth century, was that set forth by François Derand in *L'Architecture des Vo tes* (Paris, 1643). That work dealt mainly with stereometry, but included (Part I, Chap. VI) the following construction (Illustr. 239).

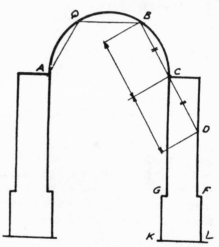

Let ABC be the soffit of the arch. Step out three equal chords AQ, QB, BC. Produce BC to D, making CD = BC. Then the vertical through D shows where the back of the pier supporting the arch should come, FG being thus the required depth of the abutment. The same construction is

Illustr. 239.—Derand's Construction for the Abutment to an Arch

assumed whether the arch be semicircular, segmental, or pointed. This rule is much superior to Palladio's, for it provides for greater depth of abutment as the rise of the arch is reduced, but, as Wren pointed out, it takes no account of the height of the pier and the load on the arch as factors in the problem.

Interest in the arch tended to decline with the growing preference among Renaissance architects for Column and Architrave construction. The Roman style in public buildings had originally been devised as a safe method of construction which could be followed by comparatively unskilled builders all over the empire; but it lacked such practical justification in seventeenth-century Europe. The brick walls and timber floors and roofs which were used in imitation classical buildings embodied certain traditional rules which were especially investigated by J. Rondelet in his *L'Art de Bâtir* (Paris, 1805, 1810). From an analysis of two hundred and eighty ancient and modern buildings, Rondelet deduced the customary ratio of height to thickness for various heights of wall and roof-spans. For instance, for a wall of length l and height h, the correct traditional thickness was found to be $\dfrac{h \times l}{N \times d}$, where d is the diagonal of the rectangle whose sides are l and h (and therefore equals $\sqrt{l^2 + h^2}$), and N is a number varying from 18 to 27, according to the class of building and to the ratio of h to l. Tables based on Rondelet's rules were inserted in the Metropolitan Building Act of 1855. They are still substantially adhered to, and have been followed in the majority of provincial by-laws.

THE SEVENTEENTH CENTURY

The best account of seventeenth-century building traditions is that given by Joseph Moxon (1627–1700), a London dealer in mathematical books and instruments, amateur in the mechanical arts, hydrographer to Charles II, and Fellow of the Royal Society. His work, called *Mechanick Exercises*, appeared in two series of monthly parts beginning in 1677, and dealt with the mechanical arts such as blacksmithing, joinery, building, etc. It merely described traditional practical knowledge, and was entirely uninfluenced by the investigations of Galilei, Descartes, and the scientific societies.

Moxon's account of the construction of timber floors (*Mech. Ex.*, Vol. I, p. 140 in 1st ed.) shows that it was recognized that the strength of a beam is more seriously weakened by cutting a mortice *across* the fibres of the wood than it is by cutting even a fairly long slot *with* the fibres, and that a small tenon at the end of the joist-span is capable of carrying a beam having considerable depth at mid-span (because, as we should say, the bending-moment increases in passing from the ends of the joists towards the middle). But the technical reasons for these properties given by Moxon were not satisfactory.

WREN

Sir Christopher Wren did not write on strength of materials, but his official reports on the condition of public buildings contain many comments on structural matters. Thus he criticized the design and construction of the roof of Old St. Paul's, which was in danger of collapse through its weight spreading the walls and thrusting the ill-built pillars outwards. Wren's structural calculations, even

Illustr. 240

Christopher Wren

William Petty

those for his St. Paul's, have not survived. They were probably
not elaborate, as he repeatedly changed his plans throughout the
process of construction. Reporting on Salisbury Cathedral in 1669,
Wren criticized the inadequate spread of foundation under the piers,
the insufficiency of the pillars to support the weights above (especially
the four which carry the steeple, which was added as an after-
thought), and the bracing of the walls by iron bands which might
contain hidden flaws or be destroyed by rust. In his report on
Westminster Abbey in 1713 Wren pointed out that the four pillars
at the crossing were not massive enough
to stand the inward thrust of so many
arches unless loaded from above by a
central tower, which exists for this
purpose in many Gothic cathedrals,
and which Wren proposed to add
to the Abbey. In the meantime he
strengthened the structure with iron,
which he also used extensively in St.
Paul's. (For the above-mentioned reports, see *Parentalia of the Wren Family*,
by Stephen Wren, 1750.) Wren was
dissatisfied with the Gothic method of
constructing vaults and their supporting
columns. He also criticized Derand's
construction (p. 479 above) for the
depth of abutment proper to a given
arch-profile, as not universally true.
Wren's own criterion for the stability
of an arch-abutment, however, was
worthless, though it did not mislead

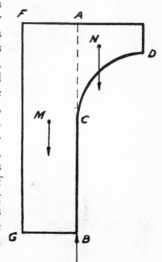

Illustr. 242.—Wren's Conception
of the Arch

him in practice. He considered (*Parentalia*, p. 356) an arch composed of a rectangular upright FB (Illustr. 175) with its centre of
gravity at M, to which is added the piece ACD, with its centre of
gravity at N. If the masses, concentrated at M and N respectively,
be equiponderant about the perpendicular AB, the whole mass of
stone will stand stably upon its base. The other half of the arch
is to be similarly constituted and to meet the first at D: the whole
arch will now stand as firmly as the two halves. Wren thus regarded
the arch as equivalent to two symmetrical and stable cantilevers and
counterpoises. He ignored the horizontal thrust transmitted through
D, together with any shearing force there due to unsymmetrical
loading of the two halves of the rib. His theory would lead one to
expect an excessive tensile stress at A, and suggested that the
maximum pressure on the base should occur at B, whereas if BC

were lofty the horizontal thrust of the arch (which he ignored) would shift the centre of pressure towards G or beyond.

HOOKE

Robert Hooke appended to his third Cutlerian lecture a list of some of his discoveries, concealed under anagrams. One of these related to "The true Mathematical and Mechanickal form of all manner of Arches for Building, with the true Butment necessary to each of them"; a second claimed to give "The true Theory of Elasticity or Springiness," while a third described "A new sort of Philosophical Scales."

The solution to the first of these anagrams was found by Waller among Hooke's papers after his death, and runs: *Ut pendet continuum flexile sic stabit continuum Rigidum inversum*, suggesting that a stable arch should have the form (inverted) of a flexible chain hanging freely under its own weight (a *catenary*). This was essentially an anticipation of the link-polygon, but would need to be modified by varying the weight of the links of the chain so as to represent the loads to be applied to the corresponding portions of the arch. Hooke's views on structural problems were supported by practical experience as Surveyor to the City of London after the Great Fire. Hooke gave evasive hints of his rule for the arch at meetings of the Royal Society in 1670–1 (Birch, *Hist. R.S.*, II, pp. 461, 465, 498). It leaked out, or was independently discovered, and was published by David Gregory without acknowledgment to Hooke, in the *Philosophical Transactions* for 1697. In the course of his paper on "The Properties of the Catenaria or Curve Line, formed by a Heavy and Flexible Chain, Hanging Freely from two Points of Suspension," Gregory (in Proposition II, cor. 6) states that "In a vertical plane, but in an inverted situation, the chain will preserve its figure without falling, and therefore will constitute a very thin arch or fornix: that is, infinitely small, rigid, and polished spheres, disposed in an inverted curve of a catenaria, will form an arch, no part of which will be thrust outwards or inwards by other parts, but, the lowest parts remaining firm, it will support itself by means of its figure. And on the contrary, none but the catenaria is the figure of a true and legitimate arch or fornix." Rondelet (*L'Art de Bâtir*, 1808, I, p. 138) claimed to have built up fifteen balls to form a stable arch of catenary profile. The catenary arch is stable only when the load carried by each section of the arch is proportional to the length of that section. Wren was believed to have solved the problem of the arch, but there is no explicit evidence on this point. It has been pointed out, however, by W. G. Allen and C. S. Peach (*Journal of the R.I.B.A.*, Vol. XXXVII, 3rd Series, No. 18,

pp. 664, 665) that the pillars and cone of St. Paul's closely follow
the form of a catenary, suitably loaded at the vertex to represent
the weight of the lantern. So Wren may independently have discovered the true form of the stable arch.

LA HIRE

Phillippe de la Hire, in his *Traité de Mécanique* (Paris, 1695) considered (Proposition CXXIII) the general problem of determining
the weights to be applied at every part of a cord (of negligible
weight) so that, being held taut by their combined efforts, the cord
might assume a curve of any form desired. Solution: Divide the

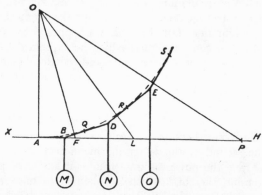

Illustr. 243.—La Hire's Treatment of the Problem of the Arch

curve AQRS into portions AQ, QR, RS, . . . and draw tangents
AB, BD, DE . . . at the points of section. Apply loads acting through
the points of intersection, B, D, E, of these tangents. The tangent
AH at A being horizontal, set off AF along AH to represent, on some
definite scale, the load M acting through B. Draw AC perpendicular
to AH, and FC perpendicular to BD to intersect AC at C. From C
draw perpendiculars to DRE, ES, etc., intersecting AH in L, P. . . .
Then AFC, FLC, LPC, etc., are what are now called the triangles
of forces for the points B, D, E, etc., respectively; ABDE is a link-
polygon; AFLP the load-line, and C the pole, of the force-polygon
CAFLP. La Hire (in Proposition CXXV) applied this construction
to find what load should be applied to each *voussoir* (arch stone) of
an arch for it to be in equilibrium even when there was no friction
between adjacent stones. The existence of friction, he recognized,
made it impracticable to apply the theory with full rigour in practice.
It is from de la Hire that the subsequent treatment of the problem
of the arch is derived.

C. ELASTICITY

PETTY

Sir William Petty, in a discourse to the Royal Society (1674), published under the title "Concerning the use of duplicate proportion in sundry important particulars: together with a new Hypothesis of springing or elastique Motions," stressed the importance of the *scale* of a structure as a factor conditioning its strength. Neglect of this factor explained why many "machinaments" which worked as models, broke down when constructed in full size. Galilei had dealt with this effect at length, but Petty did not refer to him.

In an appendix to his book, Petty sought to explain the recovery of form, and the oscillations, of elastic bodies. He supposed that atoms tended to arrange themselves in chains like magnets, with their axes in a straight line, but that this was opposed by a tendency of their centres to come together, which he explained by a sexual analogy, supposing atoms to be male and female. These two tendencies balanced each other by their "Contra-colluctations" into a state of apparent rest.

HOOKE

In his Cutlerian Lecture *De potentia restitutiva* (1678) Hooke revealed the second of the anagrams mentioned above (p. 482): *Ut tensio sic vis*, "the power of any spring is in the same proportion with the tension thereof," which he claimed to have discovered eighteen years before. Hooke's Law is often formulated nowadays as "stress is proportional to strain." Hooke illustrated the law by reference to the behaviour of four types of elastic bodies:

(1) A helix of metal wire with its axis vertical, fixed at the top and loaded with scale-pan and weights at the bottom. Increasing the load caused proportionate extension of the helix.

(2) A watch-spring coiled into a vertical spiral with the inner end fixed and the outer end attached to the rim of a light wheel, pivoted concentrically with the spring, and carrying round its rim a silk thread with a light scale-pan hanging from its loose end. Equal increments of load in the pan produced equal angular rotations of the wheel.

(3) A long wire (Hooke suggested lengths of 20, 30, and 40 feet) vertically suspended from one end and carrying a scale-pan at the other. Additions of weights produced corresponding extensions of the wire which were ascertained by measuring the distance of the pan from the floor, with compasses.

(4) A cantilever of dry wood loaded at the free end was employed to show that bending deformation followed the same law.

In his *Micrographia* Hooke had already shown that the same law applied in the compression of air, and he now sought to generalize it as a law of nature for elastic bodies, which was capable of several useful applications, e.g. to the construction of watch-springs. The third of his anagrams on this subject, *ut pondus sic tensio*, as the load so the stretch, was the principle underlying his "Philosophical Scale"—the spring-balance in which weights are measured by the extension of a spring, and which Hooke used in vain attempts to detect the variation of gravity with altitude.

Hooke at first explained elasticity as due to air contained in the elastic body (Birch: *History of the Royal Society*, II, p. 316), but this was disproved when, using Papin's air-pump, he found that the exhaustion of the receiver did not affect the elastic properties of a loaded spring suspended therein. His later theory invoked the agency of a subtle, all-pervading medium keeping the mean positions of the vibrating particles which composed the elastic body at fixed distances one from another, and resisting any attempt to separate them more widely, or to compress them more densely. Hooke's sketch (*Gunther*, VIII, p. 347) of a bent beam indicated a *neutral layer* half-way down the beam section, separating the regions of extension and compression.

NEWTON

Newton dealt with cohesion and elasticity in the 31st Query of the *Opticks*. He supposed that these phenomena, together with chemical attractions, and the refraction of light-corpuscles, must all be referred to the properties of the ultimate particles composing bodies—probably to their mutual *attraction* at close quarters. The *repulsive* forces required for elasticity and the emission of light were supposed to supervene on the attractive forces at a certain distance from the particles, just as the sign of a mathematical function may change from positive to negative for certain values of the independent variable.

(See J. Gwilt, *Encyclopaedia of Architecture*, 1842, etc.; R. T. Gunther, *Early Science in Oxford*, Vol. VIII, Oxford, 1930; W. Petty, *Concerning the Use of Duplicate Proportion*, 1674; I. Todhunter and K. Pearson, *History of Elasticity and Strength of Materials*, Vol. I, Cambridge, 1886; S. B. Hamilton, "The Development of Modern Ideas on the Behaviour of Materials under Stress," M.Sc. Dissertation, 1933, Library of the University of London.)

CHAPTER XXII

TECHNOLOGY

V. MINING AND METALLURGY. VI. MECHANICAL ENGINEERING

V. MINING AND METALLURGY

MINING and the associated metallurgical processes belong to the oldest of the world's industries. They were fully developed long before the advent of the modern period, and the sixteenth and seventeenth centuries did very little for their further advancement. The various mining and metallurgical processes were, however, but little known outside the ranks of those actually engaged in mining operations. This was due partly to trade secrecy, and partly to the lack of literary power or literary interests on the part of those who had a practical knowledge of the subject. The sixteenth century witnessed the first considerable attempts to describe the various aspects of mining fully and accurately. From about 1500 onwards a number of smaller treatises on the subject made their appearance. The oldest of them was the anonymous *Ein Nützlich Bergbüchlein* ("A Useful Mining Booklet"). It was followed (about 1510) by the more valuable *Probierbüchlein* ("Assaying Booklet"), which was also anonymous. In 1540 Vannucio Biringuccio, an Italian of Siena, published a still more important work called *De la Pirotechnia*, the first systematic book on mining and metallurgy (English translation, *The Pirotechnia of Vannoccio Biringuccio*, by C. S. Smith and M. T. Gnudi, New York, 1943). But the greatest mining treatise of the period, and one which for two centuries remained the standard work on the subject, was *De Re Metallica* (1556), by Agricola, who has already been referred to, and who had published a smaller book on mining in 1530 (*Bermannus*).

Agricola, though in some ways a child of his age, was realistic enough to have more faith in observation than in abstract reasoning. Although he was not a practical mining engineer, but a doctor, by profession, he made it his business to see things with his own eyes. The following assurances contained in his *Preface* to *De Re Metallica* are worth quoting. "I have devoted much labour and care, and have even gone to some expense, upon it; for with regard to the veins, tools, vessels, sluices, machines, and furnaces, I have not only described them, but have also hired illustrators to delineate their forms, lest descriptions which are conveyed by words should either not be understood by men of our own times, or should cause difficulty to posterity. . . . I have omitted all those things which I have not myself seen, or have not read or heard of from persons upon whom I can rely. That which I have neither seen, nor carefully considered after reading or hearing of, I have not written about. The same rule must be understood with regard to all my instruction, whether I enjoin things which ought to be done, or describe things which are usual, or condemn things which are done." The numerous and picturesque illustrations constitute one of the characteristic features of the treatise; and English-reading students of Agricola are particularly fortunate in having Mr. and Mrs. Hoover's version, which contains all the illustrations, and is in every way worthy of the great original (Georgius Agricola: *De Re Metallica*, translated by H. C. Hoover and L. H. Hoover, London, 1912).

The treatise consists of twelve books and covers every phase of the mining industry and the associated metallurgical processes. It describes scores of mining operations, deals with the relevant problems of surveying, administration, geology, engineering, smelting, and assaying, and contains also some sound comments on the more dubious aspects of mining enterprise.

The first book contains a general vindication of the mining industry against the critics of the sordid search for wealth, and an indication of the kind of knowledge that is requisite in order that mining may be carried out successfully. The second book describes the character and qualities of competent miners, and discusses problems of mine-prospecting, mine-ownership, mining companies, and shares. Some of his remarks about mining shares and the use of the divining rod are still worth repeating. "In the buying of shares," he writes, "as in other matters, there should be a certain limit of expenditure which miners should set themselves, lest, blinded by the desire for excessive wealth, they throw all their money away. Moreover, a prudent owner, before he buys shares, ought to go to the mine and carefully examine the nature of the vein, for it is very important that he should be on his guard, lest fraudulent sellers of shares should deceive him" (English trans., p. 29). Agricola's account of the divining rod is apparently one of the first, if not the first, of its kind, and reads as follows: "There are many great contentions between miners concerning the forked twig, for some say that it is of the greatest use in discovering veins, and others deny it. Some of those who manipulate and use the twig first cut a fork from a hazel bush with a knife, for this bush they consider more efficacious than any other for revealing the veins, especially if the hazel bush grows above a vein. Others use a different kind of twig for each metal, when they are seeking to discover the veins, for they employ hazel twigs for veins of silver; ash twigs for copper; pitch pine for lead and especially tin; and rods made of iron and steel for gold. All alike grasp the forks of the twig with their hands, clenching their fists, it being necessary that the clenched fingers should be held towards the sky in order that the twig should be raised at that

Illustr. 244.—The Divining Rod

end where the two branches meet. (See Illustr. 244, and *cf.* the earliest known picture of the dowser, Illustr. 265, on p. 511.) Then they wander hither and thither at random through mountain regions. It is said that the moment they place their feet on a vein the twig immediately turns and twists, and so by its action discloses the vein; when they move their feet again and go away from that spot, the twig becomes once more immobile" (*Idem,* pp. 38 f.). Agricola connects the divining rod with magic, and rejects the claims made for it. "A miner," he says, "since we think he ought to be a good and serious man, should not make use of an enchanted twig, because if he is prudent and skilled in the nature of signs, he understands that a forked stick is of no use to him, for, as I have said before, there are the natural indications of the veins which he can see for himself without the help of twigs" (*Idem*, p. 41). By "natural indications" of the presence of metal veins, Agricola means the bubbling waters of springs; the croppings, or pieces of stone, washed out by the water; the absence of hoar-frost on herbage, when it shows on neighbouring herbage; and the presence of trees "whose foliage in springtime has a bluish or leaden tint, the upper branches more especially being tinged with black or with any other unnatural colour, the trunks cleft in two, and the branches black or discoloured" (*Idem*, p. 38). These phenomena he regards as natural indications because they are caused by the intensely hot and dry exhalations emitted by the metal veins. It is remarkable that Robert Boyle still believed in divining rods a century after Agricola's rejection of them, and they still enjoy a certain vogue.

The third book describes the different kinds of veins, stringers, and seams in the rocks, and the use of the compass (or "wind-rose") to describe their directions. The fourth book deals with the administration of mines and the functions of mine officials. The fifth book explains the principles of underground mining, the art of surveying, and the digging of ore; and describes various ores to be found in mines. It depicts different kinds of shafts, of plummet levels, and other surveying instruments; and contains the strati-graphic account already quoted in Chapter XVI. Some of the illustrations are reproduced in Illustrs. 245–248.

The sixth book gives a description of the various tools, implements, vessels, and machines used in mining operations—hammers, wedges, picks, hoes, shovels, baskets, buckets, wheelbarrows, trucks, ropes, pulleys, windlasses, gear-wheels, chain-pumps, piston-pumps with valves, bellows, etc. Some of them will be described in the next section. All these tools had, of course, been invented long before Agricola's time. The book ends with an account of "the ailments and accidents of miners, and of the methods by which they can guard against these."

The seventh book describes the methods of assaying ores, "because it is desirable to first test them in order that the material mined may be advantageously smelted, or that the dross may be purged away and the metal made pure." The necessary assay furnaces, scorifiers, crucibles, cupels, moulds, and assay balances are described and illustrated, and an elaborate account is given of different kinds of touch needles for use with the touchstone. Most of the methods of assaying had first been described in the above mentioned *Probierbüchlein* (? 1510), and again in *Pirotechnia* (1540); but not so

Illustr. 245.—Vertical Shafts

A does not reach the Tunnel; B does; C has as yet no Tunnel near it

Illustr. 246.—Construction of a Shaft
A, Wall-plates; B, Dividers; C, End-posts; D, End-plates

Illustr. 247.—Standing Plummet-level

fully as in *De Re Metallica*, which also contains original instructions on the assaying of tin, bismuth, quicksilver, and iron. The touch-stone was used in ancient times already for the testing of metals,

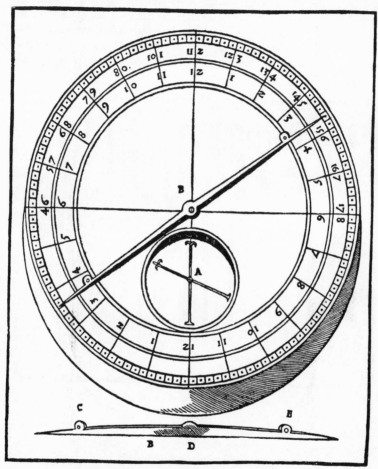

Illustr. 248.—Swiss Compass
A, Needle; B, Tongue; CDE, Holes in the Tongue

especially precious metals, although there was no adequate account of its use before the sixteenth century. It is a black or dark green stone. When a metal is rubbed on it a coloured mark is made which varies with the nature of the metal. By comparing these marks with the marks made by metal needles of known composition one can determine approximately the character of the metal or ore to be assayed. Agricola enumerates a large number of such standard touch needles, and gives elaborate tables of the effects produced by rubbing them on a touchstone. Illustr. 249 shows twenty-four such needles, the first eleven of which were meant for determining the proportion of gold in a bar of silver, and the remaining thirteen for determining the proportion of silver in a bar of gold. They could also be used for determining the proportion of gold or silver in coins. Other touch needles were used for assaying alloys containing copper, etc:

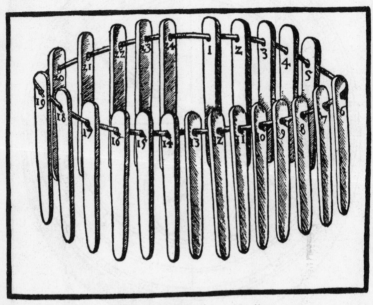

Illustr. 249.—Touchstone Needles

The eighth book describes the processes of preparing ores for smelting—sorting, crushing, grinding, sifting, washing, and roasting. It describes also the method of using quicksilver for recovering gold, but makes no mention of the method of recovering silver by amalgamation, although it had already been dealt with in the above-mentioned *Pirotechnia* of Biringuccio. The illustrations include several pictures of stamp mills, which were invented, by some unknown person about 1500, to replace the method of grinding in mill-stones. Illustr. 250 reproduces an illustration showing a stamp-mill worked by a water-wheel. Illustr. 251 shows the method of roasting metal ores containing sulphur or bitumen.

The ninth book treats of the various methods of smelting ores.

It describes the various kinds of furnaces used, the different kind of bellows, and other apparatus, and all the necessary processes. The metals dealt with are gold, silver, copper, iron, lead, tin, antimony, quicksilver, and bismuth. Agricola was the first to describe the treatment of the ores of bismuth; even the first description of the metal itself was given by him, namely, in his earlier book *Bermannus*

Illustr. 250.—A Stamp-Mill worked by Water-Wheel

(1530). Most of the operations dealt with in the ninth book were of earlier origin, but some of them were only introduced in the six-teenth century. The latter include the process of roasting copper ores before smelting them, the reduction of bismuth from ore, and the reduction of zinc from ore. Illustrs. 251–255 show some of the furnaces, etc. The sixteenth-century blast-furnace was usually a trun-cated cone about 24 feet in diameter and about 30 feet high. The blast for it was commonly supplied by bellows worked by a water-wheel. A steel furnace was built in England in 1523. Until the nine-

Illustr. 251.—Furnaces for Metal Ores containing Bitumen or Sulphur

Illustr. 252.—Furnaces for Smelting Lead Ore

A, Carni Furnace; F, Moulds; H, Slabs of Lead; K, Saxon Furnace; I, L, Openings; N, T, Crucibles; O, Dipping Pot; P, Westphalian Method of Smelting on Heaps of Charcoal; V, Polish Hearth

teenth century, however, steel was expensive and difficult to work, and its use was confined to tools, weapons, and machine parts subject to special wear and tear.

In the tenth book Agricola explains "in what manner the precious metals are parted from the base metals, or on the other hand the

Illustr. 253.—Lusitanian Furnaces, with Round Bellows, for Smelting Tin

base metals from the precious." He adds that "frequently two metals, occasionally more than two, are melted out of one ore, because in nature generally there is some amount of gold in silver and in copper, and some silver in gold, copper, lead, and iron; likewise some copper in gold, silver, lead, and iron, and some lead in silver, and lastly, some iron in copper." The methods of refining gold and silver are also dealt with. The book inevitably repeats to some extent what had already been said, in the seventh book, on assaying. The two books between them describe most of the re-agents and operations still made use of in the dry analyses of gold, silver, lead, copper, tin, bismuth, quicksilver, and iron; and they reveal even such assaying devices as the method of granulation, duplicate assays, the use of test lead, the use of beer to damp bone ash, etc., which are still in use. Agricola deals fully with what he calls *aqua valens* ("strong water"), used for separating gold and silver. He

Illustr. 254.—Furnace for Smelting Bismuth or Ores of Iron
E, Crucible; F, Pipe; G, Dipping Pot

means by it the mineral acids, or mixtures of them, previously known as *aqua fortis* (nitric acid) and *aqua regia* (a mixture of nitric and hydrochloric acid). His *aqua valens* was mostly prepared by distilling vitriol with salt, or with saltpetre, or with both. His recipes for it appear to have been taken mainly from the *Probierbüchlein*. The only kind of *aqua valens* of which he appears to have had practical experience is *aqua fortis*. Most of the methods of separation which he recounts, namely, by means of *aqua fortis*, by means of cementation with salt, or sulphur, or antimony sulphide, had already been described by others before him. But he was the first to explain the method of cementation with saltpetre.

The eleventh book speaks of "the methods by which silver must be separated from copper, and likewise from iron." The greater part of it, however, is taken up with the "liquation" method of separating silver from copper. This process was first introduced in the sixteenth century, and Agricola's appears to be the first account of it. The characteristic feature of "liquation" is this. An alloy of copper and lead, having an excess of lead, is heated in a reducing atmosphere (which prevents oxidation) to a temperature above the melting point of lead but short of the melting point of copper, so that the lead "liquates" or melts. But as it still carries with it a quantity of the silver, a number of additional processes are required before the silver is finally separated. Illustr. 255 shows the liquation furnace.

The last book of *De Re Metallica* treats of "solidified juices," that is to say, of soluble salts, their sources, and their preparation. It describes the methods of manufacturing salt, soda, alum, vitriol, sulphur, bitumen, and even glass. These topics are perhaps not altogether in their right place in a treatise on mining and metallurgy, and Agricola felt it necessary to defend their inclusion. It will, however, be convenient to follow Agricola's example to the extent at least of saying something at this point about glass-making in the sixteenth and seventeenth centuries.

GLASSMAKING

The art of glassmaking is one of the oldest, going back to prehistoric times. The sixteenth and seventeenth centuries probably added very little that was new. But during these centuries some old discoveries which had been lost in the intervening centuries were rediscovered independently, and, above all, the first important treatises on the art were written. Agricola dealt with the subject to some extent, and gave a picture of the three-chambered furnace used by glassmakers (see Illustr. 256). But the first work specially devoted to a description of the manufacture of glass was published in 1612, at Florence. It was called *De Arte Vetraria*, and was written by Antonio Neri, a Florentine priest, who had collected a great deal of information on the subject during his travels in Italy (which possessed famous glass factories at Florence and Venice) and the Low Countries (where Antwerp was an important centre of glassmaking). Neri also made some discoveries of his own. His book was translated into English by Christopher Merret (*The Art of Glass*, 1662). This version contained considerable additions by the translator, and a number of woodcut illustrations. Another

Illustr. 255.—Liquation Furnace

Illustr. 256.—Three-Chambered Furnace for Glass

Georgius Agricola

A Glass-Blower's Lamp worked by Pedal-Bellows

Illustr. 259.—Old Method of Glass-Blowing

important book on *The Art of Glassmaking* was published in 1679. It was written, in German, by Johann Kunckel, who also made use of Neri's work. Kunckel's book contains a considerable number of illustrations, the most interesting of which is that of a glass-blower's lamp worked by pedal bellows (see Illustr. 258), which may be compared with the earlier method of glass-blowing (Illustr. 259). A French version of all these works was subsequently published, in one volume with additional comments by M. D. The title of the volume is *L'Art de la Verrerie* (Paris, 1752), and M. D. was Baron d'Holbach.

The rediscoveries made during the sixteenth and seventeenth centuries all related to the processes of making coloured glass and artificial gems. They were made independently by several different chemists, most of whom treated their discoveries as important secrets.

The first of these discoveries, so far as is known, was made about 1540, when Christoph Schürer, of Neudeck, in Germany, found a method of making glass cobalt-blue in colour. Apparently he fused the glass with the residues that were left after he had extracted some bismuth from its ores. (See Ernst von Meyer's *History of Chemistry*, ed. 1906, p. 95.)

The other discoveries all related to processes of making red or ruby glass and artificial rubies. Andreas Libavius discovered, during the closing years of the sixteenth century, that ruby glass could be made by mixing gold and iron (?) with the materials from which the glass was made (*Alchemia*, 1597, Lib. II, Tr. I, C. 34). Next, Johann Rudolf Glauber made a similar discovery by a happy accident. He was melting calx of gold and added some saline flux to aid the fusion. On removing the crucible from the furnace he found that it contained some beautiful red glass. He concluded that the colour was due to the gold, since the saline flux which he had added was white. He then devised a more convenient method of colouring glass, namely, by precipitating the gold from its solution in *aqua regia* by means of "liquor of flints" (i.e. a solution of potassium silicate prepared by the action of water on a fused mixture of sand or powdered flints and excess of potash), and fusing this precipitate. This process, he remarks, can be applied also when any other metal is used to colour glass or to produce artificial gems (*Philosophical Furnaces*, 1651, Part II, Chs. 182, 183). Neri, in 1612 (*op. cit.*), also suggested that gold dissolved in *aqua regia* might be used for colouring glass. He also explained a method of preparing lead glass.

In his *Experiments and Considerations about the Porosity of Bodies* (1684), Robert Boyle pointed out that in coloured glass the colouring agent sometimes penetrates the whole glass, and sometimes affects the surface only. In fact, glass was often stained by covering it with mineral pigments, laying it on lime or some other suitable powder, and keeping it in a fire below the point of fusion of the glass. When St. Paul's Cathedral was destroyed during the Great Fire of London, in 1666, Boyle examined some fragments of stained glass from its windows and found that the colour was only on the surface. He pondered the possibility of staining glass red throughout. One day, when distilling some gold amalgam, he found that part of the glass containing vessel had turned golden; and, after a prolonged distillation in which the vessel burst, he found that the glass was red through and through, and in fact it had "so fine and glorious a Red colour, that I have seen several Rubies themselves inferior to it" (*Works*, ed. 1772, Vol. IV, p. 793). Kunckel appears to have made the same discovery independently about the same time.

VI. MECHANICAL ENGINEERING

Owing to its intimate association with mining, mechanical engineering was comparatively advanced at the beginning of the modern period. These two branches of engineering were indeed the pioneer arts which prepared the world for the Industrial Age. Increased mining activity led to a demand for better hauling and pumping machinery, and so stimulated the invention of mechanical appliances. And once mechanical inventiveness was awakened, it led to other inventions not connected with mines.

The machines described by Agricola were for the most part worked by men or animals. And when the increasing demand for metal ores necessitated deeper mining, new devices became necessary in order to meet the new situation. Labour-saving methods had to be invented, and special measures had to be taken to meet the special difficulties of deep mining—effective means of haulage, removal of subsoil water, and ventilation. The surface or outcrop miner did not have to provide for ventilation, and the simple windlass and the village pump served his needs. Not so when work had to be carried on at a considerable depth underground.

HAULING MACHINES

Agricola describes five types of hauling machines. Illustr. 260 represents a simple windlass. That shown in Illustr. 261 differs from the former in having only one crank, the place of the second man being taken by a fly-wheel. It appears to be suggested that the steadying effect of the fly-wheel constituted an actual increase of available work. As the Conservation of Energy is a nineteenth-century conception, such a view was by no means improbable or altogether unreasonable, although Agricola made far fewer mistakes in this respect than did most of his literary contemporaries.

"All windlass workers," wrote Agricola, "whatever kind of a machine they may turn, are necessarily robust, so that they can

Illustr. 260.—Simple Windlass

sustain such great toil." A shortage of men sufficiently robust, reinforced by a growing humanitarianism, eventually drove the industrialist to replace nearly all sheer brute force by power-driven machinery, but that idea was foreign to the sixteenth century. The third machine Agricola describes as "less fatiguing for the workman, while it raises larger loads." Two men (see Illustr. 262) grasping a stationary horizontal bar, walked upon a turn-table fixed to a vertical axle which carried overhead a large horizontal wheel, studded near its rim with vertical teeth. These teeth engaged with slots in a wooden drum, mounted on the square part of a horizontal axle, another part of which, being cylindrical, acted as a winch barrel winding buckets up and down an adjacent shaft, as in the first and second types.

Timber wheels, built either like the wheels of heavy wagons, or of boards in layers laid alternately transverse to those above and

Illustr. 261.—Windlass with Fly-wheel

below, carrying hardwood teeth morticed into the rim or near the edge of the body, so as to be replaceable when worn, were a feature of sixteenth-century machinery, and persisted in agricultural machinery well into the nineteenth century.

Iron was used for journals, which turned in iron sockets, or upon iron pillows. Iron was also used to hoop the edges of the pinion drums, but seldom, at that time, for wheels or axles.

The fourth machine was a whim, worked by horse-power; the parts ran into large scantlings. The vertical axle, for instance, is described as 40 feet long and 1½ feet square, furnished at the top with an iron pin running in an iron journal at the meeting of the sixteen inclined timbers, which roofed in a circular horse-track, 50 feet in diameter. The foot of the axle carried a pivot which

Illustr. 262.—Windlass worked by Treadmill

turned in a *steel* socket fixed to a sill, which spread the load on to a timber grillage, sunk well below the floor.

The fifth machine differed from the fourth in that the winding drum was driven through gearing instead of being formed on the vertical spindle. Illustr. 263 also shows a brake drum operated by the man at the foot of the shaft. As an iron winding chain was used, the axle was protected by replaceable rundles. The iron straps and connections at the ends of timbers to which chains were attached were strikingly similar to the iron parts fitted to

Illustr. 263.—Horse Whim with Brake

Illustr. 264.—Surface Transport at the Mine

the timber connecting rods of Watt's steam engines two centuries later.

Following his account of hauling machinery, Agricola described

Illustr. 265.—Sixteenth-Century Rails

the methods used to transport ore from the minehead in mountainous country. The two straight timbers which appear at the rear of the two-wheeled cart at the right of Illustr. 264 are not, as might be imagined, railway lines. They are two trunks tied behind the cart to check its motion by dragging along the surface of the corduroy track. Agricola nowhere describes, or even alludes to, the existence of rails. Yet wooden railroads were already in use in German mines at that time, or even earlier; and were adopted in some English mines early in the seventeenth century. The earliest known illustration of such a timber railway, with a truck drawn along it, is given in Sebastian Münster's *Cosmographia Universalis*, 1550 (p. 9), and is reproduced in Illustr. 265.

WATER-PUMPS.

Agricola describes several kinds of water-pumps. The first (Illustr. 266) is of especial interest. It was operated by one man through an all-metal gear-frame, obviously adapted from the familiar clock mechanism. Frame, wheels, pinions, and shafts were of iron; journals and pillows of steel. Each pair of wheels gave a speed reduction of six to one. It is worthy of note that the end of the shaft which carried the heavy chain rested on a roller made of pure steel. Details of the chain and the metal dippers, which held about three pints each, are worth observing. In detail the machine was a well-conceived piece of mechanical engineering; but it suffered from a fatal drawback in principle. In order that it might work with the power of one man, a high mechanical advantage was necessary. This can only be obtained in any machine at the cost of still higher velocity ratio. As Agricola said: "It cannot be constructed without great expense, and it carries off but little water, and is somewhat slow, as also are all other machines, which possess a great number of drums."

The next two machines were direct-driven: the winding axle carrying in one case a large wheel in which two men walked; in the other a water-wheel.

Agricola's description of the suction pump shows that this device had made little if any advance on ancient Roman practice. Illustr. 267 shows the construction and the simplest use of such pumps. Hardwood trunks, commonly of elm, were drilled out to a bore of 5 or 6 inches, and in length up to 12 feet. One end was tapered to form a spigot, or male end: the other cut to the corresponding female form. These pipes joined end to end, clamped at the joint with iron, formed either pump barrels or water mains. When used as pump barrels the lowest pipe rested on a trunk containing side inlets and a simple clack-valve. The piston consisted of a leather bag, which closed on the down-stroke, and opened to fill the bore on the up-stroke, of a wooden disc loosely fitting the bore about 4 inches thick, or a metal disc $\frac{3}{4}$ of an inch thick. The discs were perforated, covered by a leather flap on the upper side, and screwed or keyed on to the piston-rod. The drive might take the form of a direct lift as shown in the illustration, where "the

Illustr. 266.—Chain of Dippers

Illustr. 267.—Simple Suction Pump

workman eager at his labour, standing on the floor-boards, pushes
the piston down into the pipe and draws it out again." Alternatively
the piston-rod could be operated through a rocking bar. More
sophisticated forms were shown, in which the piston-rod was
continued by a square timber carrying a tappet. A cam consisting
of a rod, morticed square into the body of a revolving shaft lifted
this tappet, the weight of the piston-rod forcing the piston down
again on release. Such devices, adapted from a stamp battery, were
illustrated, in which three or more such pumps were worked in
parallel by cams from the same shaft, driven by hand or water-
wheel. The sudden engagements, however, of the tappet must have
tended to inefficient working, and necessitated frequent repairs.
More elaborate still is the device for deep well pumping represented
in Illustr. 268, where a number of suction pumps work in series.
"This," said Agricola, was "invented ten years ago, is the most
ingenious, durable, and useful of all, [and] can be made without
much expense." It was driven through a water-wheel 15 feet in
diameter through a crank with a 2-foot throw. It is evident from
the drawing that no effective steps were taken to keep the piston-
rods in parallel motion, while wear in the numerous pins connecting
together the claws and links, must have been considerable. However,
the device seems to have served its purpose, and a small working
model is now exhibited in the Science Museum, in London, constructed from Agricola's specification.

The object of using suction pumps in series, instead of one force
pump at the bottom, is clearly to avoid the difficulty and risk
attending the use of pipes, of the form described, under any considerable pressure. Attempts do appear, however, to have been
made to pump against a moderate pressure head. Illustration 269
illustrates the apparatus employed.

Two suction pumps discharged into a common crankcase, hol-
lowed out of a solid block of beechwood, 5 feet long, 2½ feet wide,
and 1½ feet thick, sawn across at the plane where the iron crank-
shaft was to run. Iron and leather washers, inside and outside at
the hole through which the axle protruded, formed a primitive
gland. "Then the upper part of the box is placed upon the lower
one, and properly fitted to it on every side, and where they join
they are bound by wide, thick, iron plates, and held with small,
wide, iron wedges, which are driven in, and are fastened with
clamps." We are not surprised that the description closed with the
ominous warning that "since a wooden box frequently cracks
open, it is better to make it of lead, or copper, or brass." Ramelli
a few years later illustrated such pumps with metal cases and
other less necessary elaborations. The crank seems to have been

Illustr. 268.—Suction Pumps in Series

Illustr. 269.—Crank-operated Force-Pump

first introduced for such a purpose at the beginning of the fifteenth century.

This brings us to Agricola's last class of pumping plant. For deep workings the chain of pots or buckets became unduly heavy: the machinery to be kept in motion was out of all proportion to the water lifted. The suction pump was subject to a natural limitation, later discovered to be the pressure of the atmosphere. The force-pump required strong, water-tight delivery pipes, the production of which was beyond the customary technique of the day. The ancients had, however, found a solution of this problem in the rag and chain system.

The chain ran in a vertical pipe, and was provided at 6-foot intervals with a series of balls "made of the hair of a horse's tail sewn into a covering to prevent it being pulled out by the iron clamps of the [driving] drum: the balls are of such a size that one can be held in each hand." A water-wheel 24 feet in diameter, Agricola stated, would draw water from a shaft 210 feet deep; a 30-foot wheel from a depth of 240 feet. Where water-power was not available the horse-gear, already described as the fifth type of hauling gear, could be adapted for the purpose.

Agricola described (p. 194) a plant erected at Chemnitz to raise water by rag-and-chain pumps in three stages. "The system of three machines of this kind is turned by ninety-six horses; these horses go down to the machines by an inclined shaft, which slopes and twists like a screw, and gradually descends. The lowest of these machines is set in a deep place, which is distant from the surface of the ground 660 feet." The horses worked in teams of eight, with four-hour working shifts and twelve-hour rests. For depths not exceeding 48 feet, the upper axle-drum could be rotated by two or four men working at cranks and capstan bars. For a 66-foot lift a treadmill and geared drive was preferable (see Illustr. 270). For really heavy work, however, there was nothing to compare for efficiency with a simple direct lift in water-bags.

The last water-raising machine Agricola described (Illustr. 271) was perhaps the most powerful built in his day. A timber wheel, 36 feet in diameter, with two sets of buckets to permit of reversal, was built up on an axle consisting of a single balk 35 feet long and 2 feet square. Even had a more powerful plant been required, the size of shaft specified must have approached the limit available or workable in timber for a single unit. Four hubs, 4 feet in diameter, at 4-foot intervals, carried wooden strips which served as a drum round which the haulage chain was wound. These strips naturally required frequent renewal. The water-wheel sluices were controlled by a man in an elevated box adjacent to the power reservoir. A

Illustr. 270.—Chain-Pump and Treadmill

Illustr. 271.—Powerful Water-driven Hoist

brake-drum, 6 feet in diameter, was also provided, so that if the sluice-man "cannot close the water-gate quickly enough, and the water continues to flow, he calls out to his comrade, and bids him raise the brake upon the drum and stop the wheel." The bucket suspended in mid-air in the Illustration is really a tell-tale, connected to a float in the sump, to show the level of the water under ground.

Illustr. 272.—Pivoted Barrel over the Flue

VENTILATION

Following the description of pumping machinery for water, Agricola describes the devices used to maintain under ground a fresh supply of air. Three types are distinguished: wind-scoops and cowls, centrifugal fans, and bellows.

Wind-scoops were either fixed or adjustable. The fixed type consisted of boards dividing the space immediately over the top of a square shaft into four, so that one quadrant was sure to obstruct the wind at the surface and divert it down the shaft. Alternatively a vertical conduit could be made to catch the wind, either by con-

Illustr. 273.—Ventilating Fans

tinuing it above the surface, or by placing a board behind its leeward edge to create the necessary obstruction. The adjustable pattern was made by placing a pivoted barrel over the flue, with a hole cut in one side, and a vane projecting from the side opposite. The detail and method of working this type is clearly seen in Illustr. 272.

Fans were made, as shown in Illustr. 273, either as cylindrical

Illustr. 274.—Ventilating Fan driven by Windmill

drums or as rectangular boxes. "The Drum," says Agricola, "is far superior to the box; for the fans so fill the drum that they almost touch it on every side, and drive into the conduit all the air that has been accumulated." Had the centrifugal action of these fans been appreciated the inlet hole would have been placed near the axle, and not as shown at C, on one side. The blades of the fans were of thin boards, shaped poplar shingles, or feathers. It was possible to make the wind itself drive the fan, by fixing sails to the fan axle, forming a small windmill, as in Illustr. 274.

The last type of ventilating device described was the bellows. These were formed of hinged boards and leather sides. One interesting example, represented in Illustr. 275, shows a giant edition of the familiar domestic fire-raising instrument applied to providing the

Illustr. 275.—Giant Bellows

draught to a furnace. Similar bellows, but usually of less gargantuan proportions, were used for pumping air into mines, or extracting it therefrom; they were also used for pumping water (Illustr. 276).

WATERWORKS

As every important town required a plentiful supply of water, experience in such work was in ready demand. The German cities led the way. Such works constructed in Augsburg, Bremen, and

several other cities were mentioned with admiration and wonder
by travellers from other countries, but neither the travellers nor
the designers have left technical descriptions.

"The Hydraulic engines at Augsburg," says Ewbank, "were at
one time greatly celebrated." They are mentioned, but not described,
by Misson (*Travels*, 5th ed., Vol. I, p. 137) and other travellers of
the seventeenth century. They raised water 130 feet. Blainville, in
1705 (*Travels*, Vol. I, p. 250) speaks of them as among the curiosities of the city. He observes: "The towers which furnish water to
this city are also curious. They are near the gate called the Red
Port, upon a branch of the Leck, which runs through the city.

Illustr. 276.—Water-raising with Bellows

Mills which go day and night by means of this torrent work a
great many pumps, which raise water in large leaden pipes to
the highest story in these towers. . . . One of these towers sends
water to all the public fountains by smaller pipes, and three others
supply with water a thousand houses in the city."

The quotation from Blainville rather suggests that piston-pumps
were employed. Beck (*Beiträge*, p. 179) quotes Paul von Stetten
(*Kunst, Gewerbe und Handswerkgeschichte der Reichsstadt Augsburg*, Augsburg, 1779) to the effect that the first public water supply scheme
in the city of Augsburg was due to Leopold Karg, who tried to distribute water to the city by seven conduits, but without success.
Four years later Hans Felber, a constructor from Ulm, began work
at the Red Port. Canals were cut to augment the sources of supply,
and several towers erected as the century advanced: and we understand that by 1558 the provision of a plentiful supply, both public
and domestic, had been achieved.

It is only incidentally, however, that an account of one of these machines used at Augsburg has been preserved in the *De Subtilitate* (*Lib.* 1) of Jerome Cardan (1550), who appears to have passed through the city about that date. In this work Cardan described the use of the Archimedean screw for raising water, and instanced the "Augsburg Machine" as an example of this class. A vertical shaft (AB in Illustr. 277, which is taken from p. 180 of Th. Beck's *Beiträge zur Geschichte des Maschinenbaues*) is driven by a metal spurwheel on the axle of the waterwheel, which supplies the motive power, and carries pinions to the same number as the screws C, D, E, etc., which raise water in turn from each of a series of horizontal troughs to the next trough higher up. By this alternation of revolving screw and stationary trough the water is made to flow up to the top of the tower from which the supply is taken. The screws in the machine described by Cardan may have been the "large leaden pipes" mentioned by Blainville; or the screw-machine may have been only one of several machines of different types used in the same city. That pipes to withstand high pressure constituted a serious practical difficulty, however, we know from other sources.

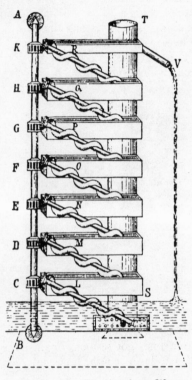

Illustr. 277.—The Augsburg Water Machine

The Waterworks at Toledo were of more than ordinary interest. The city, founded and fortified in remote antiquity, the ancient capital of Spain, like most ancient, lofty cities, stands on a group of seven hills, surrounded on three sides by the River Tagus. The Romans brought water from the surrounding highlands, whence it flowed into the city by gravity, through a long aqueduct crossing the river on a series of arches. Under the Moors the city's population rose to two hundred thousand, when it ranked second in size and importance only to Cordova. In the sixteenth century it was still the capital, though the aqueduct was ruined and water had to be brought on the backs of animals from the deep valley below.

In 1526 the palace at Toledo, known as the Alcazar (built by a Gothic king in the seventh century), was being modernized and extended, and a fuller and better water-supply was considered desirable. German waterworks were already famous, and the king's steward hailed an ingenious German engineer to solve the problem of bringing water from a distance of 2,000 feet through a height of about 250 feet. So far as we know such a problem had never hitherto been solved, unless by several successive chains of pots, or the rag-and-chain pump. Neither of these schemes, however, was suitable to a long sloping path: even the famous Augsberg machine had lifted water only half this height. There was then, as now, only one practical solution to this problem: forcing-pumps, driven by a water-wheel at the riverside; and a pipe-line to the palace. The pipes must, however, be able to withstand a pressure of about eight atmospheres, which was probably unprecedented. "This device," wrote the Chronicler of the Monastery de la Conception Francisca, "worked with great pistons, and the water hammered so furiously and was driven with such terrific force through the metal pipes, that all the mains were fractured, strong enough material out of which to cast them not being available." So "it befell that this apparatus was short-lived."

It seems probable that the German engineers used pumps with long, solid plungers, and that they omitted the air-vessel which Ctesibus had prescribed, such an omission being common; and with the low lifts customary at the time, not serious. Against the inertia of a column of water half a mile in length, however, such an omission might well occasion dangerous hammering. Even so, however, the immediate failure of the pipes suggests that the intensity of pressure was not understood, or was seriously underestimated. Cast brass or bronze pipes could have been made to stand the pressure, but would have cost a vast sum of money. Cast-iron, although used at this period in Germany and France for cannon-balls, fire-backs, and oven-plates, was of poor quality, and had probably not been tried for pipes. Lead pipes had long been in use, made from cast sheets, soldered down at the seam and, on erection, around the butts: but if large-bore mains were attempted on the lines laid down by Vitruvius, we need look no farther for the cause of failure, for that author's rule, that the Weight per Unit Length should be proportional to the Bore, led to one thickness, about a third of an inch, for all diameters (see Gwilt's *Translation of*

Vitruvius, 1828, p. 253). Wooden pipes, as described by Agricola, would obviously be out of the question.

The failure of the plant installed by the German engineers seems to have led to the abandonment of the Alcazar water project, for some years, until solved in a unique manner by an ingenious clockmaker, Juanelo Turriano (1500–85), who had been appointed Court Mathematician by the Emperor Charles V, as a reward for his success in repairing an amazingly complicated clock at Bologna, which had baffled all his colleagues. Juanelo subsequently built several clocks, which included mechanism to show the position of all the planets, according to the Ptolemaic system; and delighted his royal master, who spent many hours in his workshop, with clockwork figures made to move and dance, and other ingenious toys. Charles V died in 1558, but Juanelo remained in the service of Philip II, who set him to solve the water-supply problem, housing him at the mill, below the Alcantara Bridge, from 1564. Naturally Juanelo, who had shared with his royal patron Charles for many years a keen interest in this problem, made a working model of the plant before attempting it full-size.

Some notes and drawings attributed to Juanelo have survived, but unfortunately no mention of this machine is included among them. The only description of the mechanism extant is a confusing account by the Chronicler Ambrosio Morales in his *Antiguedades de la ciudades de España*, p. 337. Morales had seen the model, which he described as the greatest and most wonderful invention. Water was first raised from the river by means of a chain and metal buckets. The substitution of these for hemp rope and earthenware was wrongly acclaimed, as we know from Agricola's previous descriptions, as an original idea of Juanelo's. After this preliminary lift, a mechanism made of crosswise beams bolted together at middle and ends "as may be seen in the machine of Robertus Valturius, designed to lift a man on high, quietly and smoothly passed the movement towards the Alcazar." Coupled to this timber framework were certain wide brass tubes about a metre and a half in length with cups of the same metal at both ends, which were so pivoted as to rock up and down with the motion of the frame. Each of these vessels when tipped back received a charge of water from the similar vessel behind, and, on tilting forward, passed it to the vessel ahead. The "Ladder of Valturius" was a lazy-tong or "Nürnberg scissors" device, which, when compressed laterally, extends lengthwise. If, however, alternate cross-joints were position-fixed, a tilting movement, such as Morales described, would be produced (see Illustr. 278). The channels, Escusura concluded, could only be of the type shown by Ramelli (see Beck's *Beiträge*, pp. 365 ff., and Illustr. 279).

Illustr. 278.—Water-raising by Means of Rocking Troughs

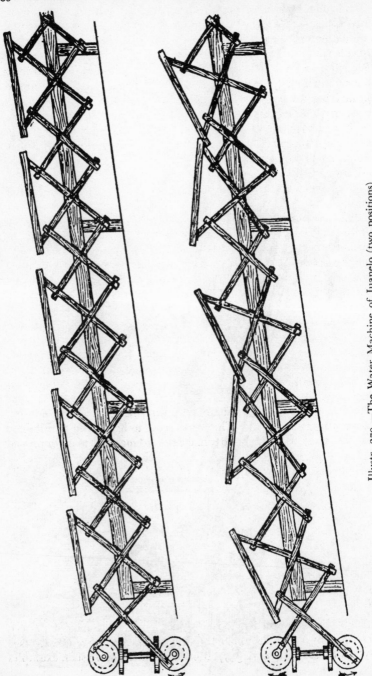

Illustr. 279.—The Water Machine of Juanelo (two positions)

Ramelli showed a scoop wheel and not a chain of pots; he included his "crash" reverse gear, and conveyed the reciprocating motion by means of stiff connecting rods. His picture may therefore have been an improved copy of Juanelo's work. Alternatively, both Ramelli and Juanelo, coming from the district where Leonardo da Vinci's influence and tradition were still strong, may have appropriated an idea suggested by that great man, or by one of his many associates, and developed it, each in his own way (see p. 539).

The construction of the machine, apart from the masonry wall to which it was fixed, consumed two hundred wagon loads of thin wood and five hundred hundredweights of brass. As the track was not straight, numerous special turning pieces had to be arranged, and at least four hundred rocking pipes kept in simultaneous motion.

The machine of Juanelo actually worked from about 1573 onwards; but, as we should now expect, it was an achievement of ingenuity rather than a commercial success. The quantity of water raised was small, and repairs were costly and incessant. Only Court pressure could compel the public to pay the heavy price of water obtained by such means, despite their pride in a possession so unique.

Juanelo's original agreement of 1565 had been to supply not only the Alcazar itself, but to bring there a stipulated quantity of water per day to supply the city as well; and he drew advances on this understanding. This agreement could not be fulfilled, and in 1575 Juanelo agreed to construct a second machine at the joint expense of the King and the town. The second machine was completed in 1581; but by that time the first was in woeful condition. Juanelo died about 1585. The works seem to have been maintained for some years, as a scheme to remake the old machine to an improved design was favourably considered by the King in 1598 on the submission of Juan Fernandez de Castillo. It is not known whether this project was ever carried out; but the entire concern had had to be abandoned some time before 1639; and the inhabitants of Toledo had reverted to their ever-reliable donkeys.

The examples quoted are sufficient to show that practical construction was attempted, not entirely without success, along the lines of freak conceptions. The general tendency, however, as experience was gained in large works, was to develop the simple, eliminating faults and weaknesses as they manifested themselves, ultimately narrowing down the design of pumps for heavy duty, though with improved materials and tools, to the ancient pattern described by Vitruvius under the title of *The Machine of Ctesibus* (see Gwilt's *Vitruvius*, 1828, p. 317). Bronze cylinders, or, in such examples as that found at Silchester (see Illustr. 280), timber lined with lead, formed in pairs, connected through valves with a chamber in the upper part of which was trapped a quantity of air. The pistons or plungers were "turned very smooth" and lubricated with oil.

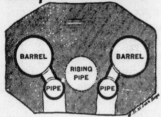

Vitruvius distinctly credited the trapped air with the duty of forcing the water up the delivery pipe. As he mentions that the purpose of such pumps was to supply the public fountains, a fairly large size must have been intended, although the few surviving examples are small. In the British Museum are to be seen two small bronze pumps, one fitted with clack-valves, the other with turned poppet valves. This type of machine never completely disappeared, and ultimately became the standard type for all heavy work, once strong castings and better methods of machining were developed.

It was perhaps used extensively in early German waterworks, although apart from such references as those already quoted in relation to quite a different pattern of machine at Augsberg, details are wanting. It was, however, without any doubt the piston pump which German engineers introduced at London, Paris, and elsewhere. Previous to the sixteenth century these cities had been supplied with water from wells, and by pipes leading from springs. The first attempt to erect power-driven pumps in London was made by a German engineer, named Peter Maurice, in

Illustr. 280.—Reconstruction of Roman Pump found at Silchester

1582. Maurice, according to William Maitland (*The History of London from its Foundation by the Romans to the Present Time*, London, 1739, p. 160), "proposed to the Court of Lord Mayor and Aldermen the erecting a Machine in the River Thames for raising Water for the more effectual Supply of the City; which, being approved of, he erected the Same in the River near London Bridge, which by Suction and Pressure thro' Pumps and Valves (the same as still performed

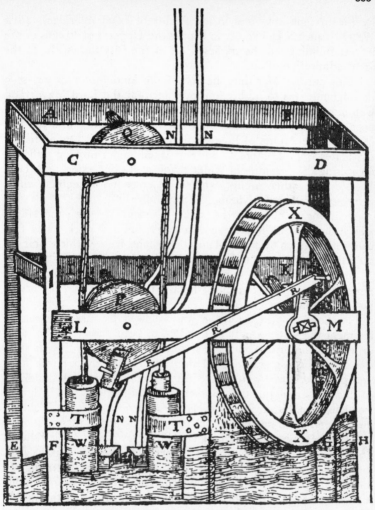

Illustr. 281.—Bate's Sketch of the London Bridge Waterworks

(*Mysteries of Nature and Art*, 1635)

ABCDEFGHIKLM, Timber Frame. XX, the Water-Wheel, in brass sockets set in the two middle Beams of the Frame IKLM, to which is also fastened the Wheel P, above which the Half-wheel Q is set. WW are two Barrels of Brass or Iron fastened with iron Bands, TT, to the Posts of the Frame. To each Barrel is fitted a Force well leathered. On the tops of the Forces are two Pieces of Wood, 2 feet long and 2 inches thick, on the tops of which are iron Chains linked up to an iron Band round Wheel Q. A Wooden Bar, RRR, comes over the Handle of the main Wheel, XX, and on the Spoke of Wheel P. The Water is forced through the Pipes, NN, to the top of a Turret near the Engine, and thence passes into the main wooden Pipes which are laid along the Streets.

by the present Machines in the Arches of London Bridge) raised Water to such a Height, as to supply the Uppermost Rooms of the loftiest Buildings in the highest Part of the City therewith, to the great admiration of all.

"This curious Machine, the first of the kind that ever was seen in England, was so highly approv'd of, that the Lord Mayor and Common Council, as an Encouragement for the ingenious Engineer to proceed in so useful an Undertaking, granted him the Use of one of the Arches of London Bridge to place his Engine in, for the better working thereof: But one Machine not proving sufficient for raising the Quantity of Water requir'd, his Successors have been allow'd Two other Arches, wherein to erect more Engines, which at present are Five in Number." (See Illustr. 281.)

According to Stow (see Ewbank's *Hydraulics*, p. 322), the Mayor and Aldermen, on inspecting Maurice's finished work, "saw him throw the water over St. Magnus's steeple, before which time no such thing was known in England as this raising of water."

The London Bridge machinery was considerably extended and altered from time to time; and finally demolished when the bridge was rebuilt in 1822.

The London Bridge scheme was followed by other projects to augment the water-supply of London, to keep pace with the rapid growth of the city. Middleton's New River, tapping the water of the Lee at Ware, was opened in 1613. Horse-driven pump units and pressure towers were erected at Durham Yard, York Buildings, Millbank, Grand Junction, Broken Wharf, Shadwell, and Wapping (see Rhys Jenkins, in *The Proceedings of the Newcomen Society*, Vol. IX, pp. 43–51). With one exception, technical details of these pumping plants are lacking; but a rough contemporary sketch of Sir Edward Ford's tower, erected just below Somerset House (see Illustr. 282), indicates a pair of piston-rods, and a long, vertical driving-rod hanging respectively from the opposite ends of what is presumably a rocking beam, although the fulcrum is omitted from the sketch. The vertical driving-rod carried a bronze friction roller, operated by a series of cams projecting from the upper surface of a horizontal face wheel, rotated, without gearing, by horses walking round on the floor below. The uneven drive was trying to the animals, and was estimated to have utilized only some 30 per cent of their power input. Except in the lift of 60 feet per pump, this plant showed no advance on machines described by Agricola a century earlier. The removal of the tower was ordered in 1664, not because it had ceased to be useful, but because of the extensive view it commanded, at close range, of the grounds of Somerset House, then occupied by the Queen Dowager.

Waterworks at Paris had a similarly interesting history. About 1608 a Flemish engineer named Lintlaer erected an engine consisting of *"lifting-pumps,"* worked by the current in the Seine beneath the Pont Neuf (then in fact as well as in name a NEW BRIDGE), in

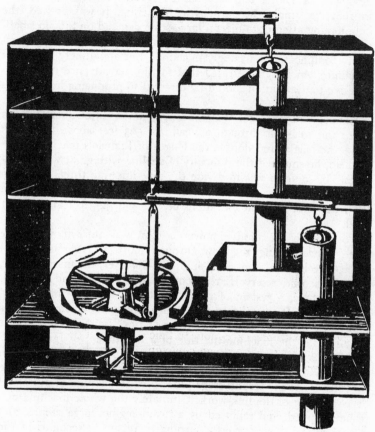

Illustr. 282.—Ford's Pump

order to supply the Louvre and the Tuilleries. The water passed upward through valves in the piston on the downstroke of the latter, and was pushed through valves in the cylinder head on the up-stroke, straight into the delivery pipe, which sprang vertically therefrom. The piston-rod was erected upon a cross-bar, suspended under water, from a rocking beam above, by a pair of vertical links.

This type of pump, being drowned, required no priming; but the working parts were inconveniently inaccessible for inspection or repair. However, their utility was sufficient to encourage the erection, in 1669, of a similar plant at the Notre Dame.

The most remarkable and elaborate mechanism constructed on a grand scale, however, was the pumping-plant erected to the designs of a Dutch engineer named Rannequin, and completed in 1682, to supply the gardens at Versailles. It was, indeed, the culminating attempt to meet a large-scale demand on the old small-scale system of construction: an attempt which produced an excessively complicated, amazingly ingenious, but appallingly inefficient machine, which demonstrated that for further advance it was imperative that attention should be directed to producing larger units of simpler forms.

Rannequin's problem was to convey water three-quarters of a mile, and to lift it through a height of 533 feet above the river: twice the height and double the length of Juanelo's machine. Like Juanelo, he shunned the difficulty of dealing with great water pressures. His solution was to divide the pipe-line into three, with two intermediate reservoirs distant 600 and 2,000 feet respectively from the river bank, and at elevations of 160 and 325 feet above river level.

To provide the motive power a dam was thrown across the river, concentrating the flow through fourteen large under-shot water-wheels. The number of pumps at the river, the first reservoir, and the second reservoir, respectively, was 64, 79, and 82; and, to drive these, a system of rods mounted on rocking links trailed up the hill. "It was the transmission of power to such elevations and extraordinary distances by these chains," said Ewbank, "that acquired for the machine the title of a Monument of Ignorance." At least 80, some say 95, per cent of the power was wasted in friction and inertia losses. Subsequent attempts to reduce these by cutting out the second stage pumps led to bursting of pipes and over-straining of the link-work. Ultimately the whole machine had to be scrapped, and replaced by a steam-engine, large pumps, and strong mains, after costing a fortune in repairs. (Accounts of the machinery employed are given by Desagulier in his *Natural Philosophy*; by Belidor in his *Architecture Hydraulique*; and by Leupold in his *Theatrum Machinarum Hydraulicorum*, Vol. I).

ENGINEERING SKETCHES

Leonardo da Vinci (1451–1519) published nothing himself, but compiled a vast collection of notes to which, after his death, numerous students and authors had access. His sketches included trains of gear-wheels, the crank, the flywheel, forcing-pumps driven by rocking-beams, lifting screws, a boring-machine with screw-feed and adjustable chuck; and a whole range of appliances for mechanizing the work of spinning and weaving. He has been credited with the invention of canal-locks; but whether he imitated or anticipated early Dutch and Flemish models is not known (see the *Early Years of Modern Civil Engineering*, by Kirby and Laurson, Yale, 1932, Chap. II). Leonardo da Vinci collected and arranged material for a projected treatise on Hydraulics. The original of this is now in the Forster Library at South Kensington, and a facsimile reproduction, under the title *Problèmes de Geométrie et d'Hydraulique*, was published in Paris in 1901. Leonardo's materials were appropriated by Jerome Cardan (1501–57) whose works (*De Subtilitate*, 1550, and *De Rerum Varietate*, 1557; both included in Cardan's *Opera Omnia*, Leyden, 1663, Vol III) served as a substitute for Leonardo's originals. Cardan also added accounts of some contemporary works, as we saw when discussing early German waterworks.

A fairer idea of the actual achievement of mechanical technology up to about 1550 is, however, given by Agricola's famous *De Re Metallica* (1556), which shows the scale of current applications of power to pumping and mining; and in other trades by a small volume by Hartmann Schopper, printed in Frankfurt in 1568 under the title of *Papoplia Omnium*. This seems to have been a Latin Reader devised on a system rediscovered in the twentieth century. Each item shows, under a heading in both German and Latin, a picture of a craftsman surrounded by the materials, tools, and products of his trade, described beneath in Latin verse. A Printer is shown printing from movable type in a screw-press. The Paper-maker is equipped with a pulping-machine, driven by tappets on the axle of a water-wheel. He, too, possesses a screw-press. The Pewterer is seen turning up metal tankards in a lathe, to which power is applied by an endless belt from a large pulley, cranked round by an assistant. The Turner is shown operating on a ball in a lathe, the mandrel of which is apparently rotated by a rope or belt, the ends being attached respectively to a treadle and a springy overhead pole. Work is individual, performed by hand tools, with the minimum of assistance from any source of power other than human muscles.

In 1579 there was issued from a press in Lyons a considerable quarto volume entitled *Theâtre des Instrumens Mathématiques et Méchaniques de Jaques Besson Dauphinois, docte Mathématicien*. Besson, who died in 1569, was a Professor of Mathematics at Orleans. His previous writings dealt with the finding of underground sources of water, and the construction of sundry mathematical and astronomical instruments. His last work, completed with explanatory notes by Beroald, was an ambitious treatise describing instruments, machine tools, pumping plants, and engines of war. Much use was made in these designs of the screw and the worm-wheel, which could hardly, at this date, have been formed with sufficient accuracy to work efficiently. Besson's own screw-cutting lathe (Illustr. 283) could have functioned only on light work of small dimensions.

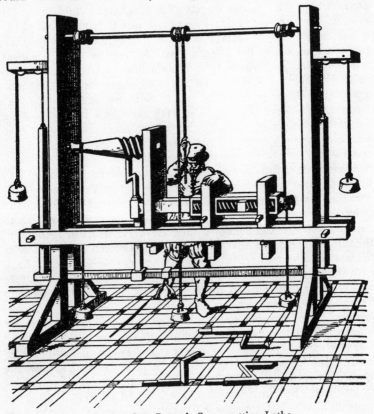

Illustr. 283.—Besson's Screw-cutting Lathe

Besson's treatise ran into several editions, and was translated into several languages. It did much to spread the Leonardo tradition among the scientific dilettanti of France.

Another work even more remarkable, in that it anticipated with detailed sketches a number of devices which were successfully manufactured and marketed two or three centuries later, is *Le Diverse et Artificiose Machine del Capitano Agostino Ramelli*, published in Paris in 1588. Ramelli (1530?–90) gained his captaincy for service under the Marquis de Marignan, who quite possibly studied under

Leonardo da Vinci. The handsome quarto volume contained one hundred and ninety-five full-page illustrations, artistically rendered, and described both in French and Italian. Most of the heavy machinery Ramelli illustrated was driven by water-wheels of the types common at this period, undershot or overshot; a few, however, possessed curved vanes radiating horizontally from a vertical shaft. Besson also had shown one of these; but, if the type was in use at all, it was probably rare. It could only run efficiently in a specially constructed cylindrical pool, through which the stream ran almost tangentially—a complication which offered few counterbalancing advantages. The water-wheel shaft, whether vertical or horizontal, provided a rotary motion, which could be used directly in water-raising by means of a chain of pots, or rag-and-chain pump. Ramelli described both types; but he was more interested in the piston-pump, and projected a variety of devices for converting rotary into a reciprocatory motion to suit this purpose. Agricola had shown one pump with a water-tight crank-case. Ramelli elaborated this, stating that the pressure case might be either of wood or of metal. Not content with this solution, however, he developed a reversing device, which would have proved disastrous in a full-sized machine. The main shaft was provided with two wheels, each toothed for half its circumference, these wheels alternately engaging the rungs of a "lantern" pinion (or else two lantern pinions on one shaft alternately engaging the teeth on one partially toothed wheel). This would effect reversal, but suddenly full speed ahead changing to full speed reverse at the first crash of each new engagement. The use of this pet device vitiated dozens of Ramelli's designs, and leaves the modern reader with the suspicion that nearly all his illustrations represent untried proposals of doubtful efficiency. The subsequent trend of current practice confirms this suspicion.

Model making and collecting was a hobby of the scientific dilettanti of the day. One such collection made by a French soldier of fortune was described by his grandson in a work entitled *Receuil d'Ouvrages curieux de Mathématique et de Mécanique, ou Description du Cabinet de M. Grollier de Servière* (Lyons, 1719). It is not clear whether all the mechanisms described were actual models, or whether some drawings and descriptions were included. That many were working models is, however, obvious; and these embodied details which could not be repeated on the grand scale.

A common feature of sixteenth-century models which rendered them unsuitable for full-sized application was the inclusion of parts requiring accurate machining, for which suitable plant was not available. Ramelli's rotary pumps fall into this category. He illustrated three types, one of which incorporates an interesting chain-drive. Numerous uses, mostly connected with fortress-breaking, were shown for the worm-wheel operated screw-jack: a practical device which came into its own as soon as accurate machine-tools permitted its economical manufacture. Ramelli illustrated windmills, both of the post and tower types, for grinding corn and pumping water respectively. The designs shown were simple, and may have represented actual models which he had seen.

Achievement in mechanical matters came more directly from the practical development of actual workable machines, such as Agricola described, than from the bold, new steps suggested by da Vinci, Besson, and Ramelli, although their influence in the direction of greater freedom and foresight may well have been considerable.

We have given to these two authors much more extended attention than we can spare to their successors, although these produced many interesting works. Draughtsmanship, however, deteriorated: there was nothing as well produced as Ramelli's book until well into the eighteenth century; and then the improvement consisted chiefly in the inclusion of scale drawings. Mention must be made, however, of several authors of illustrated descriptions of machinery, although for fuller details the reader must refer either to Th. Beck's admirable summaries (in his *Beiträge sur Geschichte des Machinenbaues*, Berlin, 1899) or to the originals.

Faustus Veranzio's *Machinae Novae* (c. 1617) contained some interesting windmill details, centrings for bridge arches, suspension bridges, and dredging apparatus.

Vittorio Zonca (1568–1602) was the author of an important work entitled *Novo Teatro di machine et Edificii* (Padua, 1621) which in rather crude sketches shows power plant extended to milling, fulling, silk-spinning by multiple spindles, and numerous other industrial purposes (see Illustr. 233, p. 464).

Giacomo Strada di Rosberg was a well-known antiquarian art collector and dealer who, in 1617–18, brought out a work entitled *Dessins Artificiaux de toutes Sortes des Moulins à Vent, à l'Eau, à Cheval, et à la Main, avec diverses Sortes de Pompes et aultres Inventions pour faire monter l'Eau au hault sans beaucoup de Peine et Despens*, etc. A German translation was published in 1629, which did much to spread the fruits of sixteenth-century Italian ingenuity in Germany.

Benedetto Castelli, a friend and pupil of Galilei, deeply influenced by the Leonardo school, and probably familiar with the Vatican Compilation of Leonardo's notes, produced *Delli Misure dell'Acque Correnti*, which was posthumously published in 1628. This work was described by Poggendorf as the first book containing sound principles on the flow of water in rivers and canals.

A work which has received less attention than it deserves is

R. D'Acres' little volume on *The Art of Water-drawing*, first published in London in 1659 (reprinted in facsimile for the Newcomen Society, 1930). D'Acres is believed to be the pseudonym of Robert Thornton (1618–79), a mining engineer with interests in the Warwickshire coalfield. He alone among the technical authors of the period analyses the machines and parts thereof according to type and function. The others describe each machine as a separate and distinct contrivance, repeating descriptions of similar details in full. D'Acres recognizes the nature of atmospheric pressure, and the limit it sets to suction devices; the "principle of work": that every water-raising machine must, whatever its construction, be supplied with more power than would suffice to lift the dead weight of water with which it deals; that perpetual motion is practically impossible; and that simplicity of construction and smoothness of action are essential to the efficient working of all machinery. Unfortunately his work contains no pictorial illustrations. This fact, together with its small size, and the troubled times in which it appeared, may account for its rarity, and the undeserved oblivion from which it has only lately been rescued by the vigilance of the Newcomen Society.

Galilei's epoch-making *Two New Sciences* appeared in 1638, when, we may say, the foundations of engineering theory were first laid. A number of treatises appeared from time to time under such titles as "Theatrum machinorum," usually followed by "novum" to suggest to the uninitiated that the author was responsible for all the ideas contained in his descriptions. Zeising (1607–18), Böckler (1661), and Leupold (1734) were the most notable contributors in this field. These works are mainly copies of other people's work; but they show some progress in detail, in magnitude of units, and in extended applications of mechanism and power. Leupold's work, although published in the eighteenth century, is mainly an encyclopaedic summary of previous work, and fitly closes the pre-steam period under review.

ADDENDA

We have now followed the development of mechanical engineering through two centuries, from the first attempts at heavy pumping and haulage in mines, and the early public waterworks, to the eve of the appearance of the steam engine. This period was characterized by improvement in two types of machine: the Water-wheel and the Pump; and both had been brought as far in size and in refinement of detail as was feasible.

Sir Samuel Morland introduced pumps with solid plungers as large as 10 inches in diameter in 1674, provided with a packing gland consisting of two "*hat-leathers*" to prevent leakage either on the suction or delivery strokes, thus obviating the necessity of drowning his cylinders to save priming.

The manual fire-engine, which attracted much attention after the disastrous fire of London (1666) was gradually improved, and practically perfected by Richard Newsham in 1721. Valves were placed in accessible positions under removable covers, and the pistons provided with "*cup-leathers.*"

Cast iron was introduced early in our period. This led in turn to increased production of wrought iron at a cheaper price, and an extension of its use. "In 1591," according to John W. Hall (*Transactions of the Newcomen Society*, Vol. VIII, p. 40), "a forge could not make more than two tons per week; and, owing to shortage of water, often made only fifty tons per year." The price of iron so produced was inevitably high. Its use was accordingly restricted to purposes for which other materials, more cheaply made and more easily worked, were inadequate. Water tanks and pipes were constructed in pewter and lead, which cost half the price of iron; indeed, Savery's engines seem to have failed because his lead pipes burst under the pressures he applied. Brewers' boilers and stills were of copper. Wrought iron at the close of the seventeenth century was made in a finery, little bigger than a smith's forge, by exposing from 50 to 100 lb. of pig iron at a time to a blast of air. The product was not infrequently insufficiently decarbonized, and crumbled when hammered to expel the somewhat infusible slag. Attempts to use raw coal, in lieu of charcoal, in iron manufacture were not successful until about 1800. Dudley (1599–1684) claimed to have succeeded on these lines as early as 1620 (*Metallum Martis*, 1665). This boast must, in the absence of confirmatory evidence, be regarded with scepticism (see T. S. Ashton, in *Transactions of the Newcomen Society*, Vol. V, p. 9).

The Rolling Mill for soft metals was probably in use in da Vinci's days. L. Darmstädter (*Handbuch z. Gesch. d. Naturw. u.d. Technik*) quotes a description of the Nürnberg iron-mill by Eobanus Hessus in which iron was rolled "by the weight of turning wheels." This account, dated 1532, is said to be the earliest description of a rolling mill with both rolling and slitting machinery. For long after that date bars and plates were formed under the tilt-hammer, and merely finished by rolling. Small bars were formed from plates by "slitting," or passing the plates between rolls in which projecting rings on one roll came opposite the spaces between projecting rings on the other, thus shearing the plates into strips. Rolls which could stand the pressure and heat necessary for the complete working of iron by this means were not in general use till the end of the eighteenth century.

CHAPTER XXIII

TECHNOLOGY

VII. THE STEAM ENGINE. VIII. MECHANICAL CALCULATORS

VII. THE STEAM ENGINE

ANTECEDENTS

The history of the steam engine goes back as far as Hero of Alexandria (*c.* 50 A.D.), who compiled several works on mechanics, including a treatise on pneumatics, in which he described various mechanical devices then existing and some of his own inventions, without indicating which was which. These devices include a machine which, by means of an altar fire, could be made to open temple doors; another which produced a steam jet on which a light ball could be supported; and, what is of greater interest, an Aeolipile, which was essentially a reaction steam turbine. Hero's Aeolipile, however, although reputed to have been used practically in later centuries (see Illustr. 284), was little more than a toy.

Until the beginning of modern times there is little to record, although the knowledge of the power of steam had not been lost. Various references from the twelfth century onwards indicate

Illustr. 284.—An Aeolipile (*left*) supplying a Blast to a Copper-smelting Fire. A hollow Bronze Ball with a small opening through which water is poured. When the water boils a strong blast issues from the Ball

this. It is stated that in 1125 at Rheims an organ, constructed by Gerbert, was blown by air, compressed by "heated water" (see R. Stuart's *History and Descriptive Anecdotes of Steam Engines*, Vol. I, p. 15). Cardan, in the middle of the sixteenth century, mentioned the power of steam and the method of producing a vacuum by condensing steam (*De Rerum Natura*, Bk. XII, Chap. 58, p. 425, in ed. 1557). Matthesius, in 1571, also mentions the power of steam; and some unknown contemporary tried to harness Hero's Aeolipile to a spit. Besson of Orleans (sixteenth century) wrote on the power of steam, and Agostino Ramelli, an Italian, in 1588 published a book on machines (*Le Diverse et Artificiose Machine*). Leonardo da

Illustr. 285.—Baptista Porta's Sketch of a Steam Machine

Illustr. 286.—Raising Water by Heat (De Caus)

The copper ball A has a vent at D through which it is partly filled with water and which is then closed by means of a tap. It has also a tube, BC, dipping down nearly to the bottom at C, with a tap at B. The ball is heated, and upon opening the tap B water spouts up through it.

Vinci described a steam gun (attributed by him to Archimedes) in which the sudden expansion produced by the vaporization of water dropped on a hot surface fired a cannon-ball.

In 1601 Baptista Porta, in *I Tre Libri de' Spiritali* (ed. 1606, p. 77), described a machine for raising a column of water by steam pressure—the condensation of the steam producing a vacuum into which the water flowed (Illustr. 285). This machine used steam pressure to expel liquid, whereas Hero used the pressure of expanding air. Porta had thus introduced something new. Moreover, Porta accurately described the action of steam in producing a vacuum by condensation, and conceived an apparatus in which the vacuum obtained in this way would be filled by water forced in by the pressure of the atmosphere. These devices, however, were not turned to practical account.

David Rivault, in *Les Elémens de l'Artillerie*, 1608, wrote that water heated in a closed bombshell burst the shell, however thick its walls. "The water," he wrote, "is converted into air, and its vaporization is followed by a violent explosion."

Solomon de Caus, in *Les Raisons des Forces Mouvantes* (1615), described a machine for raising water by the expansive power of steam (p. 4) (see Illustr. 286).

Branca, in *Le Machine deverse del Signor Giovanni Branca, etc.* (Rome, 1629), described a kind of turbine, in which the steam rotated a wheel by impinging on its vanes. This apparatus—if it was ever constructed—was probably only a toy (see Illustr. 287).

In 1630 David Ramseye obtained a patent from Charles I for various inventions, including one "to raise water from low pitts by fire . . . to make any sort of mills to goe on standing waters by continual motion, without help of wind, waite [weight?] or horse . . . to raise water from low places and mynes, and coal pitts, by a new waie never yet in use"—all evidently applications of steam power. (See T. Rymer, *Fœdera, conventiones, literae*, etc., 1732, XIX, p. 239, and p. 17.)

Bishop Wilkins, in his *Mathematical Magick* (1648), stated that aeolipiles were used "for the moving of sails in a chimney corner, the motion of which sails may be applied to the turning of a spit, or the like" (p. 149).

THE MARQUIS OF WORCESTER

None of these devices appears to have been applied to any large-scale work, and of some of them it is very doubtful whether construction ever followed suggestion. But *A Century of the Names and Scantlings of Inventions by me already practised* (written in 1655, published in 1663), by Edward Somerset, second Marquis of Worcester, describes an apparatus for raising water by means of steam. The author gives no diagram of the engine, but various diagrams have since then been made in conformity with the description, and one of these is in the Science Museum in London. Essentially, it was a more elaborate form of De Caus' machine, improved from a mere fountain to an engine for raising water. Such an engine was erected at Vauxhall, and raised water to a height of 40 feet. There are records of eye-witnesses who saw it in

Illustr. 287.—Branca's Turbine

Water in the metal vessel A is heated over a fire, and the pressure of the steam escaping through D drives round the wheel E, which, acting through a train of wheels, works a stamp-mill.

1663 and 1669. In 1663 the Marquis obtained rights for ninety-nine
years by Act of Parliament for his "water commanding engine."
The Museum drawing "shows a high pressure boiler, and two

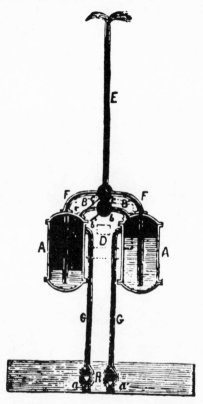

Illustr. 288.—Worcester's Water Commanding Engine

AA are two Vessels connected by a Steam-pipe with the Boiler behind. D is
the Furnace. E is a vertical Water-pipe connected with the Vessels AA by the
Pipes FF. Water is supplied by the Pipes GG, with Valves aa, dipping into the
Well H. Steam is admitted alternately into A and A, and, condensing there,
allows the pressure of the Atmosphere to force the Water from H through G and G.
While one is filling, the Steam forces the Water from the other up along E.
When one is emptied, the Steam is diverted from it into the other, and it fills again.

vessels into which the water to be pumped was forced by atmospheric pressure after the contained steam had condensed; this
water was afterwards discharged by steam pressure on the system
subsequently extensively practised by Savery" (*Science Museum Catalogue, Stationary Engines*, p. 28, Exhibit 40) (see Illustr. 288).

This "water-commanding engine" was the first known serious

attempt to make practical use of an invention. But the time was not yet ripe for it. Worcester failed to form a company to develop his invention, and although his widow made long efforts after his death she met with no success.

HUYGENS

In 1680 Huygens devised a machine-driven by the expansive force

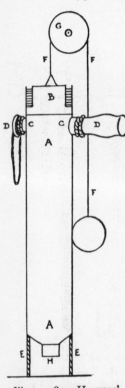

of gunpowder. This was the first gas engine with cylinder and piston. It is represented in Illustr. 289, in which A is the cylinder and B the piston. CC are relief pipes with check values. Powder is exploded at H and expels air from the cylinder. When the engine cools, the pressure in A falls and the atmospheric pressure forces down the piston B, thereby raising the weight suspended over the pulley system F. But Huygens' proposed engine never materialized.

PAPIN

The next notable advance was made by Denys Papin (1647–1712), a Frenchman who became assistant to Huygens. In 1675 Papin came to England and worked with Robert Boyle. In 1680 he was elected to the Royal Society. In 1681 he published an account of a "Digester" (Illustr. 290), which is noteworthy here because it included a new invention—the safety valve. The "Digester" was an apparatus for softening bones by boiling them with water in a closed vessel—the water, boiling under pressure, boiled at a higher temperature, as we now know, and this

Illustr. 289.—Huygens'
Gas Engine

increased its power of solution. "I took beef bones," wrote Papin, "that had never been boiled but kept dry a long time, and of the hardest part of the leg; these being put into a little glass pot, with water, I included in the engine together with another little glass pot full of bones and water too, but in this case the bones were ribs, and had been boiled already. Having pressed the fire until the drop of water would dry away in 3 seconds and ten pressures I took off the fire, and the vessels being cooled I found very good jelly in both my pots, but that which was made out of ribs had a kind of reddish colour, which, I believe, might proceed from the medullar part; the other jelly was without taste or colour, like hartshorn jelly; . . . and . . . having seasoned it with sugar and juice of lemon, I did eat it with as much pleasure, and found it as stomachical, as if it had been jelly of hartshorn" (*New Digester for Softening Bones*, 1681, p. 22). This vessel was subject to considerable steam pressure, and to avoid an explosion Papin inserted in the top of the digester a tube, HH. The end of this tube was closed by a valve, P, kept closed by means of the weight N, suspended from the end of the lever LM, which was pivoted about the support LQ.

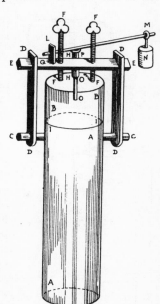

In 1687, after an absence of some years in Italy, Papin once more in England outlined another invention— the transmission of power from one point to another. "At the point where power was available, he exhausted a chamber by means of an air-pump, and, leading a pipe to the distant point at which it was to be utilized, there withdrew the air from behind a piston, and the pressure of the air upon the latter caused it to recede into the cylinder, in which it was fitted, raising a weight, of which the magnitude was proportionate to the size of the piston and the degree of exhaustion. Papin was not satis- factorily successful in his experiments; but he had created the germ of the modern system of pneumatic trans- mission of power. His disappointment

Illustr. 290.—Papin's Digester, with Safety Valve

at the result of his efforts to utilize the system was very great, and he became despondent and anxious to change his location again" (Thurston, *The Steam Engine*, p. 49). In 1687, therefore, Papin accepted the Chair of Mathematics at Marburg in Germany, where he remained for many years.

At Marburg Papin attempted to improve Huygens' gunpowder engine by substituting steam for the gunpowder, the condensation of the steam producing a higher degree of vacuum; and he thus produced the first steam engine with a piston, and in which con- densation was used to obtain a vacuum. (Papin's design was published in the *Acta Eruditorum*, Leipzic, August 1690, pp. 410 ff., as *Nova Methodus ad vires motrices validissimas levi pretio comparandas*, i.e. "A New Method of securing cheaply Motive Power of Considerable Magnitude.") Papin's engine is shown in Illustr. 291. A small quantity of water is placed at the bottom of the cylinder A, which is heated—the bottom being of very thin metal. The steam produced pushes up the piston, B, to the top. A latch, E, engages in a notch in the piston-rod, H, and holds it until it is let go. On the removal of the fire, the steam condenses, producing a partial vacuum. E is disengaged, and atmospheric pressure drives the piston down, thus raising the weight attached to the rope, L, passing over the pulleys, TT. The diameter of the cylinder was 2½ inches. It raised 60 lb. per minute. Papin calculated that, with a cylinder of diameter a little over 2 feet and a 4-foot stroke, one could raise 8,000 lb. 4 feet per minute.

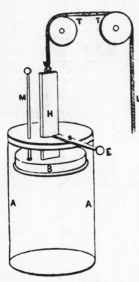

Illustr. 291.—Papin's Steam Engine

Papin suggested the use of this machine for raising water from mines, throwing bombs, and driving ships by means of paddles. "The principal difficulty," he wrote, "is that of making these large cylinders." In a reprint in 1695 (*Recueil de diverses Pièces touchant quelques nouvelles Machines*, Cassel) he described an improved furnace for the engine—the fire being surrounded by water, produced steam at a sufficiently rapid rate to give four strokes per minute Further, he suggested a furnace within which the fuel was burned on a grate by a *down draught*.

Later, in 1705, Papin heard from Leibniz of Savery's engine, and received from him a sketch of it. In 1707 Papin published, in his *Nouvelle manière pour lever l'eau par la force du feu* (Cassel), details of a new engine, a modified Savery engine—not a modified Huygens' engine, as his previous one was. This, however, was no advance on his first engine.

In 1707 Papin used his steam engine (originally conceived as a pumping engine) to drive a model boat on the river Fulda at Cassel; the pumping engine forcing up water to turn a water-wheel, which drove the paddles. (The story of these experiments is contained in Papin's correspondence with Leibniz, preserved in the State Library at Hanover.) Meanwhile, the problem had been attacked by Morland and by Savery.

MORLAND

Sir Samuel Morland, Master Mechanic to Charles II, carried out various experiments on steam and made various fire-engines. He invented the speaking-trumpet, calculating machines, and a capstan, and paid much attention to pumps. In a book published at Paris in 1685 (*Élévation des Eaux par toute sorte de Machines, etc.*) and in an earlier manuscript (now in the British Museum) he wrote on steam. In the latter he says: "Water being evaporated by fire, the vapours require a greater space (about two thousand times greater) than that occupied by the water; and, rather than submit to imprisonment, it will burst a piece of ordnance. But being controlled according to the laws of statics, and, by science, reduced to the measure of weight and balance, it bears its burden peaceably (like good horses) and thus may be of great use to mankind, especially for the raising of water." He then gives a table "which indicates the number of pounds which may be raised six inches, 1,800 times an hour, by cylinders half-filled with water, and of the several diameters and depths of the said cylinders."

The increase in volume given by Morland for the change from water to steam is considerably nearer accuracy than are those of other early experimenters. Desaguliers gave it as 1 to 14,000, and his figure was accepted for many years—until the experiments made by Watt, who estimated it as 1 to 1,800 or 1,900.

Morland would naturally be acquainted with the work of Worcester, his contemporary. His apparatus may have been a modification of Worcester's, but little is known about his work. He died in 1696.

SAVERY

By the end of the seventeenth century the English miners, now going deeper down, were very seriously harassed by the accumulation of water in the mines, and the problem was a vital one. The problem was attacked by Thomas Savery (*c.* 1650–1716), a military engineer greatly interested in mechanics, mathematics, and natural philosophy. Much given to experimenting and the contriving of curious mechanisms, he patented an apparatus in which paddle-wheels were driven by a capstan, for driving ships in calm weather, and he tried to persuade the Navy Board to adopt it. He was reproved by an official of the Navy Board with the remark, "What have interloping people, that have no concern with us, to do to pretend to contrive or invent things for us?" Savery demonstrated his invention on the Thames, but it was not adopted by the Navy.

Later, Savery invented a steam engine resembling Worcester's. Whether he knew of the work of Worcester or his predecessors we cannot say. On July 25, 1698, Savery patented his design of the first engine actually employed to pump water out of mines. A working model was successfully demonstrated to the Royal Society in 1699 (see *Phil. Trans.*, 1699, Vol. XXI, pp. 189 and 228). Savery's patent bears the title: "A grant to Thomas Savery,

Illustr. 292.—Savery's Steam Engine

A, furnace; B, boiler, connected by pipes C with receivers D, from the bottom of which branch pipes turned upward joined to form a "forcing pipe," G. From the top of D, pipes turned downward united to form a suction pipe, H, which led to the water which was to be pumped. (Maximum lift was given as 24 feet.) Steam from B was led, by opening cock C, to fill receiver D. C was closed, and the steam condensed. Water, therefore, rose through the suction pipe into D. C was opened, the check-valve was closed, and the steam forced the water out through G, the clack-valve now opening before the water. The cycle was then repeated. While one receiver was being filled with steam, the other was discharging water—the two receivers and pipes working alternately.

Gentleman, of the sole exercise of a new invention by him invented, for raising of water, and occasioning motion to all sorts of millworks, by the impellant force of fire, which will be of great use for draining mines, serving towns with water, and for the working of all sorts of mills, when they have not the benefit of water nor constant winds; to hold for 14 years; with usual clauses."

Savery knew not only how to invent but also how to make his invention known, and he seems to have had a proper appreciation

of the value of advertisement. He made his plans known and understood even in matters of detail; and his working model made a
great impression on the Royal Society, who approved of it. He
presented the Society with a drawing of his engine, and an engraving
with description appeared in the *Philosophical Transactions, loc. cit.*
(see Illustr. 292).

Another engine is shown in Illustr. 293. This, built at Campden
House, Kensington, in 1712, was a simpler contrivance. It cost £50
and raised 3,000 gallons per hour. The receiver was filled four times
a minute, and the engine required a bushel of coal per day. It
"succeeded so well that there has not been any want of water since
it has been built." Its capacity was nearly one horse-power.

Then came a more effective engine, specially designed to deal
with accumulation of water in the Cornish mines. It was described
in a pamphlet entitled *The Miner's Friend, or, An Engine to raise
Water by Fire, Described, And of the Manner of Fixing it in Mines, With
an Account of the several other Uses it is applicable unto; and an Answer
to the Objections made against it* (London, 1702). The pamphlet was
circulated among the mining interests, whose profits were disap-
pearing under the excessive cost of drainage—e.g. one mine used
five hundred horses in raising water by horsegins and buckets.
Savery acknowledged the approval of the King and the Royal
Society, and by astute advertisement made his invention known.

Savery's was the first practicable steam engine. Like Worcester's,
it had a boiler separate from the water reservoir; but it employed
the method of surface condensation, which allowed of the vessels
being charged when they had to be refilled, and it had a secondary
boiler, supplying the working boiler with water without interruption. The engine, in other words, would work uninterruptedly
until worn out. Savery also introduced gauge-cocks in the boilers
to indicate the height of the water. Savery, it must be noted, did not
use safety valves, and in deep mines his engine had to stand higher
pressures than it could safely bear. The engine is shown in Illustr. 294.

This engine was used for supplying water to towns and private
residences. It was also used in some mines, but not in many, because
of the dangers from boiler explosions, where the steam pressure
had to be high in order to raise the water in considerable amounts
to the height required. In a mine the engine had to be put within
30 feet of the lowest level, and if flooding occurred the engine was
"drowned." In a deep mine the height to which the water had to
be raised necessitated the use of steam at pressures of several atmospheres; at a time when three atmospheres was considered the
safety limit. So separate engines were put at intervals of 60 to 80 feet
in the shaft, and each engine pumped from the sump of the one

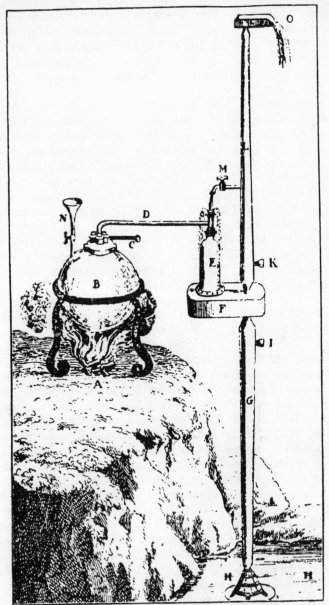

Illustr. 293.—Savery's Smaller Steam Engine

G, suction pipe, 16 feet long, diameter 3 inches. E, receiver, 13 gallons.
B, boiler, 40 gallons. L, forcing-pipe, 42 feet high. DMN, connecting-pipe and
cocks. Operation as in Illustr. 231, except that surface condensation was
employed, the cock, M, being opened to run water on to the receiver E from
the rising main.

below. If one engine was disabled, pumping had to be interrupted until repairs were effected. Savery's boilers did not exceed $2\frac{1}{2}$ feet in diameter, and several engines had to be placed at each level in

Illustr. 294.—Savery's Final Steam Engine

It resembled the first (Illustr. 292), except that the vessels were cooled by water run on to them from reservoir, C, filled from the "forcing pipe," F, and that the main boiler was kept constantly supplied with water by means of the secondary boiler, shown on left of diagram.

the shaft. It was costly and dangerous, so the mine-owners stuck to horses. Moreover, the consumption of fuel was most wasteful. The boiler had too small a heating surface. And there was still more serious waste in the method of condensation. The defects in Savery's engine were eventually overcome, but only after his death (1716), and when the eighteenth century was well under way.

(See R. H. Thurston, *A History of the Growth of the Steam-Engine*, 1878; H. W. Dickinson, *A Short History of the Steam Engine*, Cambridge, 1938.)

VIII. MECHANICAL CALCULATORS

The desire to economize time and mental effort in numerical computation, and to eliminate human liability to error, has led to the design and construction of numerous mechanical aids to calculation of varying types and degrees of complexity. Early attempts in this direction led to such devices as the abacus and the so-called "Napier's Bones." The slide-rule developed during the seventeenth and eighteenth centuries into a practically useful instrument. Calculating machines, such as are generally understood by the term, which mechanically perform arithmetical operations (e.g. by means of interlocking wheels) and exhibit the results, remained in the experimental stage during this period, and first became practically useful in the nineteenth century.

THE ABACUS

The abacus or swan-pan is of great antiquity. It seems to have spread eastward and westward from India, but there is a suggestion that it is of Semitic invention, and may have originated with the Accadians. It still retains its hold on the East, and though now employed in Western lands only for elementary educational purposes, it was used extensively in Europe in ancient and mediaeval times, down to the seventeenth century, as a means of calculation, and it influenced the written arithmetical notation which superseded its use. In its more primitive form the abacus consisted merely of pebbles (Lat. *calculi*, hence the verb *to calculate*), or other such objects, which were placed in grooves drawn in the sand, or on a table ruled into strips. Later it assumed the more familiar form of a number of parallel, equally spaced wires or rods which were fixed into the sides of a shallow box, and on which a number of beads were threaded so as to slide easily. A number was represented by forming groups of beads on successive wires to represent the number of units of successive denominations. Gerbert (*c.* 1000 A.D.), however, is said to have introduced the use of numbered counters (*apices*) which could be used to represent numbers in place of groups of beads. In mediaeval Western Europe the apparatus was variously known as *mensa Pythagorica* (a name also applied to the multiplication table), and as *mensa* or *tabula geometricalis*, as well as *abax* or *abacus*. The table divided by lines into strips (*spacia*) to represent successive denominations was a common European form.

In these strips the appropriate numbers of counters were placed, and the whole table was called in England a "counter"—a name which still survives. This line-abacus was extensively used in European commerce during the fifteenth century, and abacus reckoning was still common in Germany and neighbouring countries in the sixteenth century. By the seventeenth century the use of the abacus in Europe had been generally relegated to the more ignorant classes of the population, being superseded by written methods of calculation from Italy. In the Chinese and Japanese forms of the

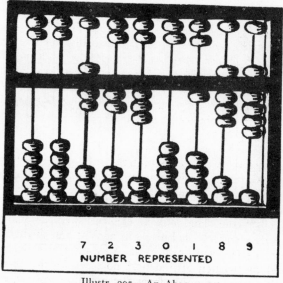

NUMBER REPRESENTED

Illustr. 295.—An Abacus

instrument the counters are threaded on wires, and each wire is divided by a partition into two segments, on one of which are five beads, and on the other a single bead, or sometimes two. Numbers up to five of any denomination are represented by moving one or more of the five beads towards the partition; five is also represented by pushing back the five beads and moving up the single bead, or one of the two beads, in the other segment; and numbers from six to ten are represented by moving up this latter bead and one or more of the five beads. Ten is also represented by moving up a bead on the next row to the left, and so on. Although primarily suited to addition and subtraction, the abacus is skilfully applied in China and Japan to the more complicated processes of multiplication and division, and to the extraction of square and cube roots (see Illustr. 295).

NAPIER'S BONES

Another form of mechanical aid to multiplication was afforded by the so-called "Napier's Bones" or numbering rods. These were described by John Napier, the inventor of logarithms, in his book *Rabdologiae, seu numerationis per virgulas, libri duo, Edinburgi,* 1617, though the principle seems to have been previously known in the East. The rods took several forms, but were generally a set of ten rectangular rods of wood, each having four flat faces. Each face was divided into nine squares. In the top square a digit was written,

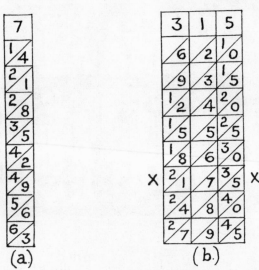

Illustr. 296.—Napier's Bones in Use

and the lower squares contained the successive multiples of it by numbers from 2 to 9. The tens and units of each multiple were separated by a diagonal of the square. The ten digits from 0 to 9 were each treated in this way. Column (*a*) shows the arrangement for the digit 7. To multiply a number by some other number lying between 0 and 9, say 315 by 7, the faces corresponding to 3, 1, and 5 were placed side by side, as in column (*b*), and the seventh multiples were noted, the tens in each square being added to the units in the next square to the left. The numbers to be thus added are seen to lie in small parallelograms. Thus, corresponding to the multiplier 7 we should have 5, 3 + 7, 1, 2, giving the digits of the required product of 315 and 7, in the reverse order, as 5, 0, 2, 2, or the product itself as 2205. When the multiplier was a number of more than one digit, this process was gone through for each digit; the partial products were recorded, and subsequently added together, account being taken of the place-value of each. The multiples of each digit were repeated on four different rods, and the distribution of the digits among the rods was such as to admit of the greatest freedom in combining the digits for multiplication.

"Napier's Bones" were modified in various ways during the seventeenth century. For instance, Schott, in 1668, showed how to mount them on rotatable cylinders which were enclosed in a box, so as to make possible the rapid manipulation of the rods.

THE SLIDE-RULE

The invention of the logarithmic slide-rule is almost as old as that of logarithms, for it dates back to about 1630. The instrument is based upon the principle that the logarithm of the product of two or more numbers is equal to the sum of the logarithms of those numbers, e.g. $\log (A \times B) = \log A + \log B$. Hence if two successive segments are set off along a straight line, of lengths respectively equal to log A and log B (on a certain scale), their sum will measure $\log (A \times B)$, on the same scale.

This was the principle of the logarithmic "line of numbers" constructed by Edmund Gunter of Gresham College, and described in his *Canon Triangulorum* (London, 1620). The "line of numbers" was a scale from one end of which were set off lengths proportional to the logarithms of the numbers between 1 and 10, and the termination of each length was marked by the number whose logarithm it measured. Thus the extremities of the scale were marked 1 and 10. The addition and subtraction of lengths on the scale was equivalent to multiplication and division of the corresponding numbers, and was effected with the aid of a pair of compasses. "Gunter's scale" had also other lines graduated on the same principle, and showing the logarithms of trigonometrical functions, for use in navigation. But it had no sliding parts, and was hence not strictly a slide-rule. This distinction, however, has not always been observed, and hence the invention of the slide-rule has often been wrongly attributed to Gunter.

The credit for that invention seems actually to belong to the English mathematician, William Oughtred (1575–1660), who superseded Gunter's compasses by making two logarithmically divided "Gunter's Scales" slide one along the other while keeping them together by hand. Besides inventing this straight slide-rule, Oughtred also devised a circular form of the instrument, in which the graduations were made on concentric circular scales. Calculations were performed with the aid of two radial pointers pivoted at the centre and traversing these scales. These pointers were the only movable parts of the instrument. Oughtred's instruments were described with his permission by his pupil, William Forster, in *The Circles of Proportion and the Horizontal Instrument* (London, 1632). It is possible that the circular rule was invented independently about the same time by Richard Delamain, a mathematical teacher in London. Certainly Delamain described the circular slide-rule two years before Forster's book appeared. Oughtred and Delamain subsequently accused each other of theft, but the rectilinear slide-rule seems certainly to have been the indisputable invention of Oughtred.

The seventeenth century saw many attempts to improve upon Oughtred's invention. Some of these aimed at increasing the length of the scale without making the instrument inconveniently large. This was doubtless the object of Oughtred's circular form to some extent, and of other designs in which the radial pointers were suppressed and the circles were made capable of turning relatively to each other. Later the logarithmic scale was sometimes set off along a spiral line; an improvement attributed to Milburne (1650). Straight rules were also constructed which could be folded up when not in use. The practice of making the movable ruler slide between two fixed ones was introduced in the middle of the seventeenth century, and it is described by Seth Partridge in a book which he completed in 1657 (*The Description and Use of an Instrument called the Double Scale of Proportion*, 1672). The slide-rule was little known, either in England or on the Continent, during the seventeenth century. Newton, however, seems to have been acquainted with the instrument, and he showed how to solve numerical cubic equations mechanically with the aid of three Gunter scales (*Opera*, ed. Horsley, Vol. IV, p. 520).

Gradually the utility of the principle of the slide-rule in the rapid evaluation of quantities of all descriptions—scientific, technological, nautical, commercial, etc.—has been recognized, and almost innumerable types of the instrument have been constructed to serve special purposes.

CALCULATING MACHINES

We come now to the earliest devices that can properly be called calculating *machines*. Johann Ciermans, in his *Disciplinae Mathematicae* (1640), mentions an apparatus with wheels for mechanical multiplication and division, which he claims to have constructed. But Ciermans gives no details, and the earliest calculating machine of which the particulars are known is an adding machine which Pascal invented in 1642 at the age of nineteen.

Pascal's machine has the appearance of an oblong box on the upper face of which is a row of wheels each with teeth numbered

Napier's Bones (Original Form)

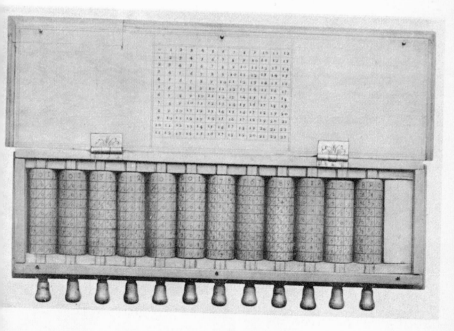

Napier's Bones (Cylindrical Form)

Pascal's Calculating Machine

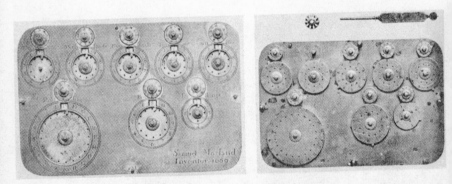

Morland's Calculating Machine

Samuel Morland

Leibniz' Calculating Machine

from 0 to 9. These wheels severally correspond to units, tens, hundreds, etc. But Pascal designed his machine to assist his father in adding up sums of money. Hence, some of his machines, besides having wheels to show ordinary numbers up to six figures, have extra wheels for the addition of *deniers* and *sous*, with 12 and 20 divisions respectively. Above each wheel is a slot in which figures on another wheel inside the box successively show themselves as the corresponding external wheel is turned. The external wheels are moved forward (or backward in subtraction) the desired number of divisions by inserting a metal point in the appropriate tooth and turning the wheel until this point is arrested by a stop projecting over the wheel. During this operation the desired number is added on to (or subtracted from) that initially shown at the slot. The difficulty in all such machines is that of carrying tens, etc., and adding them on to the number next on the left. Pascal's device for this purpose was an ingenious and complicated apparatus called the *sautoir*. The craftsmanship of the period, however, was not equal to putting Pascal's design into satisfactory practical form. (For a description of the instrument, see the *Encyclopédie* of Diderot and d'Alembert, Paris, 1751, Vol. I, p. 680 *et seq*. A replica of the machine is on view at the South Kensington Science Museum, London.)

Another machine of the seventeenth century for the addition and subtraction of sums of money was that invented in 1666 by Samuel Morland, who did not know, however, of Pascal's invention. Morland's machine is made of metal and measures 4 inches by 3 inches by less than $\frac{1}{4}$ inch. (In Illustr. 298 the right figure shows the instrument with the cover plate removed.) There are eight dials on the front plate, respectively intended for counting farthings, pence, shillings, units, tens, hundreds, thousands, and ten-thousands of pounds. The first three are respectively graduated into 4, 12, and 20 parts, and the others each into 10 parts. Within the dials similarly graduated discs revolve about their centres, and can be turned through any number of divisions with the aid of a style which can be inserted into holes opposite each division. Each complete revolution of a disc records itself by turning a small counter disc (seen just above it) through one of its ten divisions by means of a tooth on the larger disc. Carrying amounts from one denomination to the next is not automatically provided for, but has to be done by the operator before the required result can be read off. Special rules have to be observed in setting the discs and turning the larger ones, according as addition or subtraction is to be performed.

Another machine of Morland's, intended for multiplication,

worked somewhat on the principle of "Napier's Bones," but the rods were represented by rotatable discs having the digits of each multiple at opposite ends of diameters of the discs. This instrument could be used also for the extraction of roots. (For accounts of the above two instruments, see Morland's book, *The Description and Use of Two Arithmetick Instruments*, London, 1673.) Still another machine by the same inventor provided for the rapid solution of triangles and the evaluation of trigonometrical functions.

Pascal's and Morland's machines were primarily intended for addition. For the convenient performance of multiplication, provision had to be made for the repeated addition of the same number to itself mechanically, e.g. by turning a handle. This was the aim of the machines constructed by Leibniz, one of which, conceived

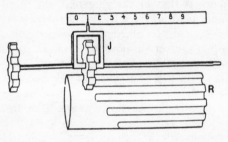

in 1671 and completed in 1694, is preserved at Hanover, while the other, completed in 1706, seems to have disappeared. In the process of designing his machines Leibniz invented two important devices which still occur as components of modern calculating machines. These are the "stepped

Illustr. 303.—The Stepped Reckoner

reckoner" and the "pin-wheel," which both serve for the mechanical addition of digits chosen at will.

The stepped reckoner consists essentially of a cylinder (Illustr. 303) with nine cogs or teeth each running parallel to its axis and progressively increasing in length by equal increments. As the cylinder is turned through a complete revolution, certain of these teeth engage with those of a cogwheel connected with a counter, and capable of being moved parallel to the axis of the cylinder. The number of teeth so engaging, and the resulting change in the reading of the counter, depend on how far along the cylinder the wheel is situated. This number is shown on an adjacent scale, with the aid of which the wheel is set in the desired position. The stepped reckoner plays an essential part in many later machines, e.g. in the Thomas de Colmar Arithmometer of 1820.

An alternative device for varying at will the number of teeth engaging a cogwheel is the "pin-wheel." This device was described by Poleni (*Miscellanea*, Venice, 1709), but seems also to have been known to Leibniz, judging from a manuscript which he left (see *Zeitschrift f. Vermessungs-Wesen*, 1897, p. 308). The pin-wheel consists of a wheel in the circumference of which are nine movable teeth. These may lie wholly within the wheel (when they cannot engage with any external wheel), or any desired number of them can be made to project from the wheel, and to engage with an external counter whenever the pin-wheel as a whole is turned through a revolution. In this way the counter can be moved forward any desired number of places. The principle of the pin-wheel is shown diagrammatically in Illustr. 304, where KKK are the pins, R a crooked ring passing through slots in the pins, or, in the older instruments, a crooked groove in a disc, in which the shoulders of the pins rest, and H the handle by which the ring or the disc is turned so as to thrust out the desired number of pins. Pin-wheels have the advantage over stepped reckoners of occupying less space.

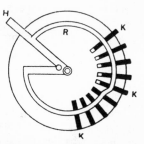

Illustr. 304.—The Pin-Wheel

They were employed in the nineteenth century by Thomas, and by the Russian inventor W. T. Odhner, whose calculating machine was later developed into the well-known Brunsviga Calculator.

Leibniz' *machina arithmetica* was invented before he had heard of Pascal's, and was described in 1710 (*Miscellanea Berolinensia*, Vol. I, p. 317; see also W. Jordan in *Zeitschrift f. Vermessungs-Wesen*, 1897). The machine consisted essentially of two parts, one of which was fixed and recorded the partial products obtained by repeated additions of the same number, while the other part was movable so as to admit of these additions of the multiplicand being made in various denominations or groups of denominations. Leibniz' machines were very complicated and, despite the large sums spent upon them they did not work satisfactorily, largely, no doubt, because of shortcomings in their construction. This remark applies generally to all machines prior to that of Thomas.

(See E. M. Horsburgh, *Napier Tercentenary Exhibition Handbook*, 1914; F. Cajori, *A History of the Logarithmic Slide Rule*, 1909; and the *South Kensington Science Museum Catalogue, Mathematics I—Calculating Machines and Instruments*.)

CHAPTER XXIV

PSYCHOLOGY

PSYCHOLOGY, as the study of human nature or of the mental processes of man, is one of the oldest studies. The first comprehensive treatises on psychology were written by Aristotle; but even his predecessors had given considerable attention to the subject. In its early history the study was intimately connected with biology and medicine, as part of the study of human behaviour; and also with speculative philosophy and theology, on account of its alleged bearing on the question of the immortality of the soul. It has taken psychology rather longer than most sciences to disengage itself from speculative philosophy; and there are still people who look upon it as a field of philosophical speculation rather than as a body of scientific knowledge, in spite of the introduction of some experimentation and statistical calculation in more recent times.

HOBBES

The first of the moderns to give a fairly comprehensive account of psychology was Thomas Hobbes, whose life and philosophy will be dealt with in the final chapter. His psychological views are contained chiefly in his book on *Human Nature* (1650) and *Leviathan* (1651). In the former treatise he attempts a description of "the sum of man's natural faculties," mental as well as physical. As regards the mental powers of man, Hobbes follows the method of introspection, and entertains no doubt that by "looking into himself" he could discover what thoughts and feelings all people experience on similar occasions. He distinguished two main classes, namely, *cognition* and *motive*. By cognitive power he means the power of forming images, ideas and conceptions. These processes or experiences have a certain amount of independence of the external objects to which they refer. Everybody knows from his own experience, Hobbes says, "that the *absence* or *destruction* of things once imagined doth not cause the *absence* or *destruction* of the *imagination* itself. This *imagery* and *representation* of the quality of the things without is that we call our *conception, imagination, ideas, notice* or *knowledge* of them" (*Human Nature*, Chapter I). Originally, all cognition is by way of the sense-organs when some external object or stimulus acts on them. But the resulting sensations, images, or conceptions are not in the external objects but in the experiencing subject. "The subject wherein colour and image are inherent," he writes, "is *not* the object or thing seen. There is nothing without us (really) which we call an *image* or colour. The said image or colour is but an *apparition* unto us of the *motion*, agitation or alteration, which the *object* worketh in the *brain*, or [vital] spirits, or some internal substance of the head. As in *vision*, so also in conceptions that arise from the *other senses*, the subject of their inherence is not the *object* but the *sentiment*" (*Ibid.*, Chap. II). All this, of course, is but the view of secondary qualities revived by Galilei. But it helps to explain why a materialist like Hobbes should deal with *mental* processes at all. Without the assumption of mental experiences of some kind it would have been impossible to accept the reduction of matter to its primary qualities, or to motion only, on which Hobbes based his materialistic philosophy. In support of the merely subjective or "phantastical" character of the perception of colour, etc., he cites such evidence as the coloured appearance of the reflected images in water or mirrors where the real objects are not; the experience of seeing one object double; of hearing one sound double or treble, by means of echoes; the fact that "the smell and taste of the *same thing* are *not* the *same* to *every man*, and therefore are not in the thing *smelt* or *tasted*, but in the men;" and so on. All such sense-qualities are "*apparitions* only: the things that really *are* in the world without use, are those motions by which these seemings are caused" in human experience. One of the most note-worthy things in Hobbes' account of sense experience is his stress on the importance of change in order to keep attention awake, "it being almost all one," he says, "for a man to be always sensible of the same thing, and not to be sensible at all of any thing" (*Elements of Philosophy*, Chap. IV, 5).

Sensations, then, are caused by external stimuli or motions. But the effects of these stimuli do not cease immediately when the stimuli are withdrawn. "Though the *sense* be *past*, the image or conception remaineth; but more *obscure* while we are *awake*. . . . And this obscure conception [cognitive process] is that we call *phantasy* or *imagination*" (*Ibid.*, Chap. III). Sometimes the residues of sense-stimulation are almost as intense as actual sensations, as, for instance, "the *image* remaining before the *eye* after looking upon the Sun," or dream-images in sleep, when the rivalry of actual sense-stimuli is eliminated. Moreover, man has also the power of remembrance; and memories are distinguished from present sense-experiences by their obscurity and incompleteness. "To see at a great distance of place, and to remember at a great distance of time, is to have like conceptions of the thing: for there wanteth distinction of parts in both; the one conception being weak by operation of distance, the other by decay" (*Ibid.*). Turning to the succession of conceptions or images in the mind, Hobbes distinguishes an orderly sequence (which he calls *discursion*) from a merely casual one (which he calls "ranging"). The sequence of conceptions is usually determined by the sequence of the original sense-experiences of which they are the residues. "For example, from St. Andrew the mind runneth to St. Peter, because their names are read together; from St. Peter to a *stone*, for the same cause; from *stone* to *foundation*, because we see them together; and for the same cause, from *foundation* to *church*, and from *church* to *people*, and from *people* to *tumult*" (*Ibid.*, Chap. IV). Such association by contiguity is the only law of association recognized by Hobbes. A man of *experience* is one who remembers what antecedents have been followed by what consequents. And all expectations relating to the future, and all explanations relating to the past, are based on such experience or remembrance. "When a man hath *so often* observed like antecedents to be followed by like consequents, that *whensoever* he seeth the antecedent, he looketh again for the consequent; or when he seeth the consequent, maketh account there hath been the like antecedent; then he calleth both the antecedent and the consequent, signs one of another, as clouds are signs of rain to come, and rain of clouds past" (*Ibid.*). Such signs, however, are only conjectural and warrant no universal conclusion.

Scientific knowledge is more than mere sense-perception and remembrance of it; it needs sequences of ideas not determined by mere contiguity in the original experiences. Such novel sequences of conceptions are rendered possible by the use of symbols. Scientific knowledge, in fact, is a knowledge of the *truth of propositions*, and is derived from *understanding*, which involves the use of language. "The *first* principle of [scientific] knowledge is, that we have such and such *conceptions*; the *second*, that we have thus and thus *named* the things whereof they are conceptions; the *third* is, that we have *joined* those *names* in such manner as to make true propositions; the *fourth* and last is, that we have *joined* those *propositions* in such a manner as they be concluding, and the truth of the conclusion said to be known" (*Ibid.*, Chap. VI). Scientific knowledge is thus a kind of linguistic calculus. Such "evidence of truth" is the prerogative of man; brute beasts can only participate in "experience of fact" and have as much "prudence" as the mere memory of it makes possible. So much for Hobbes' chief views about the *cognitive* power of man. We turn next to his account of the *motive* power of the mind.

By the *motive* power of the mind Hobbes means what is now usually described as conation. Cognitive processes are mainly the result of external stimuli acting upon the sense-organs and thereby setting up motions towards and in the brain; "motive" or conative processes involve motions from the brain outward through the heart. Such outward motion either helps or hinders the vital motion of the heart. "When it helpeth, it is called *delight, contentment* or *pleasure* . . . ; but when such motion *weakeneth* or hindereth the vital motion, then it is called *pain*. . . . This motion, in which consisteth *pleasure* or *pain*, is also a *solicitation* or provocation either to draw *near* to the thing that pleaseth, or to *retire* from the thing that displeaseth; and this solicitation is the *endeavour* or internal beginning of *animal* motion, which when the object delighteth is called *appetite*; when it *displeaseth* it is called *aversion*, in respect of the displeasure present; but in respect of the displeasure *expected, fear*" (*Ibid.*, Chap. VII). And, "every man, for his own part, calleth that which *pleaseth*, and is delightful to himself, *good*; and that *evil* which *displeaseth* him: insomuch that while every man differeth from another in *constitution*, they differ also from one another concerning the common distinction of good and evil" (*Ibid.*). "As all conceptions we have immediately by the *sense* are *delight* or *pain*, or *appetite* or *fear*; so are all the *imaginations* after sense. But as they are weaker imaginations, so are they also weaker pleasures or weaker pain" (*Ibid.*). So, besides pleasures and pains of the senses (or sensual pleasures and pains) there are also pleasures (or joys) and pains (or griefs) of the mind.

Appetite and aversion are the rudimentary form of will. The joy and grief of the mind, its hopes and fears, constitute a higher stage in the development of will. "*Appetite, fear, hope* and the rest of the passions [emotions] . . . are *the will*" (*Ibid.*, Chap. XII). Actions follow our wills, and our wills follow our opinions; and so "the world is governed by opinion" (*Ibid.*). Hobbes emphasizes the selfish impulses which prompt human conduct, and lays particular stress on man's "perpetual and restless desire of power after power that ceaseth only in death" (*Leviathan*, I, xi). His stress on the "will to power," like that of Nietzsche long afterwards, was no doubt the result of his observations of the political struggles of the time, and would seem to be still further confirmed by the political lunacies of the twentieth century.

DESCARTES

According to the dualistic philosophy of Descartes, which will be explained in the final chapter, minds and bodies are entirely different and independent substances, and can exercise no direct influence on each other. Mind or the rational soul can accordingly "act independently of the brain, for certainly the brain can be of no use in pure thought," says Descartes (*Meditations*, Reply to Objections V, Tr. by Haldane and Ross, Vol. II, p. 212). The mind or soul is equipped with certain innate ideas which it applies to, but does not derive from, external objects. These ideas are not always explicit in consciousness. But they are present in "thinking substance" as latent potentialities at least. In any case, they are not originated by experience, which only elicits them, that is, serves as an occasion for their explicit recall. All this is more or less in accordance with Plato's doctrine of reminiscence. Descartes' list of innate ideas includes the idea of God, the idea of the self as a thinking substance, the axioms of mathematics, and the "common notions" of space, time, and motion. Most characteristically the mind as an active substance (in contrast with inert matter) expresses itself in acts of will, a term under which Descartes includes not only voluntary decisions, but also attention, recollection, and deliberate judgment or thought. In contrast with the mind, the bodies of animals, and even of human beings, are treated by Descartes as mere machines, or automata, the processes of which can be explained sufficiently by reference to mechanical principles. This dualism of material substances and thinking substances failed entirely to explain certain experiences which seemed to furnish *prima facie* evidence of an intimate relation between the body and the soul of man. For, as Descartes says, "there is nothing which nature teaches me more explicitly than that I have a body which is adversely affected when I feel pain, which has need of food or drink when I feel hungry and thirsty, and so on; nor can I doubt that there is some truth in all this. Nature also teaches me by these sensations of pain, hunger, thirst, etc., that I am not in my body merely as a pilot in a ship, but that I am very closely united with it, and, as it were, so intermingled with it that we seem to form one whole. For if it were not so, then when my body is hurt, I, who am only a thinking thing, should not feel pain, but should perceive the wound by the understanding only, just as the sailor perceives when his ship is damaged; and when my body has need of drink or food, I should clearly apprehend the fact without being made aware of it by confused feelings of hunger and thirst. For all these sensations of hunger, thirst, pain, etc., are in truth only confused modes of thought which are produced by the union and apparent intermingling of mind and body" (*Meditations*, VI).

All experiences in which the mind appears *prima facie* not to be entirely self-active, but affected by bodies, Descartes called "passions," as involving a certain amount of passivity on the part of the mind. His main interest in psychology was therefore to explain the "passions" in a manner consistent with his general philosophy. This he attempted in his *Les Passions de l'Âme*, which was published in the same year as Hobbes' *Human Nature* (1650). In the wide sense of the term, "passion" includes sensation, perception, retention, imagination, and all adventitious ideas, as well as feelings and emotions. But Descartes concentrates on the latter experiences and has little of importance to say about the former; so we may confine ourselves mainly to his treatment of the emotional experiences.

Notwithstanding the apparent repudiation of the ship-pilot view of the body-soul problem, Descartes did cling to the mediaeval idea of the soul's imprisonment in the body; and he exercised all his ingenuity to explain the "passions" in harmony with this view, which was in consonance with his dualistic philosophy. His method of getting over the difficulty was to interpose between the body and the soul the agency of the good old "vital spirits" or "animal spirits," whose material character was conceived to be sufficiently refined to permit of a nodding acquaintance with the soul; and he lodged the soul in the conarion, or pineal gland, in the middle of the brain, where it would receive messages from the body and whence it could more or less control bodily movements by deftly piloting the animal spirits from the brain along the nerves to the muscles. The animal spirits were supposed to consist of the finest part of the blood, and to be "like a very subtle wind, or rather a very pure and vivid flame" (*Discourse on Method*, V). More will be said about this in the final chapter. Here we are only concerned with the psychological side of the subject.

"Passions," in the narrower sense of the term, are defined by Descartes as "feelings or emotions of the soul which we relate specially to it, and which are caused, maintained, and fortified by some movement of the spirits" (*Passions*, I, 27). The clause "which relate specially to it" is meant to exclude feelings relating to external objects (such as scents, sounds, and colours) or to our body (such as hunger, thirst, and pain); and the reference to "some movement of the [animal] spirits" is meant to exclude desires, which are caused by the soul itself. Now, the objects which arouse passions in us do so not in virtue of what they are themselves, but in virtue of their significance to us. "The objects which move the senses do not excite diverse passions in us because of all the diversities which are in them, but only because of the diverse ways in which they may harm or help us, or in general be of some importance to us" (II, 52). There are many different passions. But only six of them are primary; the rest are either varieties or combinations of the primary ones. The six primary passions are wonder, love, hatred, desire, joy, and sadness. "Wonder is a sudden surprise of the soul which causes it to apply itself to consider with attention the objects which seem to it rare and extraordinary" (II, 70). "Love is an emotion of the soul caused by the movement of the spirits which incites it to join itself willingly to objects which appear to it to be agreeable. And hatred is an emotion caused by the spirits which incite the soul to desire to be separated from the objects which present themselves to it as harmful" (II, 79). "Joy is an agreeable emotion of the soul which constitutes the enjoyment that the soul finds in the good which the impressions of the brain represent to it as its own" (II, 91). "Sadness is a disagreeable languor which constitutes the discomfort and unrest which the soul receives from evil, or from the defect which the impressions of the brain set before it as pertaining to it" (II, 92). The function of the five primary passions is "to incite the soul to consent and contribute to the actions which may serve to maintain the body, or to render it in some manner more perfect" (II, 137). Thus, for instance, sadness is induced by pain, which warns us that something is harmful to the body, whereas joy is a mark of the usefulness of the thing that pleased us. Descartes points out that there are also purely intellectual forms of love and hatred, joy and sadness, which are not passions inasmuch as they originate in the soul alone; but he adds that so long as the soul is united to the body the intellectual emotions are generally accompanied by the corresponding passions. Nevertheless, by means of the intellectual emotions, Reason can, according to Descartes, master the passions.

Turning to the secondary or derived passions, Descartes describes simple affection, friendship, and devotion as three species of love, according as we esteem an object less than, as much as, or more than ourselves. Hope is confidence in the attainment of the good that is desired; fear is diffidence in the desired result. Confidence is the highest form of hope; despair is extreme fear. Courage is the hope which induces us to exert great effort in order to achieve some desired end under great difficulties. "Scorn is a sort of joy mingled with hatred, which proceeds from our perceiving some small evil in a person whom we consider to be deserving of it" (III, 178). Envy "is a kind of sadness mingled with hatred, which proceeds from our seeing good coming to those whom we consider unworthy of it" (III, 182). "Pity is a species of sadness mingled with love or goodwill towards those whom we see suffering some evil of which we consider them undeserving" (III, 185). And so on.

What is perhaps most striking in Descartes' lengthy account of the passions is the great trouble he takes in describing not only the physical expressions of the various emotions, but even the flow of the blood and the various movements of the "animal spirits" which he supposes to be associated with them. In laying so much stress on the physical factors involved in the passions, Descartes may be credited to some extent with having anticipated the James-Lange theory of the emotions. But one is left wondering about his motive in laboriously indulging in such sheer guesswork. Yet his main motive is not difficult to surmise. It was chiefly his determination to keep body and soul as distinct as possible that forced him to resort to the highly conjectural scheme of "animal spirits," etc., in order to explain, or explain away, the apparent intimacy between body and soul. And this extreme dualism was probably an attempt to vindicate the supremacy of the human mind or soul against the tendency of that age to minimize the differences between man and the lower animals. This tendency was encouraged by the results of comparative anatomy, which revealed striking similarities between the bodies of man and of lower animals. Descartes attempted to save the prestige of man by treating all lower animals and even human bodies as mere automata. All experiences which the lower animals appeared to share with man had consequently to be explained on mechanical lines. But by claiming the rational soul for man alone, and treating it as quite independent of the body, Descartes thought that the tradition of man's privileged position in creation might be saved.

SPINOZA

Descartes' account of the passions, as we have seen, was more physiological than psychological, and his physiology was mainly of the traditional (Galenic) and speculative type. Such was the result of his extremely dualistic philosophy. The philosophy of Spinoza enabled him to adopt a very different psychological attitude. A general account of Spinoza's philosophy will be given in the final chapter. Here it will be sufficient to note that for Spinoza body and soul are not two utterly different substances which cannot stand in direct relationship to one another, needing all sorts of intermediaries and ultimately supernatural intervention; they are rather two parts or aspects or expressions of one and the same reality. Physical and mental processes are concurrent manifestations of one and the same living organism, and there is no need of outside mediation between them. Bodily and mental activities can therefore be described separately, the physical without the psychical, and the psychical without the physical, while postulating that each of these two kinds of process has its parallel in the other. The result is that Spinoza has a psychology, whereas Descartes had only a physiological psychology. And although the passions are even for Spinoza psycho-physical in character, yet they are not conceived as the product of the *interaction* between body and soul, but as the manifestation of the joint organism.

The human organism, as a psycho-physical whole, is characterized by a tendency (*conatus*) to self-preservation. This tendency, or "appetite," as he also calls it, may be conscious or subconscious. When it is conscious it is called "desire." (The purely mental aspect of the *conatus*, when there is an explicit consciousness of its activity, is what is commonly called "will.") When the desire which results from the *conatus* to self-preservation is successful we experience pleasure, otherwise we experience pain. It is of the essence of human nature not merely to persevere in its actual state but to strain after a fuller life. And in this effort pleasure is the conscious experience of increased vitality, while pain is the conscious experience of diminished vitality. Whatever is regarded as promoting self-preservation and a fuller life is sought after and, for that reason, is called "good"; whatever is regarded as having the contrary tendency is shunned and, for that reason, is called "bad" (*Ethics*, III, ix, Schol.). Desire, pleasure and pain constitute for Spinoza the primary feelings. The more complex emotions result partly from the extent to which adequate or inadequate ideas combine with the primary feelings, and partly from the extent to which the experiences are the outcome of the individual's own activity as distinguished from external influences. The two factors just referred to, namely, the adequacy of ideas and the autonomous activity of the mind, are intimately connected in the psychology of Spinoza, as will appear from a consideration of his account of the cognitive processes.

The mind, according to Spinoza, is essentially thought, that is, cognition in the widest sense. The activity most characteristic of it is that of knowledge. Spinoza distinguishes three main grades of cognitive activity. Sense-perception and imagination belong to the lowest grade, that of "vague experience." At this stage objects and events are apprehended in comparative isolation or only in accidental relationships of space and time. This kind of cognition varies from individual to individual according to their physical conditions and their environment. It is subject to error, and is inadequate at best. The only kind of universals possible at this stage are such generic images or ideas as those of "man" or "horse," which arise from the limitations to its capacity of forming more than a certain number of images. These consequently run together, so to speak, and are represented by general terms. At the next higher stage of cognition, the stage of "reason," the personal equation is eliminated, and things and events are apprehended as subject to universal laws which determine their necessary interrelations, as distinguished from their chance relations in space and time. This kind of knowledge has real universality; it apprehends reality in its essential, universal relationships; it is the same for all rational minds; and it is characterized by "adequate ideas of the properties of things" (*Ethics*, II, xl, Schol. 2), so that objects and events are apprehended as constituting an orderly world, not a merely fortuitous collection. At the stage of "reason" the mind is much more active than at the stage of "vague experience," which involves a marked sub-ordination to stimuli outside the mind, which is affected by them more or less passively. The third and highest kind of cognition Spinoza calls "intuitive knowledge." It is the apprehension of the whole universe as a unity or system, which determines all its parts in accordance with universal laws immanent within it. It is the philosophic ideal of a synoptic view of the world. At this stage reality is apprehended in the light of the infinite unity or system which is immanent in it. "For although each individual thing is determined by another individual thing to exist in a certain way, yet the force by which each thing perseveres in its existence follows from the eternal necessity of the nature of God" (*Ethics*, II, xlv, Schol.). This kind of knowledge no longer suffers from finite limi-tations, as do the lower grades of cognition. In it man exercises his highest intellectual activity, and acquires the most adequate ideas.

Now, according to Spinoza, the feelings or emotions are inseparable from the accompanying cognitions or thoughts, for "the essence of the mind consists of ideas, adequate and inadequate" (*Ethics*, III, ix); and emotions are "the affections of the body, by which its power of acting is increased or diminished, helped or hindered, together with the ideas of these affections" (III, Def. 3). When an emotion is accompanied by an inadequate cognition in which the mind is affected by external stimuli rather than self-active, the emotion is a "passion"; but when the mind is the adequate cause of the emotion, that is, when the emotion accompanies adequate ideas, then we experience an "active emotion," instead of a "passion." So long as man is mainly influenced by external factors, as happens at the stage of inadequate ideas, of "vague experience" of sense and imagination, he is in bondage to passions; by cultivating the higher stages of knowledge, the adequate ideas of "reason" and "intuition," the mind develops its own active powers, becomes free, and experiences the joy or blessedness of the ensuing active emotions. "The impotence of man to govern or restrain his feelings I call bondage, for a man who is under their control is not his own master, but is mastered by fortune, in whose powers he is, so that he is often forced to follow the worse, although he sees the better" (IV, Preface). But "everyone has the power, partly at least, if not absolutely, of understanding clearly and distinctly himself and his emotions, and of bringing it about that he should be less subject to them" (V. iv, Schol.). "An emotion which is a passion ceases to be a passion as soon as we form a clear and distinct idea of it" (V, iii), that is, as soon as the passion is seen adequately in its causal relation to the rest of reality, or from a cosmic, rather than from an individual, standpoint. And man attains to freedom when his mind is fully active in the acquisition of adequate knowledge, for "a man acts absolutely from the laws of his own nature when he lives according to the guidance of reason" (IV, xxxv, Corol. i); and what Spinoza understands by freedom or free-will is self-determination.

Spinoza's conception of free-will is original and noteworthy. According to the older view, which is still widely current, free-will was contrasted with every kind of necessity. The idea was that free-will implied the ability to do, or not do, any act at any time irrespective of the individual's character, so long as external circumstances did not hinder. According to Spinoza, the opposite of free-will or freedom is not necessity or determination, but external compulsion. In the absence of external compulsion that man is most free whose conduct is self-determined, that is, necessitated by his own character; the least free is he who acts from impulse or from momentary caprice. For Spinoza, moreover, cognition and volition are most intimately interwoven. Cognition, especially higher knowledge (as distinguished from the confused ideas of "vague experience") is essentially active; and will is essentially intelligent. Ideas, especially adequate ideas, result from the spontaneous activity of the mind; and volition presupposes thought, which is just what distinguishes human will from merely animal impulse. For Spinoza, the dictum that "knowledge is power" had a much profounder meaning than it had for Bacon.

In the light of the doctrines just sketched, Spinoza describes the whole gamut of emotions as compounded of desire, pleasure or pain, and ideas, inadequate or adequate, of the objects, presented or represented, to which they relate. Thus love is "pleasure [or joy] accompanied by the idea of an external cause"; and hatred is "pain with the accompanying idea of an external cause" (*Ethics*, III, xiii, Schol.). By association of ideas, objects which are themselves a matter of indifference to us may rouse our love or hatred. Similar emotions may also be produced by yet other kinds of transference. "He who imagines that what he loves is affected with joy or sorrow will also be affected with joy or sorrow" (III, xxi). Similarly, "if we imagine that a person affects with joy a thing which we love, we shall be affected with love towards him"; and vice versa (III, xxii). Pride is "the joy which arises from a man's thinking too much of himself"; it "is a kind of delirium, because he dreams with his eyes open, that he is able to do all that he imagines he can" (III, xxiv). The mere perception or imagination of others as like ourselves may induce in us a kind of sympathetic participation in their joy or sorrow (III, xxvii). Self-love is the joy induced by the contemplation of our power; humility is "sorrow accompanied by the idea of our own weakness" (III, lv). Many passions are distinguished only according to the kind of objects by which they are induced—for instance, voluptuousness, drunkenness, lust, avarice, and ambition. These have no contrary passions, for temperance, sobriety, and chastity are not passions, but merely indicate the power of the mind to restrain the above passions (III, lvi). Spinoza describes many other passions, but does not pretend to exhaust them, for "so many variations can arise, that no limits can be assigned to their number" (III, lix, Schol.). As regards the "active emotions," which are accompanied by adequate ideas, enough has been indicated in the foregoing paragraphs. The "active emotions" culminate in the "intellectual love of God," that is, the joy or blessedness that comes of that supreme mental activity which Spinoza calls the "intuitive knowledge" of the cosmic system, and an "adequate idea" of our place in it.

It is commonly asserted that the tripartite division of mental processes into knowing, feeling, and willing was first introduced by Moses Mendelssohn in the eighteenth century. But the recognition of the three mental functions is obviously present in the writings of Spinoza, if not in the works of Descartes already. In this connection it is significant that Mendelssohn, though he disagreed with the pantheistic philosophy of Spinoza, made nevertheless a close study of his writings.

LOCKE

Like the other psychologists considered in the present chapter, Locke was primarily interested in philosophical rather than in psychological problems. As will be explained in the final chapter, his chief concern was to ascertain the nature and limits of human knowledge. But his method of dealing with the epistemological problem was to a large extent psychological. He tried to draw up an inventory of the apparently simplest ideas, or elements of human cognition, and to analyse the complex ideas into the simpler ones. Incidentally, therefore, his *Essay Concerning Human Understanding* (1690) contains a considerable amount of psychology.

Like Boyle and Newton and Sydenham, Locke disliked the intrusion of philosophical speculations into science. General theories he regarded as "the curse of the time and destructive not less of life than of science." He preferred to keep as close as possible to sensible experience. He was particularly opposed to "innate ideas" which were claimed to be independent of experience, and beyond challenge; and, like Spinoza, he repudiated the current explanations of acts of volition by reference to the agency of a Will. So the whole drift of Locke's psychology is towards empiricism. Nevertheless, in the very process of laying bare the lack of strictly empirical foundations for such ideas as those of "body," "soul," "cause," "infinity," etc., he reveals the existence of mental activities which, however much he may doubt their epistemological value, Locke has yet to admit as psychological facts.

The psychological aspect of the *Essay* is indicated by the author in these words: "I shall inquire into the original of those ideas, notions, or whatever else you please to call them, which a man observes, and is conscious to himself he has in mind; and the ways whereby the understanding comes to be furnished with them" (Book I, Chap. I, § 3). First of all, Locke dismisses "innate ideas." He does this easily by supposing them to be ideas which are alleged to be explicitly in consciousness from the very beginning. Locke has no difficulty in showing that there are no *such* innate ideas. He then states his main thesis. "Let us then suppose the mind to be, as we say, white paper, void of all characters, without any ideas: How comes it to be furnished? Whence comes it by that vast store, which the busy and boundless fancy of man has painted on it with an almost endless variety? Whence has it all the materials of reason and knowledge? To this I answer, in one word, From experience. In that all our knowledge is founded, and from that it ultimately derives itself. Our observation, employed either about external sensible objects, or about the internal operations of our mind, perceived and reflected on by ourselves, is that which supplies our understandings with all the materials of thinking. These two are the fountains of knowledge from whence all the ideas we have, or can naturally have, do spring" (Book II, Chap. I, § 2). Of the two fountains or sources of ideas or cognitions just indicated, *sensation* supplies us with ideas of the sensible qualities such as "yellow, white, heat, cold, soft, hard, bitter, sweet," which are the result of external stimulation; but Locke declines to discuss the psycho-physical problems involved. "I shall not at present meddle with the physical consideration of the mind, or trouble myself to examine wherein its essence consists or by what motions of our [animal] spirits, or alterations of our bodies, we come to have any *sensation* by our organs, or any *ideas* in our understandings" (Book I, Chap. I, § 2). The other source of ideas is *reflection*, "the perception of the operations of our own minds within us, as it is employed about the ideas it has got; which operations when the soul comes to reflect on and consider, do furnish the understanding with another set of ideas which could not be had from things without; and such are perception, thinking, doubting, believing, reasoning, knowledge, willing, and all the different actings of our own minds; which we, being conscious of and observing in ourselves, do from these receive into our understandings as distinct ideas, as we do from bodies affecting our senses" (Book II, Chap. I, §§ 3, 4). "Reflection," according to Locke, "though it be not sense, as having nothing to do with external objects, yet it is very like it, and might properly enough be called 'internal sense' " (Book II, Chap. I, § 4). The term "reflection" suggests rather more initiative than Locke intended. Hence perhaps his alternative designation, "internal sense." For the flow of ideas of sensation comes first; the "inner sense" can only follow it, and indeed must do so more or less—"as the bodies that surround us do diversely affect our organs, the mind is forced to receive the impressions, and cannot (by any act of will) avoid the perceptions or ideas that are annexed to them" (Book II, Chap. I, § 25). In accord with Locke's empirical standpoint, external sense thus receives a certain primacy over the "inner sense."

Both ideas of sensation and ideas of reflection are distinguished as complex and simple according as they are analysable into simple ideas or not. The several sensations of touch, temperature, taste, smell, sound, and sight are simple ideas of sense. Even when they are caused by the same object, they are "perfectly distinct" ideas. Corresponding to the ideas in the mind, there are certain qualities or powers in the objects, and Locke makes the usual distinction between primary and secondary qualities. Solidity, extension, figure, motion or rest, and number are primary qualities and really exist in bodies "whether any one's senses perceive them or no" (Book II, Chap. VIII, § 17). Colours, sounds, tastes, smells, etc., are secondary qualities and "are no more really in them than sickness or pain is in manna"—they are the effects of certain "powers" possessed by the bodies "to produce various sensations in us, and depend on those primary qualities" (§ 14). Noteworthy in this connection is Locke's experimental evidence that heat and cold are secondary qualities. "The same water," he writes, "at the same time, may produce the idea of cold by one hand, and of heat by the other; whereas it is impossible that the same water, if those ideas were really in it, should at the same time be both hot and cold" (§ 21). Simple ideas of reflection are those of perception, retention, discerning, comparing, compounding, abstraction, and volition. Lastly, there are certain simple ideas which enter the mind both by way of sensation and of reflection. They are the ideas of pleasure, pain, power, existence, unity, and succession. Such, in brief, is Locke's inventory of simple ideas, "the materials of all our knowledge."

"When the understanding is once stored with these simple ideas, it has the power to repeat, compare, and unite them, even to an almost infinite variety, and so can make at pleasure new complex ideas. But it is not in the power of the most exalted wit or enlarged understanding, by any quickness or variety of thoughts, to invent or frame one new simple idea in the mind, not taken in by the ways before mentioned; nor can any force of the understanding destroy those that are there" (Book II, Chap. II, § 2).

Turning to complex ideas, Locke remarks that there are only three kinds of such ideas. "Complex ideas, however compounded or decompounded, though their number be infinite, and the variety endless wherewith they fill and entertain the thoughts of men, yet I think that may all be reduced under these three heads: (1) Modes, (2) Substances, (3) Relations" (Book II, Chap. VIII, § 3). (1) "*Modes* I call such complex ideas which, however compounded, contain not in them the supposition of subsisting by themselves, but are considered as dependences on, or affections of, substances; such are the ideas signified by the words 'triangle, gratitude, murder,' etc." (2) "The ideas of *substances* are such combinations of simple ideas as are taken to represent distinct particular things subsisting by themselves." (3) *Relation* "consists in the consideration and comparing one idea with another" (§§ 4-6). Locke does not explain why he considers these three categories of complex ideas exhaustive. But he asserts confidently that "even *the most abstruse* ideas, how remote soever they may seem from sense, or from any operation of our own minds, are yet only such as the understanding frames" in one or other of these ways out of its stock of simple ideas (§ 8). As examples of Locke's treatment of abstruse complex ideas we may take his account of the ideas of infinity and of substance. Locke holds that infinity is a mode of quantity and that it is attributed primarily to such things as space, duration and number, which have parts and are capable of increase by additions. The mind comes by the idea in this way. "Every one that has any idea of any stated length of space, as a foot, finds that he can repeat that idea . . . without ever coming to an end of his additions. . . . The power of enlarging his idea of space by further additions remaining still the same, he hence takes the idea of infinite space." Similarly with infinite duration and infinite number. In so far as the idea contains anything positive it is really based on something finite, and is derived from our experience of finite spaces, times, and numbers. Nobody really has a positive idea of infinite space, etc. The idea is partly at least negative, and refers to the unceasing process of further additions to each finite result. And it is the failure to appreciate the negative character of the idea of infinity that

Locke considers to be the cause of the "perplexities and contra-
dictions" which mar so many discussions of the theme (Book II,
Chap. XVII). The idea of substance Locke traces to the fact that we
commonly observe a certain number of simple ideas occurring constantly together. They are consequently assumed to be united in
one subject, and are called by one name. This habit misleads us
into supposing that what is really "a complication of many ideas
together" is one simple idea; and "not imagining how these simple
ideas can subsist by themselves, we accustom ourselves to suppose
some *substratum* wherein they do subsist, and from which they do
result; which therefore we call 'substance.' " But, Locke continues,
"if anyone should be asked, 'What is the subject wherein colour or
weight inheres?' he would have nothing to say but 'The solid
extended parts.' And if he were demanded, 'What is it that solidity
and extension inhere in?,' he would not be in a much better case
than the Indian . . . who, saying that the world was supported by
a great elephant, was asked, what the elephant rested on, to which
his answer was 'A great tortoise': but being again pressed to know
what gave support to the broad-backed tortoise, replied, 'Something,
he knew not what'" (Book II, Chap. XXIII, §§ 1, 2).

It will be clear now that though Locke persisted in regarding
the mind as essentially passive in its apprehension of simple ideas,
he abandoned the notion of a *tabula rasa* when he credited it with
the power of forming complex ideas out of simple ideas, and even
with the power of adding some confusions of its own. But, as will
be explained more fully in the final chapter, Locke's main problem
was to restrain speculative flights and the use of abstruse but dubious
ideas. And from this point of view the fact of the mind's active
intervention in the construction of certain complex ideas was, in
the eyes of Locke, not in their favour.

The psychological views of Leibniz, too, were part of his philosophy, though they were to some extent formed in conscious opposition to Locke's *Essay*, on which Leibniz wrote a very elaborate
commentary bearing the title of *New Essays Concerning the Human
Understanding* (English translation by A. G. Langley, 1894). His
philosophical theories will be dealt with in the final chapter. For
our present purpose it is enough to state that for Leibniz reality
consists of *monads*, that is, of animated units. Broadly speaking, there
are three kinds of monads, regarded from a psychological point of
view. The highest are the self-conscious spirits, or rational souls, or
intelligences. Next below them are conscious (but not self-conscious)
souls, like those of the lower animals. Lastly, there are the uncon-

scious or subconscious monads, such as those which constitute what is called matter. The higher monads have the powers of the lower ones as well as their own distinctive ones. Even the lowest monads have perceptions of some sort, for no monad can exist without them. But such unconscious or subconscious perceptions are also experienced by animals and men, in a state of sleep, for instance, or of faintness. Corresponding to the three grades of perception there are also three grades of appetition or conation, namely, mere impulse, animal instinct, and self-conscious will; and the higher monads may experience the lower forms of appetition as well as their own distinctive type. But all the changes which a monad undergoes come from within, and are not caused from outside. For each monad, once created, is entirely self-contained, "windowless," isolated from all others, except for the "pre-established harmony" which gives an illusory appearance of mutual influence. Whereas Locke set out from the assumption that the mind is a blank tablet the impressions on which come mainly from outside, though Locke also admitted a secondary "inner sense" besides the primary "outer senses," Leibniz conceived the mind or the monad as having nothing but an "inner sense," and regarded the whole mental life of the individual monad as unfolding from within. Nothing reaches us from outside through the bodily senses. In fact, the body is only a society of lower monads, and the so-called sensations are merely confused perceptions. Whereas Locke rejected all innate ideas, Leibniz regarded all ideas as innate, evolving only from within, even if some of them take time to grow into conscious ideas. The soul is therefore never a *tabula rasa*, but is from the first rather like a block of marble, whose veins predetermine its final sculptural form. The sublimation of subconscious, confused perceptions into clear, conscious ideas Leibniz called "apperception."

Leibniz is largely responsible for the importance attached to the unconscious or subconscious in the subsequent history of psychology. He was led to his doctrine of *petites perceptions* (unconscious or subconscious perceptions) by applying the Law of Continuity to mental life. This induced him to postulate an endless variety of grades of minds or grades of mentality; and some misleading physical analogies or assumptions confirmed him in his way of thinking. He thought that just as the roaring noise of the sea is the sum of the sounds produced by the individual waves, so what is called the perception of the raging sea must be made up of many component perceptions of which we have no separate consciousness, and which are therefore unconscious or subconscious perceptions. The example set by Leibniz in treating the problem in this way did, however, direct the attention of later psychologists to the possible influence of obscure elements upon our states of mind.

In the psychology of Leibniz stress is laid on the Cartesian distinction between obscure ideas, on the one hand, and clear and distinct ideas on the other. But stress is also laid on the Spinozistic conception of the essential activity of the mind, and on the distinction between adequate and inadequate ideas. For Leibniz, as for Spinoza (whose writings he had studied), distinctively human knowledge consists of adequate ideas of necessary truths or laws. Particularly striking is the similarity, not to say identity, of their views on the conational functions of the human mind. The passions, according to Leibniz, proceed from confused perceptions. Freedom consists in following the clear and distinct (or adequate) ideas of reason. And the will is free in the sense of being exempt from external compulsion, not in the sense of an entire absence of necessity, for a rational soul must always have a sufficient reason for its volitions, which are thus determined by what seems good for it.

(See G. S. Brett, *History of Psychology*, Vol. II, 1921.)

CHAPTER XXV

THE SOCIAL SCIENCES

THE study of social phenomena dates back to antiquity. Socrates, Plato, and Aristotle were deeply interested in them. For Socrates, indeed, as for Pope many centuries later, "the proper study of mankind is man." The ancients and their mediaeval and early modern followers were interested mainly in social and political ideals; and the discussion of ideals falls outside the domain of science, and is consequently beyond the scope of the present volume. Some attention was, however, also given to the description of societies and States. Thus Aristotle is reputed to have described as many as one hundred and fifty-eight States, though only his description of the Athenian State has come down to us. In this we find an account of the history of Athens, its foreign relations, its political constitution, its cultural and religious life. Presumably the lost treatises describe other States on similar lines. The sixteenth and seventeenth centuries carried on and developed these ancient traditions. On the one hand, they produced Utopias after the manner of Plato's *Republic* and St. Augustine's *City of God*; on the other hand, they produced numerous descriptions of States, after the pattern of Aristotle's descriptive study of Athens. Of such descriptive studies, the following may be mentioned. In 1562 Francesco Sansovino (1521–86) published his *Del governo e amministrazione di diversi regni e republiche*, containing accounts of more than twenty States. In 1593 Giovanni Botero (1540–1617) published his *Le relazioni universali*, containing geographical, economic, and religious accounts of a number of States. In 1614, a similar, if more ambitious, work appeared under the title *Les Etats, Empires, Royaumes, Seigneuries, Duchez et Principautez du Monde*, by Pierre d'Avity (1573–1635). And early in the seventeenth century the Elzevirs commenced the publication of a whole series of *Respublicae*, in which a considerable number of volumes appeared by the middle of the century.

The sixteenth and seventeenth centuries, however, did not merely continue older traditions, but made important contributions of their own to the study of social phenomena. During these two centuries a start was made with the consideration of the influence of physical environment upon human beings and societies, with the study of economic problems, and, above all, with the use of statistical method in the study of society. The work done in all these fields was rather sporadic and unsystematic, so that it is difficult to see the wood for the trees. Still, it was a beginning which did credit to the centuries under review.

I. GEOGRAPHICAL AND CLIMATIC INFLUENCES

The idea that human nature is influenced to some extent by the climate and other physical properties of the countries in which men live was first given prominence in the sixteenth century. The writer who was chiefly responsible for this was Jean Bodin (1520–96). His principal work, *De la République*, 1577 (English translation by Richard Knolles, bearing the title of *The six bookes of a Commonweale*, 1606), was mainly concerned with the problems of the ideal forms of government. Bodin felt, however, that different types of people really need different forms of government, and that the differences which distinguish various peoples are due to some extent to differences in their physical environment. Accordingly, he found it necessary to deal with these environmental differences, and their influences, before proceeding to solve his main problem. His views about the influences exercised on human character by geographical and climatic differences are expressed chiefly in Book V, Chapter I, of his work (English translation, pp. 545 ff.). They may be summarized as follows.

The animals found in different regions of the Earth vary considerably with regional differences. Men likewise vary greatly in character and disposition according to the different nature of the countries in which they live. People living in the eastern part of a given region are different from those living in the western part, even when the climate is essentially the same in both parts. In regions having the same latitude and distance from the Equator the people of the northern part are different from those of the southern portion. Moreover, in regions having the same climate, and the same latitude and longitude, the people who occupy the hills are different from those who dwell in the plains. The inhabitants of cities situated upon hills are more given to revolutions and seditions than are the inhabitants of cities which are situated on level ground. The city of Rome, for example, with its seven hills, was never long without a revolution of some sort. Bodin goes so far as to correlate the three political parties in the ancient State of Athens, with its three different geographical areas, believing that the differences in the geography of these areas induced different temperaments in its inhabitants. Thus the occupants of the higher parts of Athens were democratic, and wanted a popular State; those who lived in the lower parts of the city favoured oligarchy or government by a few; whereas those who lived around the harbour, the Piraeus, were in favour of a kind of aristocracy, or a mixed government by the nobility and the people. These differences in temperament and disposition among the Athenian citizens could not, according to Bodin, have been due to differences in ethnic origin, for the Athenians themselves insisted that they had originally all come from the land of Attica. Similar differences may be observed among the Swiss, Bodin thinks. For although they have the same racial origin, having all come from Sweden originally, yet the cantons of the mountains are fierce and warlike, and democratic, whereas the other cantons are more tractable, and are governed by an aristocracy.

Bodin next divides the terrestrial hemisphere between the Equator and the North Pole into three zones, each corresponding to 30 degrees of latitude, and compares the races which inhabit these several zones. The people who live in the extreme north, that is, between the 75th degree and the Pole, are small, thin, and tamed with cold. Those who live between the 70th and 75th degree do not suffer so badly; in fact, the outer cold, when not extreme, somehow enables them to preserve their inner heat, and so gives them a certain amount of vigour and power. On the other hand, the inhabitants of Africa have little inner heat, because the external heat of the Sun somehow exhausts them, so that they are inferior in natural powers to the northern peoples. The influence of climate is particularly noticeable when people from the north move southwards, or when people from the south move northwards. Those armies which come from the southern parts into the north become more vigorous and lusty as they proceed; conversely, the armies that come out of the north and move southwards gradually languish and become more and more feeble as they go farther south.

However, what the southern peoples lose in physical vigour, in consequence of the hot climate, they make up in cleverness or policy. The peoples who inhabit the intervening region, between the northern and the southern regions, have some of the vigour of the northern peoples and some of the wit of the southern peoples. And, having more wit than the northern peoples, and more strength than the southern peoples, these peoples of the middle regions have founded great and successful empires, which their moderation enabled them to govern well and justly.

Just as the vigour induced by the climate of the north has helped to create the powerful militancy of the people of that region, so the wit induced by the climate of the south has enabled the southern peoples to create and cultivate the study of philosophy, mathematics, and the other sciences, also the study of law and politics, and "the grace of well speaking and discoursing." Bodin sees no kind of cultural grace in the people of the north. All he can say in this respect is that "the people of the north are and have always been great drinkers"; but he is gracious enough to add by way of mitigation that this "is not the fault of the men, but of the region."

Bodin then proceeds to correlate geographic and climatic differences with differences in temperament. For this purpose he follows the traditional, Hippocratic classification of temperaments, namely, the sanguine, the choleric, the melancholic, and the phlegmatic, which medical tradition dating from the days of Hippocrates had associated with the preponderance in the body of one of the four bodily "humours" or juices, namely, blood, yellow bile, black bile, and phlegm respectively. This ancient pseudo-physiological theory of the "humours" and temperaments naturally misled Bodin, as it misled others, to associate a black complexion with melancholy, a yellow complexion with a choleric temperament, and a red complexion with a sanguine temperament. Accordingly, he describes the people who live near the Poles as phlegmatic, those who live in the south as melancholic, those who live 30 degrees south of the North Pole as more sanguine, those who live still nearer the middle region as more sanguine and choleric, and those living more towards the south as more sanguine and melancholic, so that their complexion is more black and yellow, "black being the colour of melancholy, and yellow of choler." The phlegmatic temperament of the northern people makes them barbarously cruel, and the melancholy of the southern people makes them revengeful; but the people living in the middle regions intervening between the northern and the southern peoples abhor both the cruelty of the former and the vindictiveness of the latter. Yet another consequence of these differences in temperament Bodin finds in the greater chastity or abstinence of the northern people, resulting from their phlegmatic character, and the passions or lustfulness of the southern people, caused by their "spongious melancholy."

Before concluding his speculative contrasts between northern and southern peoples, Bodin turns to the consideration of the origin of religion. If we bear in mind his views on the greater wit of southern people, and on their creation and development of philosophy and the sciences, and all the arts and graces of life, we shall naturally expect Bodin to credit them also with the origin of religion. And so it is, as the following passage, quaint in its thought and presented in the quaint dress of Tudor English, shows.

"All religions have in a manner taken their beginning from the people of the south, and from thence have been dispersed over the whole earth: not that God hath any acception of places and persons, or that he doth not suffer his divine light to shine upon all men; but even as the Sunne is seene more easily in a cleere and still

water than in that which is troubled and filthie, so in my opinion
the heavenly light doth shine far more brighter in pure and cleane
spirits, than in those which are poluted with base and earthly affections. And if it be so that the true purifying of the soule is by his
heavenly light, and by the force of contemplation in the most
perfect subject; without doubt they shall soonest attaine unto it
which have their soules ravished up into heaven; the which we see
happen unto melancholike men."

After his examination of the differences which, he thinks, distinguish people according as they live in the north or in the south,
or betwixt and between, Bodin turns to the consideration of the
differences which distinguish people according as they live in the
east or in the west. He admits his difficulty about drawing the line
between east and west, but is not deterred thereby from indicating
the distinctive characters of the peoples who live in the east and
those who live in the west. People of the east are bigger in stature
and fairer in complexion than are people living in the west. These
differences Bodin attributes to "the natural beauty of the air, and
of the easterly winds." As regards disposition, the people of the east
are less warlike, more gentle, more courteous, more tractable, and
more ingenious than those of the west.

Of all the differences in physical environment as regards their
influence on human nature Bodin singles out the difference between
hills and valleys as the most important. To some extent this difference coincides with that between north and south. At all events,
mountains, wherever they may be situated, are very like northern
countries, because, as Bodin remarks, mountains "are oftentimes
more cold than the regions that are far northward." As regards
valleys, their influence upon people is very different according as
they are turned towards the north or towards the south, even when
they are in the same climate, in the same latitude, and in the same
degree. This, he thinks, is evident from a study of valleys which lie
at the foot of a mountain range that stretches from the west to the
east. He instances those of the Apennines, the Auvergne, and the
Pyrenees. And he regards these differences as responsible for the
difference in character between the people of Tuscany and those of
Lombardy, and the people of Aragon and Valencia from those
of Gascony and Languedoc. There is yet another difference between
people who live in the mountains and those who live in plains. The
barren soil of mountains forces the people to work hard, to be
temperate and resourceful. On the other hand, people who live in
rich valleys "become soft and slothful through the richness of the
soil."

Some indication has already been given above of Bodin's belief that winds exercise an influence on human beings. He maintains that differences in the kind of prevailing winds will make peoples different even if they live in places having the same latitude and climate. People living in places exposed to violent winds are less steady and grave in manner than are people who live in places where "the air is calm and temperate."

Lastly, Bodin considers also the question as to how life on the sea-coast or in busy cities or centres of much traffic affects the character of people. His view is that people whose life is cast in such places are usually more subtle, more tactful, and more knowing than those who live far from the sea and traffic.

Such in substance were Bodin's speculations about the influence of geographical and climatic conditions upon human nature. It will have been noticed that his categories for the classification of human character and of geographical and climatic differences were far too few and simple to keep pace with such extremely complex phenomena. His conclusions, accordingly, were highly speculative and little scientific. It is, however, well to bear in mind that even now, after many generations of extensive and detailed investigation into these problems, we are still a long way from really satisfactory answers to them. Moreover, Bodin's views appear sober and almost scientific when compared with the hysterical ethnology on which contemporary Germany has based its new *Kultur*.

II. POLITICAL ARITHMETIC

The introduction of statistical method into the study of social phenomena in the course of the seventeenth century was an event of first-rate importance, and destined to prove very fruitful in subsequent centuries. The term "statistics" was not yet invented; and when it was introduced in the eighteenth century it was at first used to designate such descriptive studies of States as have been referred to in the opening paragraph of this chapter. But the thing now called statistics *did* exist in the seventeenth century, and was christened "political arithmetick" by Sir William Petty, one of the three chief pioneers in this branch of study, the other two being John Graunt and Gregory King. The absence of an adequate census made the task of demographers extremely difficult; and it is very interesting to follow the attempts of the early pioneers to arrive at reliable statistical results by all sorts of ingenious devices.

GRAUNT

Valuable pioneer work was done by John Graunt (1620–74), a London haberdasher, in his book *Natural and Political Observations, mentioned in a following Index, and made upon the Bills of Mortality* (1662; fifth edition, with further observations, 1676). The Bills of Mortality upon the study of which Graunt's book was based, were originally weekly and yearly returns of the numbers of burials in the several London parishes. The practice of making such returns seems to have arisen at some time of plague (when they would be followed with especial interest), and to have dated back to the early years of the sixteenth century. The bills seem to have been regularly made out, if not actually published, from 1563 onwards, and they gradually became more explicit in the information which they afforded. The number of deaths due to plague was always specified, and, from early in the seventeenth century, the attempt was made to classify all the deaths in respect of their several causes, the burials of males and females being likewise distinguished, though the ages at death were not given. Count was also kept in the bills of the number of christenings. In Graunt's time about one hundred and thirty parishes were included in the scope of the bills, which were issued every Thursday at a cost of 4s. *per annum.* The cause of each death was established by the "two honest and discreet matrons" appointed in every parish, whose sworn duty it was, upon being informed of a death by the sexton, to "search the body," and to report to the parish clerk whether it was a case of plague, and, in general, what was the cause of death. Graunt in his book expresses doubts about the accuracy of the reports given by the "perhaps ignorant and careless Searchers," especially in cases of death from obscure or disreputable diseases. Considered as indices of the death-rate, the records of burials would also be affected by their taking no account of Roman Catholics and Non-conformists, who formed some 5 per cent of the population, and who were not buried with the rites of the Established Church; they also excluded cases in which persons dying in London were buried in the country. Similarly the birth-rate appreciably exceeded the corresponding number of christenings, in consequence of the scruples of the period as to the lawfulness or necessity of infant baptism.

Graunt begins his book (after dedicatory letters to Lord Roberts and Sir Robert Moray) with an account of these bills of mortality, their history (so far as he could carry it back), and their gradual increase of scope as more parishes were included and more information was afforded (Chapter I). He gives examples of the yearly summaries which were given on the Thursday before Christmas

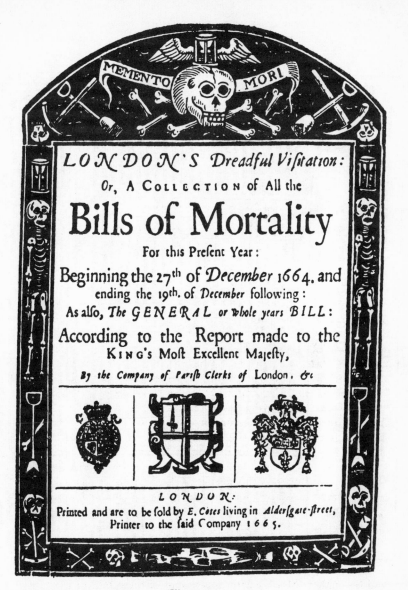

LONDON'S Dreadful Visitation:

Or, A COLLECTION of All the

Bills of Mortality

For this Present Year:

Beginning the 27th of December 1664. and ending the 19th. of December following:

As also, The GENERAL or whole years BILL:

According to the Report made to the KING's Most Excellent Majesty,

By the Company of Parish Clerks of London, &c

LONDON:

Printed and are to be sold by E. Cotes living in Aldersgate-street, Printer to the said Company 1665.

Illustr. 305

A generall Bill for this present year, ending the 19 of *December* 1665 according to the Report made to the KINGS most Excellent Majesty.

By the Company of Parish Clerks of *London*, &c.

Parish	Buried	Pla.
St Albans Woodstreet	200	121
St Alhallowes Barking	514	330
St Alhallowes Breadst	35	16
St Alhallowes Great—	455	426
St Alhallowes Honilane	10	5
St Alhallowes Lesse—	239	175
St Alhall. Lumbardstr	90	62
St Alhallowes Staining	185	112
St Alhall. weathe Wall	500	356
St Alphage	271	115
St Andrew Hubbard	71	25
St Andrew Vndershaft	274	189
St Andrew Wardrobe	476	303
St Anne Aldersgate	282	197
St Anne Blacke-Friers	652	467
St Antholins Parish—	58	33
St Austins Parish—	43	20
St Barthol. Exchange—	73	23
St Bennet Fynch—	47	23
St Bennet Grace chur.	57	41
St Bennet Pauls Wharf	355	172
St Bennet Sherehog—	11	—
St Botolph Billingsgate	83	50
Christs Church—	653	467
St Christophers	47	—

Parish	Buried	Pla.
St Clements Eastcheap	38	20
St Dionis Back-church	78	27
St Dunstans East	265	150
St Edmunds Lumbard	70	36
St Ethelborough	104	70
St Faiths	144	103
St Fosters	69	39
St Gabriel Fen-church	112	69
St George Botolphlane	41	27
St Gregories by Paul—	376	232
St James Dukes place	190	108
St James Garlickhithe	189	118
St John Baptist	138	83
St John Euangelist	9	—
St John Zacharie	85	54
St Katherine Coleman	299	213
St Katherine Creechu	335	231
St Lawrence Iewrie	94	48
St Lawrence Pountney	214	140
St Leonard Eastcheape	42	27
St Leonard Fosterlane	335	255
St Magnus Parish	103	60
St Margaret Lothbury	100	66

Parish	Buried	Pla.
St Margaret Moses	38	25
St Margar. New Fishst.	114	66
St Margaret Pattons	49	24
St Mary Abchurch	99	54
St Mary Aldermanbury	181	109
St Mary Aldermary	105	75
St Mary Alhermary	—	36
St Marie Bow	64	30
St Mary Bothaw	55	—
St Mary Colechurch	17	64
St Mary Hill	94	37
St Mary Mounthaw	56	262
St Mary Summerset	342	27
St Mary Stainings	47	33
St Mary Woolchurch	65	38
St Mary Woolnoth	75	11
St Martins Iremonger	21	128
St Martins Ludgate	196	71
St Martins Orgars	110	34
St Martins Outwich	100	349
St Martins Vintrey	417	17
St Matthew Fridaystr.	24	22
St Maudlins Milkstreet	44	121
St Maudlins Oldfishstr	176	164
St Michael Bassishaw	253	

Parish	Buried	Pla.
St Michael Cornhill	104	52
St Michael Crookedla	179	133
St Michael Queenhithe	203	122
St Michael Querne	47	18
St Michael Royall	152	116
St Michael Woodstreet	122	62
St Mildred Breadstreet	59	26
St Mildred Poultrey	68	46
St Nicholas Acons	46	28
St Nicholas Coleabby	125	91
St Nicholas Olaves	90	62
St Olaves Hart-street	237	126
St Olaves Iewry	54	32
St Olaves Silverstreet	250	132
St Pancras Soperlane	30	15
St Peters Cheape	61	35
St Peters Cornehill	136	76
St Peters Pauls Wharfe	114	66
St Peters Poore	79	47
St Stevens Colemanst	560	191
St Stevens Walbrooke	34	17
St Swithins	93	56
St Thomas Apostle	163	110
Trinitie Parish	115	79

Buried in the 97 Parishes within the walls —— 15207   Whereof of the Plague —— 9887

Parish	Buried	Pla.	Parish	Buried	Pla.
St Andrew Holborne	3958	3103	St Dunstans West	958	665
Bridewell Precinct	230	179	St George Southwark	1613	1260
St Bartholmew Great	493	344	St Botolph Aldersgate	997	755
St Bartholmew Lesse	193	139	St Botolph Algate	4926	4051
St Bridget	2111	1427	St Botolph Bishopgate	3464	2500
			St Saviours Southwark	4235	3446
			St Sepulchres Parish	4509	2746
			St Giles Cripplegate	8069	4838
			St Thomas Southwark	475	371
			St Olaves Southwark	4793	2785
			Trinity Minories	108	123
			At the Pesthouse	159	156

Buried in the 16 Parishes without the walls —— 41351   Whereof of the Plague —— 28888

Parish	Buried	Pla.	Parish	Buried	Pla.
St Giles in the Fields	4457	3216	St Magdalens Berm̃on	1943	1362
Hackney Parish	132	132	St Mary Newington	1272	1004
St James Clarkenwell	1803	1377	St Mary Islington	696	593
St Katherines Tower	956	601	St Mary Whitechap.	4766	3855
Lambeth Parish	798	537	Redriff Parish	304	210
St Leonards Shoreditch	2669	1949	Stepney Parish	8598	6583

St Paul Covent Garden 408|261 | St Margaret Westmin 4710|3742
St Martin in the Field 4804|2883| whereof at the Pelthouk--156
Uni..d in the 9 Parishes in the city and Liberties of Westminster-- 11194
whereof of the Plague ---- 6403

This Total of all the Burials this year --- 97306
Whereof, of the Plague --- 68596

Diseases and Casualties this year.

A Bortive and Stillborne — 617	Executed — 21	Palsie — 30
Aged — 1545	Flox and Smal Pox — 655	Plague — 68596
Ague and Feaver — 5257	Found dead in streets, fields, &c. — 20	Plannet — 6
Apoplex and Suddenly — 116	French Pox — 86	Plurisie — 15
Bedrid — 10	Frighted — 23	Poysoned — 1
Blasted — 5	Gout and Sciatica — 27	Quinsie — 35
Bleeding — 16	Grief — 46	Rickets — 557
Bloudy Flux, Scowring & Flux — 185	Griping in the Guts — 1288	Rising of the Lights — 307
Burnt and Scalded — 8	Hang'd & made away themselves — 7	Rupture — 34
Calenture — 3	Headmouldshot & Mouldfallen — 4	Scurvy — 105
Cancer, Gangrene and Fistula — 56	Jaundies — 110	Shingles and Swine pox — 2
Canker, and Thrush — 111	Impostume — 127	Sores, Ulcers, broken and bruised — 127
Childbed — 625	Kild by several accidents — 46	Limbes — 82
Chrisomes and Infants — 1258	Kings Evill — 86	Spleen — 14
Cold and Cough — 68	Leprosie — 2	Spotted Feaver and Purples — 1929
Collick and Winde — 134	Lethargy — 14	Stopping of the Stomack — 332
Consumption and Tissick — 4808	Livergrowne — 20	Stone and Strangury — 98
Convulsion and Mother — 2036	Megrom and Headach — 12	Surfet — 1251
Distracted — 5	Meazles — 7	Teeth and Worms — 2614
Dropsie and Timpany — 1478	Murthered, and Shot — 9	Vomiting — 51
Drowned — 50	Overlaid and Starved — 45	Wenn — 1

Christned { Males — 5114, Females — 4853 } In all — 9967
Buried { Males — 48569, Females — 48737 } In all — 97306 { Of the Plague — 68596 }

Increased in the Burials in the 130 Parishes and at the Pest-house this year — 79009
Increased of the Plague in the 130 Parishes and at the Pest-house this year — 68590

Illustr. 306

The Diseases and Casualties this Week.

		Imposthume	8
		Infants	22
		Kingsevil	4
		Lethargy	1
		Livergrown	1
		Meagrome	1
		Palsie	1
Abortive	4	Plague	4237
Aged	45	Purples	2
Bleeding	1	Quinsie	5
Broken legge	1	Rickets	23
Broke her scull by a fall in the street at St. Mary Woolchurch	1	Riling of the Lights	18
		Rupture	1
		Scurvy	3
Childbed	28	Shingles	1
Chrisomes	9	Spotted Feaver	166
Consumption	126	Stilborn	4
Convulsion	89	Stone	2
Cough	1	Stopping of the stomach	17
Dropsie	53	Strangury	3
Feaver	348	Suddenly	2
Flox and Small-pox	11	Surfeit	74
Flux	1	Teeth	111
Frighted	2	Thrush	6
Gowt	1	Tissick	9
Grief	3	Ulcer	1
Griping in the Guts	79	Vomiting	10
Head-mould-shot	1	Winde	4
Jaundies	7	Wormes	20

Christned	Males — 90		Buried	Males — 2777		Plague — 4237
	Females — 81			Females — 2791		
	In all — 171			In all — 5568		

Increased in the Burials this Week —————— 249
Parishes clear of the Plague —— 27   Parishes Infected —— 103

The Assize of Bread set forth by Order of the Lord Maior and Court of Aldermen,
A penny Wheaten Loaf to contain Nine Ounces and a half, and three
half-penny White Loaves the like weight.

Illustr. 307

Day. In the general bill for the year December 18, 1623, to December 16, 1624, the parishes were grouped together as follows:

Buried this Year in the Fourscore and seventeen Parishes of
  London within the Walls   3,386
Whereof of the Plague   1
Buried this Year in the Sixteen Parishes of London, and the
  Pesthouse, being within the Liberties, and without the Walls.. 5,924
Whereof, of the Plague   5

London 35			From the 15 of August to the 22.			1665		
	Bur.	Plag.		Bur.	Plag.		Bur.	Plag.
St Alban Woodstreet	11	8	St George Botolphlane			St Martin Ludgate	4	4
Alhallows Barking	13	11	St Gregory by St Pauls	9	5	St Martin Orgars	8	6
Alhallows Breadstreet	1	1	St Hellen	11	11	St Martin Outwitch	1	
Alhallows Great	6	5	St James Dukes place	7	5	St Martin Vintrey	17	17
Alhallows Honylane			St James Garlickhithe	3	1	St Matthew Fridaystreet	1	
Alhallows Lesse	3	2	St John Baptist	7	4	St Maudlin Milkstreet	2	2
Alhallows Lumbardstreet	4	4	St John Evangelist			St Maudlin Oldfishstreet	8	4
Alhallows Staining	7	5	St John Zachary	1	1	St Michael Bassishaw	12	11
Alhallows the Wall	23	11	St Katharine Coleman	1		St Michael Cornhil	3	1
St Alphage	18	10	St Katharine Crechurch	7	4	St Michael Crookedlane	7	4
St Andrew Hubbard	1		St Lawrence Jewry	2		St Michael Queenhithe	7	6
St Andrew Undershaft	14	9	St Lawrence Pountney	6	5	St Michael Quern	1	
St Andrew Wardrobe	21	16	St Leonard Eastcheap	1		St Michael Royal	2	1
St Ann Aldersgate	18	11	St Leonard Fosterlane	17	13	St Michael Woodstreet	2	1
St Ann Blackfryers	22	17	St Magnus Parish	2	2	St Mildred Breadstreet	2	2
St Antholins Parish			St Margaret Lothbury	2		St Mildred Poultrey	4	3
St Austins Parish			St Margaret Moses	1		St Nicholas Acons		
St Bartholomew Exchange	2	1	St Margaret Newfishstreet	1		St Nicholas Coleabby	1	
St Bennet Fynck	2	2	St Margaret Pattons	1		St Nicholas Olaves	3	1
St Bennet Gracechurch			St Mary Abchurch	1		St Olave Hartstreet	7	4
St Bennet Paulswharf	16	8	St Mary Aldermanbury	11	5	St Olave Jewry	1	1
St Bennet Sherehog			St Mary Aldermary	2		St Olave Silverstreet	23	17
St Botolph Billingsgate	2		St Mary le Bow	6	6	St Pancras Soperlane		
Christs Church	27	22	St Mary Bothaw	1	1	St Peter Cheap	1	1
St Christophers	1		St Mary Colechurch			St Peter Cornhil	7	6
St Clement Eastcheap	2	1	St Mary Hill	2	1	St Peter Paulswharf	5	2
St Dionis Backchurch	2	1	St Mary Mounthaw	1		St Peter Poor	3	2
St Dunstan East	7	3	St Mary Sommerset	5	5	St Steven Colemanstreet	15	11
St Edmund Lumbardstr.	2	2	St Mary Stayning	1		St Steven Walbrook		
St Ethelborough	13	7	St Mary Woolchurch	1		St Swithin	2	2
St Faith	6	6	St Mary Woolnoth	1	1	St Thomas Apostle	8	7
St Foster	13	11	St Martin Iremongerlane			Trinity Parish	5	3
St Gabriel Fenchurch	1							

Christned in the 97 Parishes within the Walls —— 34 Buried —— 538 Plague —— 366

St Andrew Holborn	432	220	St Botolph Aldgate	238	212	Saviours Southwark	160	120
St Bartholomew Great	58	50	St Botolph Bishopsgate	283	236	S. Sepulchres Parish	403	274
St Bartholomew Lesse	19	15	St Dunstan West	36	29	St Thomas Southwark	24	21
St Bridget	147	119	St George Southwark	80	60	Trinity Minories	8	5
Bridewel Precinct	7	5	St Giles Cripplegate	847	572	At the Pesthouse	9	9
St Botolph Aldersgate	70	61	St Olave Southwark	235	131			

Christned in the 16 Parishes without the Walls —— 61 Buried, and at the Pesthouse —— 2861 Plague —— 2139

St Giles in the fields	204	175	Lambeth Parish	13	9	St Mary Illington	50	45
Hackney Parish	12	8	St Leonard Shoreditch	252	168	St Mary Whitechappel	319	270
St James Clerkenwel	172	172	St Magdalen Bermondsey	57	36	Rotherith Parish	2	
St Kath. near the Tower	40	34	St Mary Newington	74	52	Stepney Parish	371	273

Christned in the 12 out Parishes in Middlesex and Surry —— 49 Buried —— 1571 Plague —— 1244

St Clement Danes	94	78	St Martin in the fields	255	193	St Margaret Westminster	220	191
St Paul Covent Garden	18	16	St Mary Savoy	11	10	Whereof at the Pesthouse		13

Christned in the 5 Parishes in the City and Liberties of Westminster —— 27 Buried —— 598 Plague —— 488

Illustr. 308

etc., the remaining parishes being grouped as "without the
Liberties, in Middlesex and Surrey," and "the Nine out-Parishes,
adjoyning to London, and out of the Freedom." The number
of christenings is similarly recorded. In the general bill for the
year 1624–5, every parish was particularized, the number of
burials being specified, and how many of these deaths were due
to plague:

London	Burials	Plague
Albanes in Woodstreet	188	78
Alhallows, Barking	397	263
Alhallows, Breadstreet	34	14
Alhallows the Great	442	302
Alhallows, Hony-lane	18	8
Alhallows the Less	259	205

etc., 122 parishes within and without the walls being included in the list, besides the Pesthouse. The total number of burials was 54,265, of which the plague was held responsible for 35,417; only one parish was found clear of plague throughout the year. After 1629 the deaths were classified according to their various causes, thus:

Abortive and Stillborn	415
Affrighted	1
Aged	628
Ague	43
Apoplex and Meagrim	17
Bit with a Mad Dog	1, etc.

In all, sixty-three causes of death are particularized, and they include such descriptions as "Dead in the street, and starved," "Executed and Prest to death," "Grief," "Jaw faln," "King's Evil," "Liver-grown," "Made away themselves," "Overlaid, and starved at Nurse," "Planet," "Rising of the Lights," and "Suddenly," while "Teeth" are held to have carried off 470 children.

In a chapter of "General Observations upon the Casualties" (Chap. II), Graunt examines the bills for the twenty years 1629–36 and 1647–58, and he draws up a table, included as an appendix in his third edition, giving the numbers of deaths in each of these years attributable to each of 81 causes. Of the 229,250 deaths so recorded, he finds that one-third were due to causes affecting children under four or five years of age, and, of deaths from certain other diseases, he estimates that one-half would be of children under six. He concludes that "about thirty-six *per Centum* of all quick Conceptions died before six years old." The table also shows that about 16,000 deaths were due to plague, 50,000 to other acute diseases "happening suddenly and vehemently, upon the like corruptions and alterations in the Air," 70,000 to other diseases depending upon "the ordinary temper of the place," and the nature of the food, and only 1 death in 60 to "outward Griefs," i.e. to injuries and diseases of the skin and flesh. Graunt observes that "among the several Casualties some bear a constant proportion unto the whole number of Burials; such are Chronical Diseases, and the Diseases whereunto the City is most subject; as for Example, Consumptions, Dropsies, Jaundice," etc., "nay, some Accidents, as Grief, Drowning, Men's making away themselves, and being Kill'd by several Accidents, etc., do the like; whereas Epidemical and Malignant Diseases . . . do not keep that equality: so as in some Years, or Months, there died ten times as many as in others." In this passage we see Graunt making a discovery of first-rate importance in statistics, the discovery, namely, that certain phenomena, like some of the diseases specified by him, though in their individual incidence apparently matters of chance or accident, may yet show great regularity when considered as a whole, or at least in large numbers.

Turning next to "Particular Casualties" (Chap. III), Graunt remarks how few die of starvation, and how few are murdered. The comparatively small death-rate from "French pox" (syphilis) —392 in 20 years—is attributed by Graunt to the practice (still largely followed) of returning deaths from this cause under the names of secondary diseases caused thereby, with the connivance of "the Old-women Searchers, after the mist of a Cup of Ale, and the bribe of a Two-groat fee, instead of one given them." He discusses whether rickets, first appearing among the casualties in 1634, was really a new disease or one previously confounded with the malady described as "liver-grown." From the comparative constancy of the latter disease accompanying the rapid increase in rickets, he comes to the conclusion that rickets was actually a new disease. Graunt proceeds to note and to comment upon the rise and fall in the death-rate from the more common diseases. "The Gout stands much at a stay . . . although I believe that more dye Gouty. The reason is, because those that have the Gout, are said to be long livers; and therefore, when such dye, they are returned as *Aged.*"

Chapter IV deals with the death-rate from plague at its various visitations, that of 1603, when four-fifths of the deaths were due to plague, being the most severe. In Chapter V Graunt demonstrates the effect of a visitation of the plague in reducing the number of christenings; he also seeks to prove that the loss of population in the City resulting from such a visitation is made good by the end of the second year following it, and chiefly, he thinks, from the influx of fresh people from the country. Thus, round the plague-year 1625, the numbers of christenings were:

In 1624 ..	.. 8,299		In 1626 ..	.. 6,701
In 1625 ..	.. 6,983		In 1627 ..	.. 8,408

Comparing the years and seasons one with another in respect of the health of the people (Chap. VI), Graunt distinguishes "sickly years" (in which the burials exceed those of the previous and of the following year), besides the "plague-years" (in which more than two hundred die of plague). He shows that, in general, "the more sickly the years are, the less fecund or fruitful of Children also they be." This holds also of the country parish considered in Chapter XII. Autumn is found to be the most unhealthy season of the year.

The bills show considerably more burials than christenings. Thus for the years 1649–56 there were 85,338 burials in London as against only 50,465 christenings. The population of the City must have been maintained and increased by influxes from the country. The country parish which Graunt studies later in the book shows an excess of christenings over burials at a rate which, if general throughout the country, would much more than make good the wastage of London, provided the total population of England were about fourteen times that of London, which seemed probable both from the fact that London contributed about one-fifteenth of the whole taxation, and from calculations based upon the total number of parishes in England and their supposed average population. The general reason assigned for the excess of burials over christenings in London is that "in London the proportion of those subject to die, unto those capable of breeding, is greater than in the Country." The special reasons are that men, coming to London on business or pleasure, mostly leave their wives in the country; that apprentices marry late; that London contains many sailors who go on long voyages; and that the "Smoaks, Stinks, and close Air" of London must shorten many lives. Further contributory causes suggested are "Intemperance in Feeding," "Adulteries and Fornications," and business anxieties.

The bills further show an excess of males over females in London (Chap. VIII). Thus in the 33 years from 1628 to 1662 (exclusive), the burials of males numbered 209,436 as against 190,474 burials of females, while christenings over the period were, males 139,782, females 130,866, so that male births exceed female by about a thirteenth part. Graunt believed the same general proportion to hold in the country. In Chapter XI Graunt seeks to estimate the population of London, then much exaggerated. "Considering, That it is esteemed an even lay, whether any man lives ten years longer, I supposed it was the same, that one of any ten might die within one year." Of the 15,000 buried in London *per annum*, according to the bills, about 5,000 died of infantile and senile diseases, so that some 10,000 *per annum* must die between 10 and 60, and, assuming the truth of the above "even lay," Graunt multiplies this number by 10 (it should be by 20) to get the number (100,000) of persons alive between these ages. To obtain a closer approximation he estimates the number of "Teeming-Women" (women of child-bearing age) as double the annual number of births (12,000), or 24,000, and he puts the number of families at twice the number of these women (or 48,000), and the average number of persons in a family as 8 (including servants and lodgers), giving a population of 384,000. From the proportion of the number of deaths to the number of families in some parishes within the walls (3 to 11), and from the total death-rate of London (13,000 of late years), he confirms that the total number of families in London must be about 48,000 (as above). This number is again confirmed by the number of men raised for the trained-bands, and also by the following calculation: "I took the Map of London set out in the year 1658 by Richard Newcourt, drawn by a Scale of Yards. Now I guessed that in 100 Yards square there might be about 54 Families, sup-posing every House to be 20 Foot in the Front; for on two sides of the said square there will be 100 Yards of Housing in each, and in the two other sides 80 each; in all 360 Yards: that is, 54 Families in each square, of which there are 220 within the Walls, making in all 11,880 Families within the Walls. But forasmuch as there die within the Walls about 3,200 *per annum*, and in the whole 13,000; it follows, that the Housing within the Walls is $\frac{1}{4}$ part of the whole, and consequently, that there are 47,520 Families in and about London." The population is thus put at about 384,000, of which, according to the proportion already arrived at (Chap. VIII) about 199,112 must be males.

In his twelfth and last chapter, "Of the Country-Bills," Graunt turns to records of christenings, weddings, and burials, kept for over 90 years in "a certain Parish in Hantshire, being a place neither famous for Longevity and Healthfulness, nor for the contrary." This parish, which numbered 2,700 souls, was almost certainly Sir William Petty's native parish of Romsey, as is proved by the close agreement between its Register and Graunt's figures. From an examination of these records, Graunt observes: that each wedding produces, on an average, 4 children; that 16 males are born for every 15 females; that the burials of males and of females are almost exactly equal in number; that the excess of births over burials, throughout the whole 90 years, only amounted to 1,059, or about 12 *per annum*, of which excess about 400 probably went to London, and about 400 emigrated, while the native population grew by about 300. Graunt was led by these records to suppose that "the proportion between the greatest and the least [annual] Mortalities in the Country are far greater than at London," for "in London . . . the number of Burials . . . within no Decad of years hath been double, whereas in the Country it hath been quintuple . . . within the same Decad. . . . Which shews, that the opener and freer Airs are most subject both to the good and bad Impressions, and that the Fumes, Steams and Stenches of London do so medicate and impregnate the Air about it, that it becomes capable of little more." Graunt did not realize that narrowing down the field from which his data were taken, from London to a single small town, must make the statistical regularities far more unstable from year to year.

In the appendix added to the third edition of his *Observations*, Graunt discusses a weekly bill of mortality from Dublin, probably supplied to him by Petty, and from the number of burials there, and the proportion of burials to population in London, he estimates the population of Dublin as about 30,000. He also reproduces other bills from Kent and Devonshire, for comparison with the Hampshire bill, summarizes the Amsterdam bills of mortality, and gives miscellaneous particulars of the mortality from plague in other European centres of population, and also some account of the burials and christenings in Paris, drawn from bills which probably owed their publication to the influence of Graunt's *Observations* in the original edition. The book concludes with analytical tables summarizing all the bills surveyed in its pages.

PETTY

Graunt's work in statistical demography was continued by his friend Sir William Petty, and the work of both received recognition by their election as Fellows of the Royal Society. Petty was the first to advocate explicitly the use of quantitative empirical methods in the study of social and political phenomena, and his words are worth quoting. "Instead of using only comparative and superlative Words, and intellectual Arguments, I have taken the Course (as a Specimen of the Political Arithmetick I have long aimed at) to express myself in Terms of Number, Weight, or Measure; to use only Arguments of Sense, and to consider only such Causes as have visible Foundations in Nature; leaving those that depend upon mutable Minds, Opinions, Appetites and Passions of particular Men, to the Consideration of others" (*Political Arithmetick*, Preface). He accordingly advocated the institution of a proper census of inhabitants, giving their ages, sexes, conjugal condition, titles, trades, religions, etc. "Without the knowledge of the true number of People, as a Principle, the whole scope and use of the keeping of Bills of Births and Burials, is impaired; wherefore by laborious conjectures and Calculations to deduce the number of People from the Births and

Burials may be Ingenious, but very preposterous" (*Observations upon the Dublin Bills of Mortality*, 1681).

Petty's *Political Arithmetick* (finished in 1676, though not published till 1690) was mainly controversial—it was intended to combat the general impression that the affairs of England were in a bad way. Some of his shorter *Essays in Political Arithmetick* (1683–7) are more relevant to the subject of this chapter. In the essay *Concerning the Growth of the City of London* (1683), Petty estimates the growth of London by reference to the increase of population in the 130 parishes covered by the bills of mortality, on the assumption that the population is proportional to the number of burials in years of normal health. His calculation is based on the following table:

There dyed in London, at a Medium, between the years

1604 and 1605	..	..	..	.. 5,185
1621 and 1622	..	..	..	.. 8,527
1641 and 1642	..	..	..	.. 11,883
1661 and 1662	..	..	..	.. 15,148
1681 and 1682	..	..	..	.. 22,331

Petty observes that these numbers are roughly consistent with the population's doubling itself in 40 years. Assuming Graunt's observation that 1 in 30 dies annually, the death-rate of 22,331 about 1682 gives the population as 669,930. This is confirmed by a report that there are 84,000 tenanted houses which, allowing 8 to a family, give a population of 672,000. Next he tries to estimate the population of England and Wales. The assessment of London is about one-eleventh of that for the whole of England and Wales; hence the whole population of London may be one-eleventh, and the whole population of England and Wales may be, say, 7,369,000, which agrees with poll and hearth tax returns, and with the bishops' list of communicants. As for the time in which the population doubles, Graunt's country bills suggest that 1 in 50 dies annually, and that there are 24 births for 23 burials. If these rules always held, they would suggest that the population doubles in about 1,200 years. But other good observations can be found that suggest a rate ten times as rapid, and "in Natural possibility" a population might double in ten years. For in a population of 600, there may be 180 men between 18 and 59, and 180 women between 15 and 44 who may bear a child once in two years, giving a birth-rate of 90 or (abating 15 for various causes) 75, which, with a burial-rate of 15, would give an annual increase of 60, the population thus doubling in 10 years. Petty takes a medium course, assuming a death-rate of 1 in 40, and allowing 10 births for 9 burials, giving, on a population of 600, an annual increase of $1\frac{2}{3}$, which would double the population in 360 years. He seems to neglect the cumulative effect of increase in population, but perhaps thinks that the effects of plague, famine, and war, which he mentions, would cancel this. Hence if there be now in England and Wales 7,400,000 people, and assuming the above rates of doubling for town and country, there must have been about 2,000,000 at the Norman Conquest. In 1840 the population of the City will be 10,718,880, and that of the country 10,917,389, "which is but inconsiderably more. Wherefor it is Certain and Necessary that the Growth of the City must stop before the said Year 1840: And will be at its utmost height in the next preceding Period, Anno 1800."

In the third of his *Five Essays in Political Arithmetick* (1687), Petty makes another attempt at estimating the population of London, and uses three independent methods for the purpose:

(i) *By estimating the number of houses.*—This is done in three ways: (a) The number of houses burnt in 1666 was 13,200. The proportion of people dying out of those houses was one-fifth of the whole in that year, whence the total number of London's houses was 66,000 in 1666. But the burials in 1666 were only three-fourths of the burials in 1686. Hence the number of houses in 1686 is 88,000. (b) The makers of a map (of uncertain identity) of 1682 told Petty that they found over 84,000 houses, and four years later there might be one-tenth more, London doubling as it does in 40 years, or 92,400 in all. (c) In 1685 there were 29,325 hearths and 6,400 houses in Dublin, and 388,000 hearths in London, the same proportion therefore giving the City at least 87,000 houses. In Bristol there were 16,752 hearths to 5,307 houses, giving London, by proportion, 123,000 houses. The medium between these two results is 105,000: this was very approximately confirmed from the Hearth Office, which gave 105,315. To find next the number of families: There are probably two families in one-tenth of the houses in London, and hence (105,315 + 10,531) families, and allowing 6 to a family, we obtain a population of 695,076.

(ii) *By the number of burials and the death-rate.*—The healthy years 1684 and 1685 gave nearly the same numbers of burials (23,202 and 23,222, medium value 23,212). Supposing that 1 dies in 30 *per annum*, as Graunt affirmed and Petty shows to be probable, then the population would be 696,360.

(iii) *By the proportion of plague-deaths to survivals in plague-years.*—Petty states (apparently incorrectly) that Graunt had said that one-fifth of the people of London died during a visitation of the plague. Now in 1665 nearly 98,000 died. Hence the population must have been 490,000, and, adding a third for the increase down to

1686, the total of 653,000 is obtained. (But Hull points out that of the total number of deaths in 1665 [97,306], only 68,596 were said to have died of plague, which would give the population in 1665 as about 343,000 and that of 1686 as about 460,000).

In the fourth of the *Five Essays*, Petty attempts an estimate of the populations of the principal cities of Europe. Assuming a death-rate of 1 in 30, and taking into account the alleged number of burials or of houses, he gives the following estimates of population for the cities named.

London	696,000
Paris	488,000
Amsterdam	187,000
Venice	134,000
Rome	125,000
Dublin	69,000
Bristol	48,000
Rouen	66,000

During his residence in Ireland, 1667 till 1673, Petty collected data for his *Political Anatomy of Ireland* (1691), which gives an idea of the kind of information which a demography, according to his views, should contain. It describes the extent and character of the land and the distribution of its ownership among various classes of people. Of the 10,500,000 Irish acres of land, 1,500,000 acres are said to consist of highways, bogs, and rivers; another 1,500,000 acres are described as unprofitable land; and 7,500,000 acres are said to be good meadow, arable, or pasture. The total value of the land, the rents, tithes, etc., are calculated. The total population of Ireland is estimated at 1,100,000, the number of families being 200,000, and the number of "Smoaks" (hearths) 250,000. The population is classified as follows:

Papists	800,000	or otherwise as	English		200,000
Non-Papists	300,000		Scots		100,000
			Irish		800,000

Of the families, 160,000 have no chimney, 24,000 have one chimney, and 16,000 have more than one chimney (and, one with another, four chimneys). Estimates are also made of the number of impotent folk (2,000), of soldiers (3,000), of children under 7 (275,000), of well-to-do people with more than six chimneys in their houses (7,200), of servants (32,400), and of ministers and students (400)—320,000 in all, leaving a residue of 780,000 persons fit for trade. These men and women are supposed to be distributed among the trades as follows:

Corn-growers	..	..	..	..	.. 100,000
Cattle-tenders	..	..	..	..	.. 120,000
Fishers	..	..	..	..	.. 1,000
Iron-manufacturers		..	..	..	.. 2,000
Blacksmiths and their servants	..		..	..	.. 22,500
Tailors	..	..	..	..	.. 45,000
Carpenters and Masons	..		..	..	.. 10,000
Shoemakers and their servants	..		..	..	.. 22,500
Millers	..	..	..	..	.. 1,600
Workers in wool	..	..	..	..	.. 30,000
Tanners and Curriers		..	..	..	.. 10,000
Ornamental Trades		..	..	..	.. 48,400

Giving a total of	.. .. ..	.. 413,000

leaving 367,000 for other trades. In Dublin, with its 4,000 families, there are 1,180 ale-houses and 91 public brew-houses, so that in Ireland as a whole, with 200,000 families, there may be 60,000, families in the drink trade (i.e. at least 180,000 persons in all—men, women, and servants), leaving still 187,000 unemployed as "Casherers and Fait-neants." These, he thinks, might be well employed in building proper houses and factories, instead of the "lamentable Sties" now in use, planting trees, repairing roads, and making rivers navigable, fortifying Dublin, etc., or in ship-building and the manufacture of textiles, estimates of the cost of each of the works proposed being supplied.

KING

The pioneer work of Graunt and Petty was carried a stage farther by Gregory King (1648–1712), whose *Natural and Political Observations and Conclusions upon the State and Condition of England*, 1696, shows some development in the conception of the function of demography. In the opening section (§ 1) of these *Observations*, the population of England is calculated on the basis of estimates of (i) the number of inhabited houses; (ii) the number of people to a house; and (iii) the number of vagrants and others not coming under regular assessment. (i) According to the books of the Hearth Office, the number of houses on Lady Day, 1690, was reckoned to be 1,319,215. As shown later (§ 5), the population is estimated to increase by about 9,000 souls *per annum*, and, at this rate, houses should be increasing by about 2,000 *per annum*, but, owing to the war with France, the annual increase in houses cannot be much above 1,000, so that by the end of 1695 the number of houses may have increased only to about 1,326,000. But about 3 per cent is to be deducted from this number in consideration of the fact that houses divided among several tenants are counted, for taxation, as so many distinct dwell-ings, while empty houses and smithies are also included in the account. Hence the *true number of inhabited houses* is given, in round figures, as 1,300,000. (ii) King next estimates the medium number of persons to a house, in various classified areas, from the returns of marriages, births, and burials in those areas, and, assuming the inhabited houses to be distributed as shown below, he arrives at the total fixed population:

	Inhabited Houses	Souls per House	Number of Souls
The 97 parishes within the walls ..	13,500 at	5·4	72,900
The 16 parishes without the walls ..	32,500 at	4·6	149,500
The 15 out parishes in Middlesex and Surrey	35,000 at	4·4	154,000
The 7 parishes in the city and liberty of Westminster	24,000 at	4·3	103,200
So London and the Bills of Mortality contain	105,000 at	4·57	479,600
The other cities and market towns ..	195,000 at	4·3	838,500
The villages and hamlets	1,000,000 at	4	4,000,000
In all	1,300,000 at	4	5,318,100

Suspected omissions are allowed for by adding on 10 per cent to the calculated population of London, 2 per cent to that of cities and towns outside London, and 1 per cent to that of villages and hamlets, giving a corrected total of about 5,422,560. (iii) Of "transitory people," such as soldiers and sailors, probably about 60,000 do not come under the above assessment, and, of vagrants, pedlars, etc., probably about 20,000 are unassessed. When these numbers are added, the total population of England appears as about 5,500,000.

The third section treats of "the several Distinctions of the People, as to Males and Females, Married and Unmarried, Children, Servants, and Sojourners." The assessments of marriages, births, and burials show the numbers of the two sexes to bear the following proportion in the specified environments:

	Males, Females	Males	Females	Both
London and the Bills of Mortality	10 to 13	230,000	300,000	530,000
Other cities and market towns	8 to 9	410,000	460,000	870,000
Villages and hamlets	100 to 99	2,060,000	2,040,000	4,100,000
	27 to 28	2,700,000	2,800,000	5,500,000

A more detailed classification of the population shows the following proportions:

		People	Males	Females
Husbands and wives, above ..	34½ %	1,900,000	950,000	950,000
Widowers, above	1½ %	90,000	90,000	—
Widows, almost	4½ %	240,000	--	240,000
Children, above	45 %	2,500,000	1,300,000	1,200,000
Servants, almost	10½ %	560,000	260,000	300,000
Sojourners and single persons ..	4 %	210,000	100,000	110,000
Total	100	5,500,000	2,700,000	2,800,000

The different proportions in which these classes occur in the populations of London, the large towns, and the villages respectively, are shown in the following table:

	London and Bills of Mortality		Other Cities and Great Towns		Villages and Hamlets	
		Souls		Souls		Souls
Husbands and wives	37 %	196,100	36 %	313,200	34 %	1,394,000
Widowers	2 %	10,600	2 %	17,400	1½ %	61,500
Widows	7 %	37,100	6 %	52,200	4½ %	184,500
Children	33 %	174,900	40 %	348,000	47 %	1,927,000
Servants	13 %	68,900	11 %	95,700	10 %	410,000
Sojourners ..	8 %	42,400	5 %	43,500	3 %	123,000
Total	100	530,000	100	870,000	100	4,100,000

In Section 4, the age-distribution of the people is next set forth as in the following table, on the assumption of 190,000 births *per annum*:

	In all	Males	Females
Under 1 year old	170,000	90,000	80,000
Under 5 years old	820,000	415,000	405,000
Under 10 years old	1,520,000	764,000	756,000
Under 16 years old	2,240,000	1,122,000	1,118,000
Above 16 years old	3,260,000	1,578,000	1,682,000
Above 21 years old	2,700,000	1,300,000	1,400,000
Above 25 years old	2,400,000	1,150,000	1,250,000
Above 60 years old	600,000	270,000	330,000

In Section 5 King estimates the *annual* increase in his time to be about 9,000. The annual number of burials in the kingdom, assuming a proportion of 1 in 32, works out at about 170,000, while the annual number of births, at 1 in 28, must be 190,000. Hence the yearly increase should be 20,000, the discrepancy between this figure and 9,000 being partly due to additional mortality in time of plague (representing 4,000 deaths *per annum*), and in war (3,500 deaths); while 2,500 may be lost at sea, and 1,000 go to the plantations, bringing the net annual increase down to 9,000. Of the gross increase of 20,000 annually, King supposes that the country produces just this increase, and the towns, exclusive of London, 2,000 more, but that London shows an annual excess of burials over births of 2,000, so that the resulting gross increase is maintained at 20,000 annually. The population of London is shown to have doubled three times since 1500, but the population of the country as a whole to have declined by 50,000 since 1688 in consequence of the war.

King gives the following table of the annual rate of marriages, births, and burials:

Population		Marriages	Births	Burials
530,000	London	1 in 106	1 in 26·5	1 in 24·1
870,000	Cities and towns ..	1 in 128	1 in 28·5	1 in 30·4
4,100,000	Villages and hamlets..	1 in 141	1 in 29·4	1 in 34·4
5,500,000		1 in 134	1 in 28·85	1 in 32·35

Hence, among any 10,000 of the population, there are 71 or 72 marriages in the country, producing 343 children; 78 marriages in towns, producing 351 children; and 94 marriages in London, producing 376 children. Thus in London there are fewer births in proportion to the number of marriages, but more marriages in proportion to the population, so that London is more prolific than other large towns, and similarly those towns are more prolific than the country. Again, if the people of London were as long-lived as those of the country, London would increase in population much faster in proportion than the country. King attributes the smaller number of births in London in proportion to marriages to the greater prevalence of adultery, to greater luxury and intemperance, to greater preoccupation with business, to the unhealthy effects of coal smoke, and to the greater inequality of age between husbands and wives in London as compared with the country.

In connection with the last-mentioned factor, King gives the

SCHEME D.—A SCHEME OF THE INCOME AN[
ENGLAND, CALCULATE[

Number of Families	Ranks, Degrees, Titles, and Qualifications	Heads per Family
160	Temporal Lords	40
26	Spiritual Lords	20
800	Baronets	16
600	Knights	13
3,000	Esquires	10
12,000	Gentlemen	8
5,000	Persons in greater offices and places	8
5,000	Persons in lesser offices and places	6
2,000	Eminent merchants and traders by sea	8
8,000	Lesser merchants and traders by sea	6
10,000	Persons in the law	7
2,000	Eminent clergymen	6
8,000	Lesser clergymen	5
40,000	Freeholders of the better sort	7
120,000	Freeholders of the lesser sort	$5\frac{1}{2}$
150,000	Farmers	5
15,000	Persons in liberal arts and sciences	5
50,000	Shopkeepers and tradesmen	$4\frac{1}{2}$
60,000	Artisans and handicrafts	4
5,000	Naval officers	4
4,000	Military officers	4
500,586		$5\frac{1}{8}$
50,000	Common seamen	3
364,000	Labouring people and out-servants	$3\frac{1}{2}$
400,000	Cottagers and paupers	$3\frac{1}{4}$
35,000	Common soldiers	2
849,000		$3\frac{1}{4}$
	Vagrants, as gipsies, thieves, beggars, etc.	—
500,586	Increasing the wealth of the kingdom	$5\frac{1}{8}$
849,000	Decreasing the wealth of the kingdom	$3\frac{1}{4}$
1,349,586	Net totals	$4\frac{1}{3}$

EXPENSE OF THE SEVERAL FAMILIES OF
FOR THE YEAR 1688

Number of Persons	Yearly Income per Family			Yearly Income in General	Yearly Income per Head			Yearly Expense per Head			Yearly Increase per Head			Yearly Increase in General
	£	s.	d.	£	£	s.	d.	£	s.	d.	£	s.	d.	£
6,400	3,200	0	0	512,000	80	0	0	70	0	0	10	0	0	64,000
520	1,300	0	0	33,800	65	0	0	45	0	0	20	0	0	10,400
12,800	880	0	0	704,000	55	0	0	49	0	0	6	0	0	76,800
7,800	650	0	0	390,000	50	0	0	45	0	0	5	0	0	39,000
30,000	450	0	0	1,200,000	45	0	0	41	0	0	4	0	0	120,000
96,000	280	0	0	2,880,000	35	0	0	32	0	0	3	0	0	288,000
40,000	240	0	0	1,200,000	30	0	0	26	0	0	4	0	0	160,000
30,000	120	0	0	600,000	20	0	0	17	0	0	3	0	0	90,000
16,000	400	0	0	800,000	50	0	0	37	0	0	13	0	0	208,000
48,000	198	0	0	1,600,000	33	0	0	27	0	0	6	0	0	288,000
70,000	154	0	0	1,540,000	22	0	0	18	0	0	4	0	0	280,000
12,000	72	0	0	144,000	12	0	0	10	0	0	2	0	0	24,000
40,000	50	0	0	400,000	10	0	0	9	4	0	0	16	0	32,000
280,000	91	0	0	3,640,000	13	0	0	11	15	0	1	5	0	350,000
660,000	55	0	0	6,600,000	10	0	0	9	10	0	0	10	0	330,000
750,000	42	10	0	6,375,000	8	10	0	8	5	0	0	5	0	187,500
75,000	60	0	0	900,000	12	0	0	11	0	0	1	0	0	75,000
225,000	45	0	0	2,250,000	10	0	0	9	0	0	1	0	0	225,000
240,000	38	0	0	2,280,000	9	10	0	9	0	0	0	10	0	120,000
20,000	80	0	0	400,000	20	0	0	18	0	0	2	0	0	40,000
16,000	60	0	0	240,000	15	0	0	14	0	0	1	0	0	16,000
675,520	68	18	0	34,488,800	12	18	0	11	15	4	1	2	8	3,023,700
450,000	20	0	0	1,000,000	7	0	0	7	10	0	Decrease 0 10 0			Decrease 75,000
275,000	15	0	0	5,460,000	4	10	0	4	12	0	0	2	0	127,500
300,000	6	10	0	2,000,000	2	0	0	2	5	0	0	5	0	325,000
70,000	14	0	0	490,000	7	0	0	7	10	0	0	10	0	35,000
795,000	10	10	0	8,950,000	3	5	0	3	9	0	0	4	0	562,500
50,000				60,000	2	0	0	4	0	0	2	0	0	60,000
So the General Account is														
675,520	68	18	0	34,488,800	12	18	0	11	15	4	1	2	8	3,023,700
825,000	10	10	0	9,010,000	3	3	0	3	7	6	0	4	6	622,500
00,520	32	5	0	43,491,800	7	18	0	7	9	3	0	8	9	2,401,200

results of his investigation of the (apparent) effect on fertility of inequality of age in the parents, as observed in the town of Lichfield. Of 1,060 children considered, the mother was the elder parent in 228 instances, and the father in 832; half were the children of parents of whom the husband was 4 or more years older than the wife; three-quarters were the children of parents whose relative ages ranged from 2 years' seniority in the wife to 6 years' in the husband, and so on. Half were the children of fathers between 28 and 35, and of mothers between 25 and 32.

In the sixth section of his book, King deals with the annual income and expenditure of the people of England for the year 1688. His calculations are summed up in a table which was by far the most elaborate demographic balance-sheet produced up to that time. Charles Davenant (1656–1714) described it deservedly as "a more distinct and regular scheme of the inhabitants in England than peradventure was ever made concerning the people of any other country." The table (Scheme D) is reproduced on page 606 f., and may be allowed to speak for itself.

King estimated the total value of England at £650,000,000, as calculated from the capital values of the rents and produce, together with the national stock in money, plates, shipping, stores, live-stock, etc.

III. LIFE OR MORTALITY TABLES

The practice of life insurance seems to date from the sixteenth century, if not earlier. But the basis of such contracts appears to have been rather arbitrary. Even in the seventeenth century life insurance was treated more or less after the analogy of a wager, or of a game of chance. A group of people paid certain sums into a common account by way of mutual insurance for a year at a time; no account was taken of differences of age, but only of such calculations of probability as had been suggested by Pascal and others. Graunt's study of the Bills of Mortality marked a period of special interest in the basis of all scientific life insurance, namely, life tables or mortality tables. Graunt himself drew up a mortality table, which is reproduced here, together with his introductory explanations (*Natural and Political Observations*, Chapter XI).

"Whereas we have found, that of 100 quick Conceptions about 36 of them die before they be six years old, and that perhaps but one surviveth 76; we having seven Decads between six and 76, we sought six mean proportional numbers between 64, the remainder, living at six years, and the one, which survives 76, and find, that the numbers following are practically near enough to the truth. . . .

Of an hundred there die within the first six years ..	36
The next ten years, or Decad	24
The second Decad	15
The third Decad	9
The fourth	6
The next	4
The next	3
The next	2
The next	1

From whence it follows, that of the said 100 conceived:

There remain alive at six years end	64
At sixteen years end	40
At twenty-six	25
At thirty-six	16
At fourty-six	10
At fifty-six	6
At sixty [six]	3
At seventy-six	1
At eighty [six]	0 "

The mortality at the younger ages is greatly exaggerated in this table. Other mortality tables were attempted, especially in Holland, where Jacob van Dael, Johan Hudde (Burgomaster of Amsterdam), Christian Huygens, and Jan de Witt were interested in the subject. But the most valuable life table, with applications to the calculation of life annuities, was published by Edmond Halley in 1693, in the *Philosophical Transactions*, No. 196, pp. 596–610. The title of the paper is, "An Estimate of the Degrees of the Mortality of Mankind drawn from curious Tables of the Births and Funerals at the City of Breslaw; with an Attempt to ascertain the Price of Annuities upon Lives. By Mr. E. Halley, R.S.S."

Referring to the work of Graunt and Petty on the bills of mortality of London and Dublin, Halley remarks that these bills failed to specify (1) the total number of the population, and (2) the ages of the people who died. Moreover, "both London and Dublin by reason of the great and casual Accession of Strangers who die therein, (as appeared in both, by the great Excess of the Funerals above the Births) rendered them incapable of being Standards for this purpose; which requires, if it were possible, that the People we treat of should not at all be changed, but die where they were born, without any Adventitious Increase from Abroad, or Decay by Migration elsewhere." But Justell had recently communicated to the Royal Society certain bills of mortality relating to the city of Breslau for the years 1687–91. These gave monthly returns of deaths in which age and sex were specified, and which were compared with the number of births. The total number of the population of Breslau, however, was not given, and Halley had to estimate this indirectly, from the table given later. Breslau lies far from the sea, "whence the Confluence of Strangers is but small," the births slightly exceeding the funerals. For the five years considered (1687–91) the average birth-rate *per annum* was 1,238, and the average death-rate *per annum* was 1,174. It appeared from the returns that 348 infants died in their first year, and that another 198 died between the ages of 1 and 6 years, so that only 692 survived the first 6 years. From the ages at death of these survivors, Halley drew up the following table, where the upper line shows the age and the lower line the *average* number of persons annually dying at that age. Where a dot is placed in the upper line, the number under it represents the deaths (at each age presumably) between the ages in the preceding and the following columns.

Age ..	7	8	9	.	14	.	18	.	21	.	27	28	.	35
Deaths	11	11	6	$5\frac{1}{2}$	2	$3\frac{1}{2}$	5	6	$4\frac{1}{2}$	$6\frac{1}{2}$	9	8	7	7

Age..	36	.	42	.	45	.	49	54	55	56	.	63	.	70
Deaths	8	$9\frac{1}{2}$	8	9	7	7	10	11	9	9	10	12	$9\frac{1}{2}$	14

Age..	71	72	.	77	.	81	.	84	.	90	91	98	99	100
Deaths	9	11	$9\frac{1}{2}$	6	7	3	4	2	1	1	1	0	$\frac{1}{5}$	$\frac{3}{5}$

Slight irregularities in the table, Halley thought, would be straightened out if a larger number of years were taken into account.

On the basis of these data, Halley drew up a table "whose Uses are manifold, and give a more just Idea of the State and Condition of Mankind, than any thing yet extant that I know of." It claimed to show the number of people in Breslau of each age, and thus to show the chances of survival and of death at all ages, so providing a sound basis for calculating the values of life-annuities, etc. Halley's table, showing "the number of Persons that are living in the Age current annexed thereto," is given on p. 611.

The numbers in the age-groups add up to nearly 34,000, being presumably adjusted so as to give this round number which Halley took as the population of Breslau.

Halley proceeds to make a number of applications of this table. (1) He first works out the proportion of men of military age in such a population. The total number of persons between 18 and 56 is 18,053, and taking half of these to be males, the total number of "Fencible Men" is just over a quarter of the total number of souls. (2) The table also serves to show the degrees of mortality or of

Age Current	Persons	Age Current	Persons	Age Current	Persons	Age Current	Persons
1	1,000	22	586	43	417	64	202
2	855	23	579	44	407	65	192
3	798	24	573	45	397	66	182
4	760	25	567	46	387	67	172
5	732	26	560	47	377	68	162
6	710	27	553	48	367	69	152
7	692	28	546	49	357	70	142
8	680	29	539	50	346	71	131
9	670	30	531	51	335	72	120
10	661	31	523	52	324	73	109
11	653	32	515	53	313	74	98
12	646	33	507	54	302	75	88
13	640	34	499	55	292	76	78
14	634	35	490	56	282	77	68
15	628	36	481	57	272	78	58
16	622	37	472	58	262	79	49
17	616	38	463	59	252	80	41
18	610	39	454	60	242	81	34
19	604	40	445	61	232	82	28
20	598	41	436	62	222	83	23
21	592	42	427	63	212	84	20

vitality at all ages, "for if the number of Persons of any Age remaining after one year, be divided by the difference between that and the number of the Age proposed, it shows the odds that there is, that a Person of that Age does not die in a Year." Thus, for instance, the table shows that, for a person of 25, the odds are 560 to 7 or 80 to 1 that he does not die within a year. Similarly the odds can be expressed that a person of any given age does not die before attaining any other given age. For instance, the odds that a man of 40 will live seven years are seen to be 377 to 68, or about $5\frac{1}{2}$ to 1. (3) Taking a person of a given age, the table shows the period within which that person has an even chance of dying and of not dying. It is the period within which the number of living persons of the age proposed is halved, e.g. for a person of 30 the period is between 27 and 28 years. (4) The price of insuring a life (for a stated period) should be regulated on these principles, and so also should (5) the prices of annuities, "for it is plain that the Purchaser ought to pay for only such a part of the value of the Annuity, as he has Chances that he is living; and this ought to be computed yearly, and the Sum of all those yearly Values being added together, will amount to the value of the Annuity for the Life of the Person proposed." That is, the present value of a pound payable after a term of years at a given rate of interest having been calculated by the ordinary methods, then "it will be as the number of Persons living after that term of years, to the number dead; so are the Odds that any one Person is Alive or Dead. And by consequence, as the Sum of both, or the number of Persons living of the Age first proposed, to the number remaining after so many years . . . so the present value of the yearly Sum payable after the term proposed, to the Sum which ought to be paid for the Chance the person has to enjoy such an Annuity after so many Years. And this being repeated for every year of the person's Life, the Sum of all the present Values of those Chances is the true Value of the Annuity." On this principle Halley worked out the following table, showing the value of annuities in years' purchase for every fifth year of age to the seventieth.

Age	Years' Purchase	Age	Years' Purchase	Age	Years' Purchase
1	10·28	25	12·27	50	9·21
5	13·40	30	11·72	55	8·51
10	13·44	35	11·12	60	7·60
15	13·33	40	10·57	65	6·54
20	12·78	45	9·91	70	5·32

To calculate chances involving two lives it is necessary only to bear in mind that "the number of Chances of each single Life, found in the table, being multiplied together, become the Chances of the Two Lives." In treating such problems, involving the chances of two persons, Halley recommends the use of geometrical diagrams.

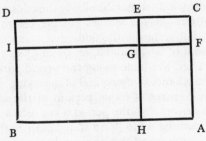

Thus in the rectangle ABCD, let AB represent the number of persons of the same age as the younger life, BH the number of them remaining alive after a given period, and AH those dead in the meantime. Let AC be the number of persons of the same age as the elder life, AF the survivors and CF the dead, after the same period. Then if the whole rectangle ABCD represent in area all the chances, the rectangle HI will represent the chance that both are living at the end of the period; the rectangle FE will represent the chance that both are dead, while the rectangles GD, AG will represent chances of one being alive and the other dead. Particular applications of this case arise in connection with the purchase of joint annuities, and provision for widows by reversion. Halley concludes by investigating the chances involving three lives, and showing how to find the value of an annuity payable during the continuance of any one of these. The appropriate diagram here is the parallelepiped.

"It may be objected," Halley concludes, "that the different Salubrity of places does hinder this Proposal from being universal; nor can it be denied. But . . . it does appear that about a 30th part die yearly [at Breslau] as Sir William Petty has computed for London. . . . So that by what I can learn, there cannot perhaps be one better place proposed for a Standard."

It is worth noting that the first life insurance companies established in London in the eighteenth century made use of Halley's tables.

IV. Economics

The production, acquisition, and use of commodities constitute such common social phenomena that even the earliest writers on social and political problems could not avoid them altogether. Some economic thoughts are accordingly to be found in ancient and mediaeval literature. The beginnings of a science of economics, however, cannot be said to date earlier than the beginning of the modern period. Even in the sixteenth and seventeenth centuries comparatively little interest was shown in the scientific study of economic phenomena. Economics was regarded rather as a part of politics or statecraft. Hence the older name of the science, "political economy," which made its first appearance in Antoyne de Montchrétien's *Traicté de l'Oeconomie Politique* (1615). The regulation of industry and trade, and especially of foreign commerce, was regarded mainly as an instrument for increasing the wealth and power of the State. And the State was rather apt to be regarded on the analogy of a farm—the monarch's farm. It is almost pathetic to find Sir William Petty, for example, assessing the cash value of the inhabitants of England or Ireland at so much per head, as if they were heads of cattle on a farm. In parts of Europe a large population is esteemed even now in the same sort of way, namely, as food—for powder! However, the advocacy of rival views concerning economic measures to be enforced by the State inevitably led to a certain amount of reflection and reasoning about economic problems, and so helped to lay the foundations of economic science. As might be expected from the nature of the case, the chief economic problems discussed during the sixteenth and seventeenth centuries were those of trade as an instrument of national wealth, and certain associated monetary problems. In the course of these discussions, a number of economic concepts, such as "wealth," "value," "rent," "interest" or "usury" received the kind of critical examination indispensable to a science of economics. To some extent, of course, the studies already described under the heading of "political arithmetic" also belong to the domain of economic science, and are certainly interspersed with various economic discussions. But in the absence of any systematic treatment of economic problems as a whole, during the period under review, it was thought best to give a separate account of "political arithmetic," especially so as it is sufficiently self-contained, and its most important characteristic, namely, the use of quantitative or statistical methods, had important percussions outside the sphere of economic studies.

Although France and Italy made valuable contributions to economic theory, and especially to the study of finance, yet, the most important economic literature of the sixteenth and seventeenth centuries was English; and the following sketch of the economic thought of the period will accordingly deal mainly with English economists, whose views may, as a whole, be regarded as representative of all contemporary theories in other countries.

NATIONAL WEALTH

The problem in practical economics which chiefly occupied the statesmen of the period was that of increasing national wealth. Conceiving a whole nation after the analogy of an ordinary tradesman, it was tacitly assumed that the wealth of a country can only grow by means of profitable transactions with other countries. Moreover, keeping a steady eye on "the sinews of war," politicians attached special importance to wealth in the form of money or precious metals. Growing armaments, the cost of a rapidly increasing Civil Service, and the rising magnificence of Royal households made great demands on cash resources. The political aim, accordingly, was to secure such a favourable "balance of trade" as would bring into the country, by way of exchange for its exports, not only all necessary commodities from abroad, but also a supply of precious metals to balance the difference in price between the imports and the exports. The phrase "balance of trade" (apparently first used by Francis Bacon in conjunction with "balance of glory," in his *Letter of Advice to Sir George Villiers*, 1615) appears in a great many

of the economic writings of the period; and the idea which it expresses ante-dated the expression. This kind of economic policy,
together with the various measures adopted to promote it, is known
as the "mercantile system," presumably on account of the special
importance which it tended to give to the merchant classes as the
principal agents in securing the desired favourable balance of
trade. The formation of various companies of merchant adventurers
was characteristic of those times. The earliest known statement of
the mercantile conception appeared in John Hales' *Briefe Conceit
of English Policy* (?1549); but its clearest formulation is found in
the writings of Thomas Mun (1571–1641), a director of the East
India Company, and the author of *A Discourse of Trade from England
to the East Indies* (1621) and *England's Treasure by Forraign Trade or the
Ballance of our forraign Trade is the Rule of our Treasure* (written about
1628, published in 1664).

"The ordinary means," says Mun, "to encrease our wealth
and treasure is by Forraign Trade, wherein wee must ever observe
this rule; to sell more to strangers yearly than wee consume of
theirs in value. For suppose that when this Kingdom is plenti-
fully served with the Cloth, Lead, Tinn, Iron, Fish, and other
native commodities, wee doe yearly export the overplus to forraign
Countries to the value of twenty-two hundred thousand pounds;
by which means we are enabled beyond the Seas to buy and bring
in forraign wares for our use and Consumption, to the value of
twenty hundred thousand pounds; By this order duly kept in our
trading, we may rest assured that the Kingdom shall be enriched
yearly two hundred thousand pounds, which must be brought to us
in so much Treasure; because that part of our stock which is not
returned to us in wares must necessarily be brought home in
treasure" (*England's Treasure*, Chap. II).

One result of this conception of the increase of national wealth
by a favourable balance of trade was that governments tried to
encourage in every possible way, even by means of bounties when
necessary, the export of goods, and to discourage, by means of
prohibitions or by means of import duties, the import of foreign
goods. In order to find foreign markets for home manufactures,
various methods were suggested, and some of them applied. In
France the attempt was made, early in the sixteenth century, and
again under Colbert in the seventeenth, to secure supremacy in
the manufacture of goods with the aid of artists, scientists, and other
experts. Famous men like Leonardo da Vinci, Benvenuto Cellini,
Christian Huygens, and many others, as well as an army of skilled
craftsmen from abroad, received attractive posts in France for that
purpose; and England secured somewhat similar advantages by

her toleration of refugees from lands of religious persecution. Another method of meeting competition in foreign markets was that of cheap production. "The natural way of promoting the woollen manufacture," urged Davenant, was "by wholesome laws to contrive that it may be wrought cheaply in England, which will enable us to command the markets abroad" (*Ways and Means of Supplying the War*, 1695). This might be achieved, in the first place, by a proper division of labour. "In the making of a Watch," says Petty, "if one Man shall make the Wheels, another the Spring, another shall engrave the Dial-plate, and another shall make the Cases, then the Watch will be better and cheaper made than if the whole work be put upon any one Man" (*Concerning the Growth of the City of London*, 1683).

Similarly, "Cloth must be cheaper made when one cards, another spins, another weaves, another presses and packs, than when all the Operations above mentioned were clumsily performed by the same Hand." Another aid to cheap production, suggested by Petty, was to compel idlers to work, namely, by "taxing unemployed persons to manufacture goods" (*Polit. Arith.*, II). Petty actually suggested the wholesale transplantation of the Irish "from the poor and miserable Trade of Husbandry, to more beneficial Handicrafts" in England (*Ibid.*, IV). Charles Davenant (in his *Ways and Means*) likewise urged the compulsory participation of the able-bodied poor in the production of cheap goods. Exports were also encouraged by means of State bounties or subsidies. The idea underlying this method was probably the same, to some extent, as that which prompted Petty's remark (*Treatise of Taxes*, 1662, Chap. VI) that it would be "better to burn a thousand men's labour for a time than to let those thousand men by non-employment lose their faculty for labouring"—a view extensively endorsed recently during the period following the Great War. The one kind of export which was not regarded favourably was that of gold and silver. The reasons for this will be considered presently.

The restriction of imports was a much simpler matter than the expansion of exports. Certain kinds of imported goods could be prohibited altogether; others could be taxed; while raw materials required for the country's home industries could be admitted free of duty. Sometimes two birds could be killed with one stone, the same measure at once restricting certain kinds of imports and helping to expand corresponding exports. This was notably the case with shipping services as affected by Cromwell's Navigation Act (1651), which at once destroyed Holland's carrying trade and helped Britannia to rule the waves. Somewhat similarly, various restrictions imposed on imported goods were intended to protect and develop

THE SOCIAL SCIENCES 617

the home manufacture of similar commodities both for home use and for export.

The spirit of the whole mercantile tendency was one of international antagonism. Commerce was regarded mainly as a political instrument; and the motto of mercantilism might have been expressed in the words, "the flag follows trade." Something of this spirit may be seen reflected even in the economic writings of Petty, who writes that, England having a sufficiency of land, and of spare labour and employment, "it is not impossible, nay, a very feasible matter, for the King of England's Subjects to gain the Universal Trade of the whole Commercial World" (*Polit. Arith.*, X). But there were not altogether wanting economists who saw the matter differently, regarding international trade mainly as a natural way of providing a mutual supply of the several needs of the different countries, and believing that international trade should be kept free from arbitrary interference. This view is expressed in Davenant's *Ways and Means* as follows: "Trade is in its nature free, finds its own channel, and best directeth its own course, and all laws to give it rules and directions, and to limit and circumscribe it, may serve the particular ends of private men, but are seldom advantageous to the public. . . . The various products of different soils and countries is an indication that Providence intended they should be helpful to each other." But the world was not yet ripe for such a view; and is not yet ripe for it even now. The ghost of mercantilism still haunts the Cabinets of the Great Powers.

MONEY AND WEALTH

Politicians and economists of the sixteenth and seventeenth centuries were, as we have seen, all alive to the importance of exports. Nevertheless, as has already been stated, they did not favour the export of gold and silver. There was a popular tendency to identify wealth with money, or at least with the precious metals and stones, so that an export of these looked like a loss of wealth. When trade was bad in England early in the seventeenth century, Edward Misselden (*Free Trade*, 1622) put the blame partly on the East India Company's exportation of bullion; and when Mun defended the Company he only pleaded that "the exportation of our Moneys in Trade of Merchandise is a means to encrease our Treasure," like the increased return which the husbandman reaps from the seed which he has sown. Mun's defence seems to admit the popular identification of wealth with money; more probably he only assumed it for argument's sake, believing that he could defend his cause even on that assumption. Hardly any economist of that period really identified wealth with money (or precious metals).

Petty, for example, in his tract *Quantulumcunque concerning Money* (?1682) puts the question (23): "Is not a Country the Poorer for having less Money?" And his answer is: "Not always. For as the most thriving Men keep little or no Money by them, but turn and wind it into various Commodities to their great Profit, so may the whole Nation also." In fact, the nation, he goes on to say, may have too much money if this exceeds "half a Year's Rent for all the Lands of England, and a Quarter's Rent of the Housing, and a Week's Expence of all the People, and about a Quarter of the Value of all the exported Commodities."

In his estimate of the wealth of England, he includes lands, houses, goods, ships, etc., as well as money and precious metals and stones. And in his *Treatise of Taxes*, etc., he estimates the total coin of the realm at only 1 per cent of the national wealth. Gregory King's views are equally clear in this respect (see p. 606 f.). Davenant is equally explicit, or even more so. "We understand that to be wealth which maintains the Prince and the general Body of his People in Plenty, Ease, and safety" (*Works*, I, p. 381). Finally, Sir Dudley North may be quoted—to "be free from Want, and enjoy most Circumstances," he writes, "is truly to be Rich, altho' there were no such thing as Gold, Silver, or the like" (*Discourses upon Trade*, 1691, I).

The writers on economic problems in the period under review did not confuse wealth with money. But they did attach a peculiar importance to money or the precious metals. Gold and silver, they realized, are commodities, yet they are commodities of a peculiar kind, inasmuch as they are imperishable, movable, and most readily exchangeable for any other commodity. Gold and silver (and money made of them) thus have great advantages over other commodities. The main points are stated very explicitly by North. "Metals are very necessary for many Uses, and are to be reckoned among the Fruits and Manufactories of the World. Gold and Silver," he explains, "being by nature very fine, and more scarce than others, are higher prized; and a little of them is very reasonably esteemed equal in value with a great quantity of other Mettals, etc. For which reason and moreover that they are imperishable, as well as convenient for easie stowage and removal, and not from any Laws, they are made a Standard or common Measure to deal with; and all Mankind concur in it, as every one knows" (*op. cit.*).

In the second *Discourse* he says: "Gold and Silver, and, out of them, Money are nothing but the Weights and Measures, by which Traffick is more conveniently carried on, than could be done without them; and also a proper Fund for the surplusage of Stock to be deposited in" (*op. cit.*).

North's view of gold and silver money in relation to wealth was true in essentials, especially in the England of his time, when any English citizen possessed of bullion could have it minted, free of charge, into coins of the realm. But it was not the whole truth, as he would have seen if he had considered the case of bronze, copper, or tin coins. Coins of the realm have an element of legislative sanction which made them legal tender. This aspect was emphasized, with some exaggeration (for a period which had no paper currency) by Nicholas Barbon (or Barebone) in his *Discourse of Trade* (1690) in the section "Of Mony," etc. "Mony," he writes, "is a Value made by a Law; and the Difference of its Value is known by the Stamp, and Size of the Piece. . . . The Value of Mony must be made certain by Law, or else it could not be made a certain Measure, nor an Exchange for the Value of all things. It is not absolutely necessary, Mony should be made of Gold or Silver; for having its sole Value from the Law, it is not Material upon what Metal the Stamp is set. Mony hath the same Value, and performs the same Uses, if it be made of Brass, Copper, Tin, or anything else. . . . Six Pence in Farthings will buy the same thing as Six Pence in Silver." Barbon realized, however, that this only applied to coins in the country where their legal sanction could be enforced. He adds, accordingly, that "Gold and Silver, as well as Brass, Copper and Tin Mony, change their value in those Countries, where the Law has no Force, and yield no more than the Price of the Metal that bears the Stamp: Therefore, all Foreign Coins go by Weight, and are of no certain Value, but rise and fall with the Price of the Metal."

So, after all, money has *not* "its *sole* value from the Law"; and Barbon's view needs to be supplemented by North's. If coins are made legal tender they become more *acceptable* thereby; but their *value* is mainly determined by general conditions of demand and supply of the metals of which they are made.

GRESHAM'S LAW

The possible difference between the value of a coin as legal tender and the value of its metal contents offered various temptations. On the one hand, in times of economic difficulty, governments or princes were tempted to make a little precious metal go a long way by reducing the metal value of coins considerably below their nominal or legal value. The economic writers of the period under consideration were almost unanimous in their condemnation of such a policy; and many of them also urged that old worn coins should be melted down and replaced by new coins having the proper amount of precious metal. Petty, for example, in his *Quantulumcunque*, points out that there would be no advantage in reducing the weight of silver coins, for they would purchase less in proportion to the reduction in their weight. He also urges that the old coins, which were of unequal weights, should be recoined uniformly to provide a fixed commercial standard, and that the new coins should have the same weight and fineness as the old coins had when they were first issued. The other temptation was that of the coin-clipper. In spite of severe punishment when caught, coin-clippers pursued their trade. Extensive experience of debased, worn, and clipped coins soon made it clear that when coins of full weight and coins of lesser weight were put into circulation the tendency was for people to hoard the better coins, or to use them for payments due to foreign creditors, so that soon only the inferior coins remained in circulation. This tendency is usually known as Gresham's Law, and is expressed in the formula: "Bad money drives out good." The formulation of this law is attributed to Sir Thomas Gresham, and is alleged to have been used by him in a proclamation composed by him, and authorized by Queen Elizabeth in 1560 (see Burgon's *Life and Times of Gresham*, 1839).

VALUE AND PRICE

One of the economic problems most widely discussed in the seventeenth century was that of value, a problem partly suggested, no doubt, by the discussions on the value of money, of which an account has already been given in the preceding paragraphs. The discussions on value were rather confused and one-sided. The writers for the most part did not always clearly distinguish between value in use and value in exchange, that is between the usefulness and the price of commodities or services. Secondly, each writer tended to regard some one factor in the determination of value as though it were the sole factor that needed to be considered. Nevertheless, the discussions taken collectively brought to light nearly all the essential aspects of a sound theory of economic value, and only needed some kind of logical synthesis.

In his *Discourse of Trade*, Barbon lays chief stress on the factor of utility. "The Value of all Wares," he writes, "arise from their Use; Things of no Use, have no Value, as the English Phrase is, *They are good for nothing*. The Use of Things are to supply the Wants and Necessities of Man: There are Two General Wants that Mankind is born with; the Wants of the Body, and the Wants of the mind; To supply these two Necessities, all things under the Sun become useful, and therefore have a Value." The principal wants of the body are "Food, Clothes and Lodging." But "the Wants of the Mind are infinite." And "amongst the great Variety of Things to satisfie the

Wants of the Mind, those that adorn Mans Body, and advance the Pomp of Life, have the most general Use."

Hence rarity or scarcity becomes a factor in value, for "things rare and difficult to be obtained are General Badges of Honour : From this Use, Pearls, Diamonds, and Precious Stones have their Value: Things Rare are proper Ensigns of Honour, because it is Honourable to acquire Things Difficult." Conversely, "the *Over-pluss* of Those Wares, which are more than can be used, become worth nothing."

Barbon also explains the fluctuation in the value of most things with changes in fashion. "The Use of most things being to supply the Wants of the Mind, and not the Necessitys of the Body; and those Wants, most of them proceeding from imagination, the Mind Changeth; the things grow out of Use, and so lose their Value" (pp. 13–15 in J. H. Hollander's Reprint, Baltimore, 1905).

Most of the discussions on value were, however, primarily concerned with the problem of prices, or the factors which determine exchange values. Granted that things must be of some use in order to have a value in exchange, or a price, it does not follow that all things that are of use can command a price, less still does it follow that the price of a commodity or service must vary proportionately with its utility, supposing that this can be measured independently. As John Law pointed out, "Water is of great use, yet of little value. . . . Diamonds are of little use, yet of great value" (*Money and Trade Considered*, 1705).

What, then, is it that determines the price of Commodities, supposing these to be of some use? The factors chiefly stressed by economic writers in the seventeenth century were those of (1) the amount of labour necessary to the production of a commodity, and (2) the relation between the supply of the commodity and the demand for it.

(1) John Locke, in his *Civil Government* (1690, § 42) laid stress on labour in the creation of value. "Bread, Wine, and Cloth," he says, "are things of daily Use and great Plenty, yet notwithstanding, Acorns, Water, and Leaves, or Skins must be our Bread, Drink, and Clothing, did not Labour furnish us with these more useful Commodities. For whatever Bread is worth more than Acorns, Wine than Water, and Cloth or Silk than Leaves, Skins, or Moss, that is wholly owing to Labour and Industry." Since, however, labour must have raw materials to work upon, and raw materials are not created by the labour of man, but by the earth, Locke has to admit that some part of the value of a commodity is due to land. Petty divided the honours evenly between land and labour in the creation of values. "All things," he wrote in his *Treatise of Taxes* (1662, Chap. IV), "ought to be valued by two natural Denominations, which is Land

and Labour; that is, we ought to say, a Ship or garment is worth such a measure of Land, with such another measure of Labour; forasmuch as both Ships and Garments were the creatures of Lands and men's Labours thereupon."

It would be more convenient, however, to express the value of a commodity in terms of labour alone or of land alone. Petty accordingly thought of finding "a natural Par between Land and Labour," by means of which it would be possible to "reduce one into the other as easily and certainly as we reduce Pence into Pounds" (*Ibid.*). The problem of such a "natural Par" was taken up again in his *Political Anatomy of Ireland* (1691, Chap. IX), and the conclusion at which he arrived was that "the day's food of an adult Man, at a Medium, and not the day's labour, is the common measure of Value." This conclusion is based on the following considerations. "Suppose two Acres of Pasture-land inclosed, and put thereinto a weaned Calf, which I suppose in twelve Months will become 1 C. [hundred-weight] heavier in eatable Flesh; then 1 C. weight of such Flesh, which I suppose fifty days' Food, and the Interest of the Value of the Calf, is the value or year's Rent of the Land. But if a man's Labour . . . for a year can make the said Land to yield more than sixty days' Food of the same, or of any other kind, then that overplus of days' Food is the Wages of the Man: both being expressed by the number of days' food."

Satisfied with his method of reducing the value of labour and the rental value of land to a common denominator, Petty proceeds to indicate how to make "a Par and Equation between Art and Simple Labour." "If," he explains, "by such Simple Labour I could dig and prepare for Seed a hundred Acres in a thousand days; suppose then, I spend a hundred days in studying a more compendious way, and in contriving Tools for the same purpose; but in all that hundred days dig nothing, but in the remaining nine hundred days I dig two hundred Acres of Ground; then I say, that the said Art which cost but one hundred days' Invention is worth one Man's labour for ever; because the new Art, and one Man, performed as much as two Men could have done without it" (*Ibid.*).

(2) On the other hand, there was a tendency to emphasize the dependence of the price of a commodity on supply and demand. John Law, for instance, insisted that the price of goods "is greater or lesser, not so much from their more or less valuable or necessary Uses, as from the greater or lesser Quantity of them in proportion to the Demand for them." He gives the example already cited above, and repeated *in extenso* here. "Water," he says, "is of great Use, yet of little Value [in exchange]; because the quantity of Water

is much greater than the Demand for it. Diamonds are of little Use yet of great Value, because the Demand for Diamonds is much greater than the quantity of them" (*Money and Trade Considered*). Hence "goods change their Value from any change in their Quantity or in the Demand for them. *Example.* If Oats be in greater Quantity than last year and the Demand the same or lesser, Oats will be less valuable."

Davenant, or perhaps Gregory King (whose statistical data Davenant made use of), made a study of the variation of the price with the supply of corn, and his conclusion was as follows: "We take it, That a Defect in the Harvest may raise the Price of Corn in the following Proportions:

Defect	Raises the Price above the Common Rate
1 Tenth [10 %]	3 Tenths [30 %]
2 Tenths [20 %]	8 Tenths [80 %]
3 Tenths [30 %]	16 Tenths [160 %]
4 Tenths [40 %]	28 Tenths [280 %]
5 Tenths [50 %]	45 Tenths [450 %]

[*An Essay upon the Probable Methods of making a People Gainers in the Ballance of Trade*, 1699, § III, p. 83.]

Locke, after emphasizing labour as a factor in the determination of value, also admitted the influence of supply and demand. "The Price of any Commodity," he writes, "rises or falls by the Proportion of the number of Buyers and Sellers" (*Some Considerations of the Consequences of the Lowering of Interest*, etc., 1696, p. 45). He also has the merit of having taken into account the influence of the existence of substitutes upon the price of a commodity. "For supposing that at the same Time that there is a great Scarcity of Wheat and other Grain, there were a considerable Quantity of Oats, Men no question would give far more for Wheat than Oats, as being the healthier, pleasanter and more convenient Food: but since Oats would serve to supply that absolute Necessity of sustaining Life, Men would not rob themselves of all other Conveniences of Life, by paying all their Money for Wheat when Oats, that are cheaper, though with some inconvenience, would supply that Defect" (*Ibid.*, p. 48).

We may conclude this section by quoting a passage from Barbon's *Discourse of Trade* (p. 18, ed. 1905), which makes good reading. "Were it not for the Waste, made of Gold and Silver, by Plate, Lace, Silks, and Guilding, and the Custom of the *Eastern* Princes, to lay them up and bury them, [so] that Half which is dug in the *West*, is buried in the *East*. The great Quantities dug out of the earth, since the Discovery of the *West-Indies*, would have so much lessened the Value, that by this time, they would not have much exceeded the Value of Tin, or Copper: Therefore, How greatly would these Gentlemen be disappointed that are searching after the Philosopher's Stone, if they should at last happen to find it? For if they should make but so great a Quantity of Gold and Silver, as they, and their Predecessors have spent in search after it, it would so alter, and bring down the Price of those Metals, that it might be a Question, whether they would get so much *Over-plus* by it, as would pay for the Metal they change into Gold and Silver. It is only the Scarcity that keeps up the Value [Price], and not any Intrinsick Vertue or Quality in the Metals; For if the Vertue were to be considered, the *Affrican* that gives Gold for Knives, and Things made of Iron, would have the Odds in the Exchange; Iron being a much more Useful Metal, than either Gold or Silver."

One may perhaps recall here the fear entertained in certain quarters, shortly after the Great War, lest Germany should pay off all her reparations by means of artificial gold. But the crucible of German alchemy has yielded neither reparations nor gold, only Frankenstein monstrosities.

THE VALUE OF LAND

In the foregoing section we have already incidentally quoted Petty's way of assessing the rental value of pasture land by the amount of food gained through allowing cattle to graze on it. The problem is discussed more fully in his *Treatise of Taxes* (Chap. IV), from which we quote: "Suppose," he writes, "a man could with his own hands plant a certain scope of Land with Corn, that is, could Digg, or Plough, Harrow, Weed, Reap, Carry home, Thresh, and Winnow so much as the Husbandry of this Land requires, and had withal Seed wherewith to sowe the same. I say, that when this man hath subducted his seed out of the proceed of his Harvest, and also, what himself hath both eaten and given to others in exchange for Clothes, and other Natural necessities; that the remainder of Corn is the natural and true Rent of the Land for that Year; and the medium of seven Years, or rather of so many years as makes up the Cycle, within which Dearths and Plenties make their revolution, doth give the ordinary Rent of the Land in Corn."

To the question, how much money this rent is worth, "I answer, so much as the money, which another single man can save, within the same time, over and above his expence, if he imployed himself wholly to produce and make it; viz; Let another man go travel into a Countrey where is Silver, there Dig it, Refine it, bring it to the same place where the other man planted his Corn; Coyne it, etc., the same person, all the while of his working for Silver, gathering also food for his necessary livelihood, and procuring himself covering, etc.

I say, the Silver of the one, must be esteemed of equal value with the Corn of the other," when the comparison is based on the results of the labour of a number of men working over a number of years.

Petty, however, realized that there are also other factors involved in determining the rental value of land, especially its nearness to densely populated areas, partly because of the saving on the cost of food transport. He explains this in his *Political Arithmetic* (Chap. IV), as follows: "If there were but one Man living in England, then the benefit of the whole Territory could be but the livelihood of that one Man: but if another Man were added, the rent or benefit of the same would be double, if two, triple; and so forward until so many Men were Planted in it as the whole Territory could afford Food unto. For if a Man would know what any Land is worth, the true and natural Question must be, How many Men will it feed? How many Men are there to be fed? But to speak more practically, Land of the same quantity and quality in England is generally worth four or five times as much as in Ireland; and but one-quarter or third of what it is worth in Holland; because England is four or five times better Peopled than Ireland, and but a quarter so well as Holland."

Petty next proceeds to determine the capital value of land in terms of the number of yearly rents, or the "number of years' purchase." He assesses it at "the number of years, which I conceive one man of fifty years old, another of twenty-eight, and another of seven years old" [grandfather, father, and son] "all being alive together may be thought to live . . . few men having reason to take care of more remote Posterity. . . . Now in England we esteem three lives equal to one and twenty years, and consequently the value of Land, to be about the same number of years' purchase," more or less, according to circumstance. The increase in the capital value of land due to the vicinity of markets, or dense populations, is, of course, already allowed for in the increased rental value, of which the capital value is a multiple.

WAGES

The account already given above (see p. 622) of Petty's attempt to establish "a natural Par between Land and Labour" contains incidentally his view of the value of agricultural labour. He measured it in terms of the "overplus of days' Food" produced by the wage-earner's labour, as compared with the number of days' food which the same land would yield if used for grazing cattle. This view, which measured wages by the productivity of labour was an advance on the view generally held by his contemporaries, namely that wages were determined by what was required for the bare subsistence of the labourer and his dependents. It was this subsistence theory of wages that was at the basis of Mun's, Davenant's, and Locke's contention that taxes imposed on the working classes really fell on their employers. This could only be maintained on the assumption that the normal wages of the workers were only just enough for their subsistence, and that if they were taxed, the employers would have to increase their wages by the amount of the tax. Petty observed, however, that "when Corn is extremely plentiful, the Labour of the Poor is proportionately dear, and scarce to be had at all" (*Political Arithmetick*, Chap. II); and Sir Josiah Child (in his *Discourse of Trade*, Preface) pointed out that the Dutch "give generally more Wages to all their Manufacturers by at least two Pence in the Shilling than the English," although there was no such difference in the cost of bare subsistence in the two countries.

INTEREST

During the Middle Ages the attitude of Christendom towards "usury" or "use-money" (that is, payment for the temporary use of other people's money or credit) was sometimes marked by a mixture of economic stupidity and sordid hypocrisy. Christians were not allowed to lend money on interest; only Jews were commonly permitted to do so; but Christian princes usually saw to it that they received a large share of the profits thus made by the Jews who lived under their "protection." In course of time, however, economic necessity over-rode pseudo-religious scruples, and under one guise or another "usury" was extensively practised among Christians, though the term still reeks of the evil odour into which it came during the "Ages of Faith," and has been steadily displaced by the term "interest." It is to the credit of the economic writers of the seventeenth century that they made it clear that to charge interest on money is essentially the same as to charge rent for land or houses. Both may be abused; but it is the abuse that is wrong, not the rent or the interest as such. The main point was stated with brevity and clearness by Barbon (*op. cit.*, p. 20): "Interest," he writes, "is the Rent of Stock, and is the same as the Rent of Land: The First is the Rent of the Wrought or Artificial Stock; the Latter, of the Unwrought, or Natural Stock. Interest is commonly reckoned for Mony; because the Mony Borrowed at Interest is to be repayed in Mony; but this is a mistake; For the Interest is paid for Stock: for the Mony borrowed is laid out to buy Goods, or pay for them before bought: No Man takes up Mony at Interest to lay it by him, and lose the Interest of it."

Petty was equally explicit, or even more so, as may be seen from the following quotation from his *Treatise of Taxes and Contributions*, 1662, (Chap. V): "When a man giveth out his money upon condition that he may not demand it back until a certain time to come, whatsoever his own necessities shall be in the mean time, he certainly may take a compensation for this inconvenience which he admits against himself: And this allowance is that we commonly call Usury."

When, moreover, money has to be paid at a certain place the question of "Exchange or local Usury" arises. Usury for money cannot naturally be less than "the Rent of so much Land as the money lent will buy, where the security is undoubted; but where the security is casual, then a kinde of ensurance must be enterwoven with the simple natural Interest, which may advance the Usury very conscionably unto any height below the Principal it self."

The question most discussed in the seventeenth century in relation to interest was whether it should be limited by law. Some urged that a maximum rate of interest should be fixed by law, and this view was sometimes put into force. Thus in England the rate of interest was limited to 8 per cent in 1623, and to 6 per cent in 1651; and some writers (Sir Josiah Child, for instance, in his *Brief Observations concerning Trade*, etc., 1668) urged its further reduction to 3 per cent, which was the rate ruling at that time in Holland, and was believed to give Dutch merchants an advantage over their English competitors. Most of the economic writers were, however, opposed to the legal restriction of interest. Petty (*loc. cit.*) opposed it. So did North, who urged that the rate of interest should be left to adjust itself in accordance with the proportion of borrowers and lenders. To those who advocated the legal enforcement of a low rate of interest in the interests of trade, he retorted, "it is not low Interest makes Trade, but Trade increasing, the Stock of this Nation makes Interest low"; and he concluded that "when all things are considered, it will be found best for the Nation to leave the Borrowers and the Lenders to make their own Bargains, according to the Circumstances" (*op. cit.*, pp. 18, 20).

V. Regularity in Social Phenomena

One of the most interesting features in the economic literature of the seventeenth century is the growing awareness of the prevalence of a measure of inherent regularity or orderliness, in the world of economic activities. The perception of law and order in the purely physical realm was, of course, one of the characteristic features of the physical sciences of that century. The great discoveries of the astronomers and physicists of that age of genius impressed all thinking men, and inspired philosophers like Descartes, Hobbes, and especially Spinoza with the conviction of the universal prevalence of cosmic law and order. Such flights of the imagination were, however, only possible to the few. Man with his free-will and his caprice seemed to be an obvious disproof of the idea of the universal reign of law. Even Descartes found it necessary to concede special privileges to the human soul, if not to the human body. Nevertheless, the spirit of the triumphant physical sciences was sufficiently infectious to prompt Bodin to seek regular correlations between the character and abilities of men, on the one hand, and geographical and climatic influences, on the other. And the workers in the field of "political arithmetic" searched for regularities in such human events as births and deaths, the incidence of disease, etc. The writers on economics were in a somewhat peculiar position, inasmuch as, during the prevalence of mercantilism, economic activities were wont to be regarded as an obvious field for arbitrary intravention and control by princes and governments. Nevertheless, as one follows the economic literature of the period one observes a steadily growing conviction that economic transactions naturally follow certain laws or tendencies of their own, and that there are limits to the extent to which they can be effectively manipulated even by governments. This appears from the increasing antagonism to government interference in matters of trade, and the emphasis laid on the way in which such interference often leads to all sorts of subterfuges which are the outlets of economic tendencies when interfered with. Some of the quotations contained in the foregoing pages may have made this clear already. We shall only add here the picturesque sentence with which North concludes his *Discourse*: "we may labour to hedge in the Cuckow, but in vain."

See *The Economic Writings of Sir William Petty—Together with the Observations upon the Bills of Mortality more probably by Captain John Graunt*, ed. by C. H. Hull, Cambridge, 1899; *The Petty Papers*, ed. by the Marquis of Lansdowne, 1927; J. Bonar, *Theories of Population*, 1931; W. G. Bell, *The Great Plague in London in 1665*, 1925; H. L. Westergaard, *Contributions to the History of Statistics*, 1932; E. Cannan, *A Review of Economic Theory*, 1930.)

CHAPTER XXVI

PHILOSOPHY

As has already been pointed out, philosophy and science were not distinguished from each other at the beginning of the modern period. The term philosophy was used in a wide sense so as to cover all secular knowledge, including all that is now called science. For a long time the pioneers of modern thought had enough to do in order to free philosophy from its subordination to Christian theology, which was the most characteristic feature of Scholasticism. The ground for this separation had been prepared to some extent by Duns Scotus (?1270–1310) towards the end of the mediaeval period. He had drawn a sharp line between revealed knowledge and natural knowledge, between theology and philosophy. Revelation was conceived as a matter of God's grace; rational knowledge, on the other hand, was conceived as a natural process of the human mind directed to perceived objects. This conception of a "twofold truth," natural and revealed, certainly helped the cause of secular study. But the progress towards the emancipation of natural knowledge was retarded by the fact that the Church had set up the philosophy of Aristotle as authoritative in all matters of philosophical and scientific theory which did not conflict with Church Dogma. Hence the frequent and violent attacks on Aristotle, and especially on his formal logic, at that time. He was severely criticized for the barrenness of his merely syllogistic methods of reasoning, and for his blindness to the proper methods of experience and induction by which alone real knowledge could advance. The criticism was quite undeserved. Aristotle knew much more about scientific method, and had done much more for the advancement of science, than most of his critics. Nor was the criticism always sincere. It was probably intended rather as a sly hit at the Church and at the Scholastic abuse of Aristotelian logic. The criticism of Aristotelian logic and the advocacy of new empirical methods in philosophy were certainly directed mainly towards securing the emancipation of natural knowledge from theology, so that philosophy and science might become purely secular. For a long time, however, science and philosophy were not divorced from each other. Works on science contained much that we should now call philosophy, and scientific workers often made all sorts of purely philosophical assumptions. Gradually, however, the two domains of natural knowledge, science and philosophy, came to be separated, though not always under these designations. Partly under the influence of

Francis Bacon, more so through the efforts of Robert Boyle, and especially through the example set by Newton, and of course entirely in consequence of the empirical methods of research which they advocated and embraced, a distinction was drawn between such theories as followed directly from the facts observed or experimented with, and such further theories as were more remote from the data in question. The former belonged properly to the domain of science (or natural philosophy, as it was often called), the latter belonged rather to the domain of speculative philosophy (or theology, or metaphysics, or first philosophy, as it was variously designated). Newton, curiously enough, restricted the term "hypothesis" to such more speculative theories, perhaps because etymologically the term suggested to him the idea of a metaphysical "substrate" or "substance." In this way an empirically verifiable body of natural knowledge came to be distinguished from a more dubious, because unverified, or insufficiently verified, body of speculations—in other words, science from philosophy, though these were not always the terms employed for the purpose. In the present chapter the term philosophy is used in the sense just indicated. This will prevent confusion, though it anticipates a somewhat later differentiation.

The persistent endeavour to free both science and philosophy from theology, and the subsequent divorce of science from philosophy must not be treated as evidence of a common hostility either to theology or to philosophy on the part of the pioneers of modern science. Most of them were sincere Christians, even if they were not particularly enthusiastic Churchmen, and all of them were addicted to various philosophical assumptions, even if they were not always explicitly aware of the fact. Instinctively, however, they tried more or less successfully to keep their theology and their philosophy out of their scientific work.

The main purpose of this chapter is to describe the leading ideas of the chief modern philosophers up to the end of the seventeenth century, with some digressions on the philosophical views or presuppositions of those pioneers of modern science who were not primarily philosophers.

BRUNO

Giordano Bruno (1548–1600) was born at Nola, in Italy. He studied in Naples, and joined the Dominican Order. Suspected of heresy, he fled, and lived a wandering life in France, England, Germany, and Switzerland. He lectured at various times in Oxford, Paris, and elsewhere. Returning to Italy he was betrayed to the

Inquisition while in Venice, was imprisoned by them for several years, and finally burned at the stake in Rome.

Bruno's world view reflects at once the enthusiasm for the living beauty of Nature so characteristic of the Renaissance under the influence of the revived Neo-platonism, the broadness of outlook encouraged by the voyages of discovery which shook his age out of its naïve provincialism and, above all, the far-reaching effects on human orientation brought about by the heliocentric astronomy of Copernicus.

Nature had been conceived by the Churches rather narrowly and treated contemptuously in contrast with the realm of the supernatural. For Bruno Nature is an infinite world full of life and beauty. It is suffused with Divinity; in fact, it is God, and has all the attributes usually assigned to God. God, according to Bruno, does not exist beyond and apart from the things of the world, but is present in them all (*De la Causa, Principio et Uno*, Dial. II and V; *Opera Latina*, 1879, I, i, 68). A finite world would be unworthy of God who pervades it all. Nature, indeed, is not only infinite, but contains an infinity of worlds, all of them full of life and activity and pulsating with Divinity. Each of these worlds has its own Sun around which it moves. Each of them has been formed out of a cruder state, into which it will return again after completing its cycle of life. The Universe, moreover, is endlessly beautiful in consequence of the law and order which are immanent in it. This orderliness results from the necessity of its own nature, which is also its freedom. For in God, or the Universe, freedom and necessity coincide. It is just in the inviolable laws of Nature, in the splendour of the Sun, in the things produced by mother Earth, that God is revealed; and everything in the Universe contributes its share to the perfection of the Highest. Finite beings are really an infinite variety of eternal "monads," each of which is a unique unit of the Universe, and contributes to its completeness. The "death" of a monad is only a phase in its incessant transformation, the phase of its involution. The birth of a monad is simply its evolution from the cosmic centre, its life is the period of its fullness, and its death is its return to, or involution into, the cosmic centre. But there is no real spatial centre in an infinite Universe. And there can be no fundamental difference between inner and outer, between a supra-lunar and a sub-lunar region, between Heaven and Earth, or between matter and spirit in Nature. For the divine spirit is everywhere, and there is no body without a soul, just as there is no soul without a body. Nor can the One be divorced from the Many, or the Many from the One. And the highest life and activity of man consists in his striving to love the Universe, with an "heroic" love, and so purge himself of all pettiness.

Bruno's poetic exuberances about the life and beauty of Nature may seem strange, but it was essentially a similar kind of aesthetic attitude towards Nature and its geometric harmony that inspired the pioneer astronomers, especially Kepler, and thereby secured for mathematics its place of supreme importance in modern science.

BACON

Francis Bacon (1561–1626) was born in London. His father was Sir Nicholas Bacon, Lord Keeper of the Great Seal under Queen Elizabeth. Francis studied at Trinity College, Cambridge, where he appears to have acquired two things—a passion for personal glory and a contempt for Scholasticism. Thanks to his unusual gifts and opportunities, the former led to his ruin, the latter secured him immortality as a leading combatant against mediaevalism. In 1576 he went to France, but returned on his father's death in 1579, and spent the next four or five years studying law. In 1584 he entered Parliament. In 1593 he incurred the Queen's displeasure by opposing a financial measure in the Commons, and so spoiled his chances of advancement in spite of the intercession of the Earl of Essex. This may have taught him to discount his conscience. He regained the Queen's favour by helping to secure the condemnation of Essex on a charge of treason in 1601. But still no important post came his way, only a knighthood in 1603. He was seriously thinking of leaving politics for scholarship when he was at last appointed Solicitor-General in 1607, under King James. In 1613 he was made Attorney-General; in 1617 Lord Keeper of the Great Seal; in 1618 Lord Chancellor and Baron Verulam; in 1621 Viscount of St. Albans. But his extravagance had involved him in certain lapses, and he was accused of bribery, condemned, and disgraced in that very year. The last five years of his life were spent in retirement, and devoted to literary work.

The voyages of discovery and the practical inventions made just before his time greatly impressed Bacon. The invention of printing, gunpowder, and the magnetic compass had, in his view, "changed the whole face and state of things throughout the world." And he was particularly impressed by Columbus' discovery of the New World, and by the disclosure of new visions through the telescope in the hands of his contemporary Galilei. Bacon, too, wished to take a hand in the making of practical inventions and in the discovery of a new world, at least of a "New Intellectual World." To this end he proposed to diagnose the defects of contemporary learning, and to elaborate the plan of such new methods of co-operative investigation as might lead to real knowledge and to practical results. His main contributions to the fulfilment of this plan are contained in his *Advancement of Learning*, 1605 (much enlarged Latin edition, *De Augmentis Scientiarum*, 1623), *Novum Organum* (New Methodology), 1620, and *New Atlantis*, 1625. It is noteworthy that the most important of these works, namely, the *Novum Organum*, had on its title-page a picture of a ship in full sail passing through the Pillars of Hercules, the limits of the Old World, into the Atlantic Ocean in search of new worlds. It was clearly Bacon's ambition to be the Columbus of the "New Intellectual World." He said so explicitly. "I publish and set forth these conjectures of mine just as Columbus acted, before that wonderful voyage of his across the Atlantic, when he gave the reasons for his conviction that new lands and continents might be discovered" (*Nov. Org.*).

The defect of the traditional learning, such as he found in the old universities, was in Bacon's eyes the characteristic defect of Scholasticism—its reliance on a few old books, and incessant logic-chopping of their contents, instead of directing attention to things themselves. "This kind of degenerate learning," he says continually, "did chiefly reign amongst the Schoolmen: who, having sharp and strong wits and abundance of leisure, and small variety of reading, but their wits being shut up in the cells of a few authors (chiefly Aristotle, their dictator), as their persons were shut up in the cells of monasteries and colleges, and knowing little history, either of nature or time, did out of no great quantity of matter and infinite agitation of wit, spin out unto us those laborious webs of learning which are extant in their books. For the wit and mind of man, if it work upon matter, which is the contemplation of the creatures of God, worketh according to the stuff, and is limited thereby; but if it work upon itself, as the spider worketh his web, then it is endless, and brings forth, indeed, cobwebs of learning admirable for the fineness of thread and work, but of no substance or profit" (*Advancement of Learning*, Book I). With one eye on the credulous Scholastics, and the other on the Sceptics of his time, Bacon described the right attitude to books as follows: "Read not to contradict and confute; nor to believe and take for granted; nor to find talk and discourse; but to weigh and consider "(*Essays*, On Studies).

Bacon not only knew what qualities of mind were a hindrance to science, he also had an excellent insight into the kind of mentality that was best fitted for it. This is how he described it: "A mind nimble and versatile enough to catch the resemblances of things (which is the chief point), and at the same time steady enough to fix and distinguish their subtler differences; . . . gifted by nature with the desire to seek, patience to doubt, fondness to meditate, slowness to assert, readiness to reconsider, carefulness to dispose and set in order; and . . . neither affecting what is new

nor admiring what is old, and hating every kind of imposture"
(*De Interpretatione Naturae Proemium*, Vol. III, p. 518 ff. in Ellis and
Spedding's edition of Bacon's Works). Bacon gave this description
of himself, when he considered his qualifications for the great
enterprise of planning the "New Intellectual World." In view of
his actual achievements it cannot be contended seriously that he
exaggerated his own qualities. One is rather inclined to think
regretfully of what great things Bacon might have achieved in the
realm of science and invention if he had devoted all his energies
to it instead of to politics.

Scientific Knowledge was not valued by Bacon for its own sake,
but as a potent instrument for improving the lot of mankind by
means of inventions which might result from it. The masses of the
people were still living under brutish, wretched conditions, and the
need of remedial measures was pressing. In their distress men
turned to magic and astrology. The traditional belief in miracles
and the current mystic and animistic views of Nature encouraged
beliefs in astrology, magic, and witchcraft. Even Kepler, it must
be pointed out again, was a mystic and an astrologer, as well as a
great astronomer; and Harvey still took part in the examination of
alleged witches. It is to the credit of Bacon that he insisted that the
only way to secure mastery over natural phenomena was by means
of scientific knowledge, not by means of magic rites or astrological
ritual. Natural phenomena cannot be coerced by mysterious mani-
pulations; they must be studied, respected, and obeyed. It is only
by understanding and respecting their character and laws that they
may be made use of for the benefit of mankind.

"Human knowledge," says Bacon, "and human power meet in
one; for where the cause is not known the effect cannot be produced. Nature to be commanded must be obeyed" (*Nov. Org.*,
Aphorism iii).

Moreover, Bacon's utilitarian view of science was far-sighted.
He took long views. He meant that in the long run science as a
whole would and should be of great service to mankind. He did
not advocate any such short-sighted view as that each scientific
investigation should be judged, either at the beginning or at the
end, by its practical fruits. On the contrary, he warned his age
that such short-sighted utilitarianism could only defeat itself, just
as Atalanta lost the race by stopping to pick up the golden apples.
"Though it is true," he writes, "that I am principally in pursuit
of works and the active department of the sciences, yet I wish for
harvest time, and do not attempt to mow the moss or to reap the
green corn. . . . And that unseasonable and puerile hurry to
snatch by way of earnest at the first works which come within

reach, I utterly condemn and reject, as an Atalanta's apple that hinders the race" (*The Great Instauration*, Plan of the Work).

In order to obtain real and fruitful knowledge two things are required, namely, the riddance of prejudices and the adoption of sound methods of inquiry. With regard to the first of these requirements, Bacon insists that all scientific knowledge must begin with unbiased observation. But this is no simple matter. For the mind of man is "like an enchanted glass," a distorting mirror, which gives false reflections instead of correct images. The distortion is due to certain prejudices or "idols" (that is, phantoms or fantasies) which haunt the human mind. Bacon enumerates four types of prejudice or bias which he calls respectively "idols of the tribe," "idols of the cave," "idols of the market-place," and "idols of the theatre." "Idols of the tribe" are prejudices which are common to the whole human race, such as the tendency to see and believe only what is agreeable, to see a purpose in all things, to interpret everything anthropomorphically, to suffer from illusions, and so on. "Idols of the cave" are prejudices peculiar to the individual, and vary from person to person. These, he says, "mostly owe their birth to the predominance of a favourite subject"; and he instances the case of his contemporary, Dr. Gilbert, who "after he had employed himself most laboriously in the study and observation of the load-stone, proceeded at once to construct an entire system of philosophy in accordance with his favourite subject." By "idols of the market-place" Bacon meant those prejudices which arise chiefly from the use of language, which is the main instrument of social intercourse. Such is the tendency to assume that there exist things corresponding to all names in use, e.g. chance, fortune, witch, etc.; also the tendency to overlook the differences between literal and metaphorical meanings of a term, e.g. finite and infinite when applied to physical and to non-physical objects. Bacon blames these "idols" for the fact that "the great and solemn disputes of learned men often terminate in controversies about words and names." Lastly, "idols of the theatre" are the prejudices due to the adoption of special systems of thought. They arise from the special loyalties to specific systems of philosophy, theology, etc. "In my judgment," Bacon asserts, "all the received systems [of philosophy] are but so many stage-plays, representing worlds of their own creation after an unreal and scenic fashion." He instances the loyal Aristotelians and Pythagoreans, and those moderns who "attempt to found a system of natural philosophy on the first chapters of Genesis, or the book of Job, and other parts of the sacred writings." The man of science must purge his mind of all the four types of "idols" if he is to obtain the kind of knowledge that will give mankind the mastery over the material world—"the entrance into the kingdom of man, founded on the sciences, being not much other than the entrance into the kingdom of heaven, whereinto none may enter except as a little child" (*Nov. Org.*, Aphorisms xxxix–lxviii).

With regard to the second requisite of scientific knowledge, namely a sound methodology, Bacon insists on the importance of combining empiricism with rationalism, careful observation with valid reasoning. In his usual picturesque way Bacon compared the mere empiricist with an ant, the *a priori* rationalist with a spider, the sound scientist with a bee. "The men of experiment are like the ant: they only collect and use; the reasoners resemble spiders who make cobwebs out of their own substance. But the bee takes a middle course; it gathers its material from the flowers of the garden and of the field, but transforms and digests it by a power of its own" (*Nov. Org.*, Book I, Aphorism xcv).

Bacon took great pains to elaborate the details of the correct method for the discovery of scientific truths. His ideas about the nature and aims of the methods which he formulated were based upon certain conceptions which he embraced concerning the constitution of the physical world. These conceptions must be described briefly before attempting an account of the scientific methods which he formulated.

While Galilei and others were already constructing a new physical science in terms of material atoms or corpuscles, motion and their mathematical laws, Bacon was still thinking in terms of the Aristotelian concepts of matter, form, qualities, and the correlated notions of material, formal, efficient, and final causes. But he was more restrained than the Scholastic physicists. Just as Copernicus still thought in terms of epicycles, but reduced their number considerably in comparison with Ptolemy, so Bacon reduced the number of qualities and forms of mediaeval physics. He proceeded on the assumption that in order to understand physical phenomena three aspects had to be taken into account, namely their sensible qualities, their intrinsic or physical qualities, and the forms which constituted their basis. Heat, for instance, is a sensitive quality, that is to say, it is a kind of sensation which certain material phenomena produce in living things under certain conditions. Such heat is not in the so-called hot substance which is alleged to be the cause, the source or the stimulus of the sensation. Rather one should say that the hot substance in question has the *power* of producing sensations of heat in living bodies (or, it may be, of increasing the volume of a gas, etc.). Now it is this power that constitutes the intrinsic or physical quality of the hot object. This and any similar physical quality or power in material objects (colour, for instance, or weight) Bacon called a "nature." Again each "nature" according to Bacon depends upon some invisible or latent process, which he called "form"; and, since such processes conform to laws, Bacon also uses the term "law" instead of "form." "When I speak of Forms," he writes, "I mean nothing more than those laws and determinations of absolute actuality, which govern and constitute any simple nature, as heat, light, weight, in every kind of matter and subject that is susceptible of them. Thus the Form of Heat or the Form of Light is the same thing as the Law of Heat or the Law of Light" (*Nov. Org.*, Book II, Aphorism xvii). Thus according to Bacon "sensible heat is a relative notion and has relation to man"; the "nature" of heat is some power of producing the feeling of heat in living bodies, and the power remains even when there are no living bodies at hand to be affected by it; the "form" of heat, or what he also describes as "heat itself, its essence, and its quiddity" is just "motion and nothing else." Now the whole material world was conceived by Bacon as consisting of a comparatively small number of such simple "natures" as heat, light, and weight (regarded as physical powers or properties). And all the simple "natures," he thought, might be explained by reference to even a smaller number of "forms," perhaps even to a single ultimate "form." The whole of human experience of material objects, the whole choir of heaven and furniture of earth is the result of the varying combinations and permutations of a limited number of "simple natures," or of an even smaller number of ultimate "forms," for such simple generic "natures" as heat, light, and sound, for instance, could be regarded as resulting from specific varieties of the same ultimate "form," namely motion. "The forms of simple natures, though few in number, yet in their communications and co-ordinations make all this variety" (*Adv. of Learning*, Book II). It should be apparent that, in spite of his more or less scholastic terminology, Bacon was really thinking of the physical world on the lines of atoms and motions and their laws, even if he did not appreciate the significance of quantitatively exact laws.

In the light of the foregoing explanations it may be intelligible that Bacon should have identified the work of real and fruitful science with the discovery of "forms" or rather of simple forms. "To enquire into the form of density, rarity, heat, cold, gravity, levity, tangibility, fluidity, volatility, fixity, and the like . . . which, like the letters of the alphabet, are not many and yet make up and sustain the essences and forms of all substances, this, I say, is what I am attempting" (*De Augmentis Scientiarum*, Book III, Chap. IV). Bacon accordingly proceeded to explain the method of discovering such simple forms. The main features of his methodology may now be described.

Scientific method must begin with systematic observation and experiment, pass on to truths of limited generality, and from these to more comprehensive generalizations by gradual successive inductions. Rash generalizations from a few observations must be avoided. "There are," he says, "and can be only two ways of searching into and discovering truth. The one flies from the senses and particulars to the most general axioms, and from these principles, the truth of which it takes for settled and immovable, proceeds to judgment and to the discovery of middle axioms. And this way is now in fashion. The other derives axioms from the senses and particulars, rising by a gradual and unbroken ascent, so that it arrives at the most general axioms last of all. This is the true way" (*Nov. Org.*, Book I, Aphorism xix). [Bacon calls any generalization an "axiom."]

Observations must be made and recorded systematically. Whatever the quality or physical property under investigation, the attempt must be made to draw up three tables of relevant data based on observation. (i) First we require a *Table of Positive Instances*, that is an enumeration of all the kinds of phenomena in which the property in question is present. The instances should be as varied as possible. "A nature being given, we must first of all have a muster or presentation before the understanding of all known instances which agree in the same nature, though in substances the most unlike. And such collection must be made . . . without premature speculation" (*Ibid.*, Book II, Aphorism xi). If, for example, the investigation is into the Form of Heat, the Table would enumerate such instances as the rays of the Sun, meteors, thunderbolts, flame, natural warm springs, sparks, rubbed minerals, moistened quicklime, acids, etc. (ii) In the next place, a *Table of Negative Instances* should be drawn up, that is, "instances in which the given nature is wanting" although they are otherwise "most akin to the others in which it is present." Negative instances in relation to heat, for example, would consist of the rays of the Moon, stars, meteors; air, water, and other fluids in a natural state; dry quicklime, etc. (iii) Thirdly, we require a *Table of Degrees or of Comparison*, consisting of "instances in which the nature under inquiry is found in different degrees, more or less." In the case of heat, the required instances would include the increase in animal heat by exercise, wine, fever, etc., the different degrees of heat in the various parts of a living body, variations in the intensity of solar heat with the different positions of the Sun, differences in heat with the amount of motion or of blowing, with the distance of a burning glass from a burning body, with the duration of a fire, etc.

With the aid of such three tables of suitable instances the form of the property or nature under investigation might be readily determined. The principle assumed is that the form of the given nature must be present when the given nature is present, absent when it is absent, and vary quantitatively when it varies. By comparing the various instances in each table, and the tables with each other, it should be possible to dismiss the claims of all but one form. Reliance on such a method of exclusions implies the existence of comparatively few forms, and a knowledge of them all. Bacon certainly believed in their small number, as has already been explained, and he hoped that by diligent co-operation among men of science the forms would all be known before very long. By applying the method of exclusions to the three tables of instances relating to heat, Bacon concluded that "the nature of which Heat is a particular case appears to be Motion. This is displayed most conspicuously in flame, which is always in motion, and in boiling or simmering liquids, which also are in perpetual motion. It is also shown in the excitement or increase of heat caused by motion, as in bellows and blasts. . . . Again it is shown in the extinction of fire and heat by any strong compression, which checks and stops the motion." To guard against misinterpretation, Bacon adds: "Heat itself, its essence and quiddity, is Motion and nothing else"; but it is a specific kind of motion, namely, "a motion expansive, restrained, and acting in its strife upon the smaller particles of bodies" (*Nov. Org.*, Book II, Aphorisms x–xx).

It was Bacon's ambition to formulate a code of scientific procedure that would enable almost any industrious person of ordinary common sense to make scientific discoveries. His *Novum Organum* (or New Logic) was intended as such an instrument, which he compared with a pair of compasses. Just as a pair of compasses enable even an unskilled person to draw a good circle, so the new method should enable ordinary people to become scientific discoverers. In this, Bacon grossly underrated the place of originality and sagacity in the work of science, and the difficulties of reducing it to rules of thumb. As a matter of fact, Bacon himself found it impossible to apply satisfactorily his own elaborate rules. The mere preparation of anything like complete tables of the three types which he required would be a very slow and laborious business. And Bacon himself had to sanction and practice certain shortcuts ("anticipations"). Nevertheless, a considerable amount of credit is due to him for his accounts of scientific methods. His three tables, even if incomplete, would supply the data necessary for the application of the most important of the simpler methods of induction. The Table of Positive Instances would supply the data for the application of the Method of Agreement; the Table of Comparison would furnish the necessary data for the Method of Concomitant Variations; while the combined use of the Tables of Positive and of Negative Instances would supply the data for applying the Method of Difference and the Joint Method of Agreement and Difference. This was no small achievement in the exposition of scientific methodology. He also deserves credit for his emphasis on the necessity of experience, and the great importance of controlled experimentation; his exclusion of teleological considerations from physical science (though not from philosophy); and his appreciation of the significance of negative, crucial, and prerogative (or abnormal) instances. These were all important contributions to the study of the methods of science.

Lastly, though Bacon himself made no direct contributions of value to scientific discovery, yet he rendered valuable help towards the secularization of natural knowledge, and his Utopian *New Atlantis*, with its picture of an institution of organized scientific research (House of Solomon), helped forward the subsequent establishment of the Royal Society of London, which may well be regarded as the deliberate realization of Bacon's dream on the part of men like Boyle and others who had been impressed by the writings and the fame of that unusually versatile and brilliant Lord Chancellor.

HOBBES

Thomas Hobbes (1588–1679) was born at Westport, near Malmesbury. He studied in Oxford, and then became companion to the heir of Lord Cavendish, whom he accompanied on his travels abroad, in the course of which he met many foreign scholars and statesmen, including Galilei, Gassendi, Mersenne, and Descartes. His chief philosophical works are *De Cive* (1642), *Leviathan* (1645), *De Corpore* (1655), *De Homine* (1658). The first of these books dealt with the political troubles of his time; the second, and best known of his works, attempted a vindication of the royal prerogative based, not on the divine right of kings, but on the idea that the king is the embodiment of the will of the people. His denial of free-will aroused much opposition; and for many decades Hobbes was the target of the chief British moralists.

In a history of science the main interest in Hobbes lies in his adoption of the mechanistic interpretation of the universe. Galilei and Descartes, and to some extent even Bacon, tried to explain the material world in terms of matter and motion. Hobbes went beyond them and attempted a similar explanation of the whole universe, the world of mind as well as the world of matter. Though

Illustr. 309

Francis Bacon

Thomas Hobbes

René Descartes

Benedictus de Spinoza

an empiricist and anti-Scholastic like Bacon, Hobbes had a deeper insight into the scientific importance of mathematics, and his affiliation is with Galilei rather than with any other predecessor or contemporary. Although Hobbes was the classical materialist of modern times, yet he was no opponent of religion. He believed in God as the first cause of the universe, but he contended that man "cannot have any idea of Him."

According to the materialistic philosophy of Hobbes, matter and motion are the only ultimate realities. They are at the basis of everything, even of feeling and thought, and therefore of all knowledge. For all knowledge is in the last resort derived from sensation or sense-perception. "There is no conception in a man's mind," Hobbes contends, "which hath not at first, totally or by parts, been begotten upon the organs of sense"; and all sense experiences are produced by the motions of matter impinging or pressing upon the organs of sense; and even inside man these pressures cannot be or produce anything else than different kinds of motions, "for motion produceth nothing but motions (*Leviathan*, Part I, Chap. I). Mind is a kind of matter; and mental experiences are all process of change, and therefore motions, for, according to Hobbes, "all mutation consists in motion." Moreover, all things, whether living or lifeless, are subject to the same law of inertia, that is, show the same fundamental tendency to persist in their present condition, whether of rest or of motion.

Hobbes may serve as a striking example of the way in which a methodological principle may be transformed into a cosmic philosophy. Galilei's method of explaining physical phenomena by reference to matter and motion was transformed by Hobbes into a one-sided materialistic philosophy. Soon afterwards one-sided materialism was countered by several systems of equally one-sided idealism. Most philosophers of the seventeenth century, however, relied upon the God of Christian tradition to keep the two worlds of matter and of mind together. The one philosopher who attempted to do justice to all aspects of the universe without resorting to the traditional *deus ex machina* was Spinoza, whose philosophy will be described presently.

DESCARTES

René Descartes (1596–1650) was born at La Haye in Touraine, France. His family belonged to the lesser nobility, and included a number of learned men. The story of his military ancestry is a legend resulting from a confusion of different people having the same name. He studied at the Jesuit school at La Flèche, in Anjou. The first five years were devoted chiefly to the study of the classical languages; the last three years there were given up mainly to the study of mathematics, physics, and philosophy. In 1612 he left school, and soon afterwards entered the University of Poitiers, where he graduated in Law in 1616. In 1618 he left France apparently in search of military experience in Holland, Germany, and Austria. But there is no evidence of any real soldiering there on his part; only of intercourse with mathematicians.

On November 10, 1619, while staying at Ulm, he appears to have realized in a flash that the mathematical method could be extended to other studies. This idea dominated his mind like a divine revelation. Three dreams followed which made such a profound impression on him that he vowed a pilgrimage to Our Lady of Loretto; and the next nine or ten years were almost entirely devoted to the elaboration of his new mathematical ideas, of which an account has already been given. In 1622 he returned to France, but went to Italy in 1623 on family business, returning to Paris about 1625, and became friendly with Mersenne, Picot, and others. In 1628 he went to Holland again and spent there nearly the rest of his life. "What other country," he wrote, "where you can enjoy such perfect liberty, where you can sleep with more security . . . where poisoning, treacheries, calumnies are less known, and where there has survived more of the innocence of our forefathers?" By 1649 Descartes had become very famous, and he was invited to Stockholm as tutor to Queen Christina, who took some interest in philosophy. But life at the Swedish Court did not suit him, and the severity of a northern winter was too much for his constitution, which had never been robust. He died on February 11, 1650, after a stay in Stockholm of barely five months.

The principal works of Descartes are the *Discourse on Method*, with important appendices on Dioptrics, Meteors, and Geometry, 1636; *Meditations of First Philosophy*, 1641; *Principles of Philosophy*, 1644; *Treatise on the Passions of the Soul*, 1649. There is an English translation of the philosophical works of Descartes in two volumes by E. S. Haldane and G. R. T. Ross (Cambridge, 1911, 1912), and an American translation of his *Geometry* by D. E. Smith and M. L. Latham (Chicago, 1924). English translations of Descartes' *Dioptrics* (by A. J. Taylor) and *Le Monde* (by A. Wechsler) exist in typescript in the Library of the University of London.

Like Bacon and others before him and after him, Descartes was thoroughly dissatisfied with Scholasticism, on which he had been nurtured at La Flèche. His genius was essentially mathematical; and in mathematics the Scholastic method of citing authorities did not count even at his Jesuit school, where it counted for much in other studies. Descartes accordingly devoted a great deal of thought to the question of the correct method of obtaining real knowledge by the natural light of reason. The problem is discussed by him in his fragmentary *Rules for the direction of the Mind* (1628), in his *Discourse on the Method of Rightly Conducting the Reason* (1637), in his *Meditations on First Philosophy* (1641), in the unfinished dialogue on *The Search after Truth* (?1641 or possibly 1628), and in *The Principles of Philosophy* (1644). The *Discourse* contains some interesting biographical matter bearing on his attitude to the question of method. The following passage is particularly noteworthy. "I have been nourished on letters since my childhood, and since I was given to believe that by their means a clear and certain knowledge could be obtained of all that is useful in life, I had an extreme desire to acquire instruction. But as soon as I had achieved the entire course of study, at the close of which one is usually received into the ranks of the learned, I entirely changed my opinion. For I found myself embarrassed with so many doubts and errors that it seemed to me that the effort to instruct myself had no effect other than the increasing discovery of my own ignorance. And yet I was studying at one of the most celebrated schools in Europe. . . I learned there all that others learned . . . and I did not feel that I was esteemed inferior to my fellow-students. . . . And this made me take the liberty of judging all others by myself and of coming to the conclusion that there was no learning in the world such as I was formerly led to believe it to be." In his *Rules* he accordingly insists that the solution of a problem must not be determined by what others have thought about it, but by the investigator's own insight. For, as he goes on to explain, "we shall not, for instance, become mathematicians even if we know by heart all the proofs that others have elaborated unless we have an intellectual talent that fits us to solve difficulties of that kind. Neither, though we have mastered all the arguments of Plato and Aristotle, shall we become philosophers if we have not the capacity for forming a solid judgment on these matters."

Mathematics was the only study which really satisfied him, because of the certainty of its demonstrations. It should therefore serve as a model for other studies; and he recalled the significant fact that Plato and other ancient philosophers "refused to admit to the study of philosophy anyone who was not versed in mathematics." Descartes did not share in the Pythagorean mathematical mysticism still in vogue among some of his contemporaries. In fact he had little respect even for pure mathematics as such, remarking that "there is nothing more futile than to busy oneself with bare numbers and imaginary figures in such a way as to appear to rest content with such trifles." It was the method of mathematics, rather than its results, that impressed him; and he was anxious to see the same method extended to other branches of study. But what is the peculiarity of mathematical method? Its peculiar virtue, according to Descartes, consists in beginning with the simplest ideas and then proceeding to draw careful inferences from them. And that is what all scientific investigators should do. Beginning with the simplest and most certain ideas they should advance to more complex ideas by a progressive synthesis of the simpler ones, that is, by deduction. Descartes knew that knowledge is also derived from experience, and by induction from experience. He had read and praised Bacon's *Novum Organum*. Descartes himself, however, put his trust in deduction from a sure starting-point. Experience, he pointed out, begins with highly complex objects, and that is why inferences from them may easily go wrong; but deduction cannot go wrong if applied with moderate intelligence. "This," he maintains, "furnishes an obvious explanation of the greatly superior certainty of arithmetic and geometry over other sciences. The former alone deal with an object so pure and simple that they need make no assumptions at all which experience renders uncertain, but wholly consist in the rational reduction of consequences."

The first problem of all natural knowledge is, therefore, to discover the simplest and surest ideas or principles. These, according to Descartes, "are given by intuition," that is, by "the undoubting conception of an unclouded and attentive mind, which springs from the light of reason." As examples of such intuitions he cites that "each individual can have the intuition of the fact that he exists, and that he thinks; that a triangle is bounded by three lines only; a sphere by a single superficies, and so on." When confronted with a more complex problem, the right course is to analyse it into its simplest elements, make sure of each of them by intuition, and then reason from them deductively. In his *Rules* Descartes made no attempt to get behind intuition, but in his *Discourse on Method* he shows a more sophisticated attitude.

In the *Discourse on Method* Descartes seeks a sure starting-point of knowledge by applying the acid test of methodical doubt. By questioning everything that can possibly be doubted he hopes to find something that is beyond all doubt. For a time everything appears to succumb to it. Not only traditional beliefs, but widely accepted ideas, even the facts of direct observation might all be mere illusions or dreams. Finally, however, he discovers something indubitable, namely doubt itself. He who doubts cannot be dubious about his doubt. Now, to doubt is to think, and thinking implies a thinker. So *cogito ergo sum*, "I think, therefore I am." This indubitable certainty is then used as a fulcrum for his logical lever in order to raise a system of real natural knowledge. What is the secret of this ultimate certainty? It consists in the clearness and distinctness of the conviction. It is an ultimate intuition beyond the possibility of doubt. This, however, implies that whatever is apprehended with similar clearness and distinctness must be accepted as true. All clear and distinct intuitions may therefore be accepted as true; also deductions from them, provided that each step in the deduction is as clear and distinct as the initial intuition, even if the connection between the final deduction and the original intuitions should rest on memory rather than on clear and distinct apprehension. One of the ultimate intuitions which Descartes implicitly accepts as true is the principle of universal causation, namely, that everything must have a cause, and that the cause must be at least as rich as its effects. With the aid of this principle he passes from his own existence as a thinking being, and his possession of the idea of God as a perfect Being infinitely superior to himself, to the existence of God as the adequate cause of the thinker and of the idea. And from the existence of a perfect God, who would not mislead this thinker (Descartes), he infers the reality of all things that are perceived clearly and distinctly. In this kind of way Descartes establishes to his own satisfaction the existence of an external world. Contrary to the usual procedure of inferring the existence of God from the existence of the world, Descartes inferred the existence of the world from the existence of God.

Descartes' argument, however, seems to have carried him too far. If the trustworthiness of human perception follows from God's veracity, how is it that there are, nevertheless, such things as errors and illusions at all? Descartes meets the difficulty by saying that error results from the neglect of the precaution that apprehensions should be clear and distinct before they can be trusted. Error arises when judgment exceeds understanding, as is often the case. For judgment, according to Descartes, is an act of decision, of will. And the will of man is free, unlimited, whereas human understanding is severely limited.

Moreover, clearness and distinctness of apprehension are not only the test of the reality of things; they are also a guide to the determination of their real character or qualities. Now, the only properties of external or material objects which are clear and distinct to thought are their extension in three dimensions and their motions. These so-called primary or mathematical properties of things are therefore objectively real. On the other hand, qualities like colour, smell, taste, etc., the so-called secondary qualities, are not clearly and distinctly thinkable, and are consequently not objective properties of things but merely sense-qualities, that is subjective experiences on the part of living beings endowed with sense-organs on which the physical objects act through their primary qualities. Descartes thus adopted explicitly the distinction between primary and secondary qualities taught in ancient times by the Atomists, and revived in modern times by Galilei, Bacon, Gassendi, and others. Motion was not regarded by Descartes as an intrinsic property of matter, but as a separate creation, constant in quantity, and arbitrarily associated with matter so as to conform to certain laws. For Descartes, accordingly, matter was practically identical with extension, that is three-dimensional space. Thus his mathematical methodology assumed the form of a mathematical physics or mechanics, more or less after the manner of Galilei, but not so extreme as that of Hobbes. One result of the Cartesian identification of matter with extension was his assumption of a plenum, or denial of a vacuum, in the material world, for space is continuous. Another was the rejection of atoms, that is, of ultimately indivisible particles, for even the smallest part of space is theoretically divisible. A third result was his assumption of the unity of the physical world, for all space is one. Some of these points must now be considered somewhat more fully.

If matter is extension and extension is continuous, how do the apparently detached bodies come into being? Descartes holds that it is their motion that leads us to distinguish separate particles of matter. Whatever part of extension moves together, appears as a separate body. As there is no vacuum the motion of one body must be followed immediately by that of other bodies. "To this end," he explains, "it is not at all necessary that all the moving parts should be arranged in a true circle, or be of like size or shape, for inequalities in these respects may be compensated for by other inequalities. We do not commonly observe these circular motions in the air, because we are accustomed to regard the air as an empty place. But if we observe fishes swimming in a basin we see that, if they do not approach too near it, they do not stir the surface, although they pass under it at a great speed. It is clear, therefore, that the water which they push before them does not push indifferently all the water in the basin, but only that which can best serve to complete the circle of their motion and enter the place which they have vacated" (*The World*, Ch. IV). In this way Descartes arrived at his theory of vortices.

Descartes made two attempts to explain the formation of the physical world, "by gradual and natural means," out of extension and motion. The first was in *The World*, in which he boldly declared: "Give me extension and motion, and I will construct the world." The second was in his *Principles of Philosophy*. His account is some-

what as follows. As there is no vacuum in the material world the
only possible motion for material bodies is circular or vortex motion
(Illustr. 313). When God imparted motion to matter, innumerable

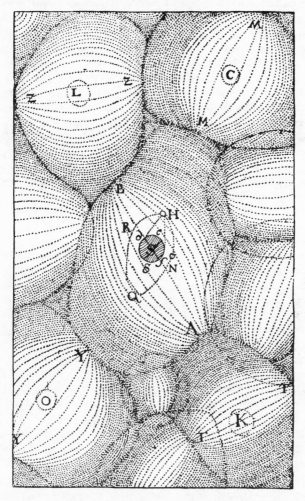

Illustr. 313.—Descartes' Vortices

vortices of all shapes and sizes of matter were set in motion with all
sorts of velocities. The friction set up by the movement of the closely
packed bodies rubbed off fine particles from many of them, and
made these smooth and spherical. The fine particles, or rubbings,
constitute "first matter" or the finest matter, which tends towards

the centre·of each vortex, and there forms self-luminous suns and fixed stars. The smooth globular particles, from which the "first matter" was separated by rubbing, constitute "second matter," which tends to move away from the centres of the vortices in straight lines towards the circumferences where it composes the transparent heavens, and transmits the light of the shining stars. There is yet a grosser "third matter," consisting of the most massive of the original particles which resist all damage from friction; all the opaque bodies are made of it, such as the Earth, and other planets and the comets. By means of the vortex theory Descartes tried to reconcile Copernican astronomy with Biblical teaching. For the Earth, like each of the other planets, is at rest in its vortex, and therefore stationary with reference to it; but the vortex moves around the sun. In his *Principles* Descartes explains the formation of planets and comets as follows. As the fine particles of a vortex pass through the interstices between the revolving globular particles they get caught and become channelled and twisted, and when they reach the stellar matter at the centre of the vortex they form crusts or "sun-spots" upon it. This sometimes causes a diminution in the expansive force of the star, which is consequently overtaken by another vortex. If the crusted star has a velocity equal to that of some part of the encroaching vortex it will stay there and continue to revolve in that vortex. In this case it is a planet. But if the velocity of the crusted star is greater than that of the encroaching vortex, the star will pass out of that vortex into another, and continue to wander from vortex to vortex, and will be known as a comet. The planets of the Solar System are those crusted stars, and their respective vortices, that have been swept up by the vortex of the Sun.

The mechanistic mode of explanation was applied by Descartes to living bodies as well as to lifeless ones. Even the human body was treated by him as mainly an automatic mechanism, or "an earthly machine." Harvey's demonstration of the mechanical processes of the circulation of the blood encouraged this tendency. By way of popular illustration of the mechanism of the body, Descartes uses the following analogy. "You may have seen," he writes, "in the grottoes and fountains which are in our royal gardens that the simple force with which the water moves when issuing from its source is enough to set in motion various machines, and to make instruments play or utter words, according to the different arrangements of the tubes which convey the water. And so one may well compare the nerves of the machine which I am describing with the tubes of the machines of these fountains, the muscles and tendons with the other engines and springs which move the machines, and the animal spirits [that is, the finest and most vivified parts of the blood], the source of which is the heart and of which the cavities of the brain are the reservoirs, with the water which puts them in motion. Moreover, breathing and similar acts, which are natural and usual to the machine, and which depend on the flow of the [animal] spirits, are like the movements of a [water] clock or of a mill which the ordinary flow of water keeps going continually. External objects, which by their presence act on the sense-organs of the machine and so determine it to move in different ways according to the disposition of the parts of the brain, may be compared with strangers who, entering one of the grottoes containing many fountains, themselves cause unwittingly the movements they witness. For on entering they tread on certain tiles or plates which are so arranged that if they approach a bathing Diana they cause her to hide in the rose bushes, and if they try to follow her they cause a Neptune to come towards them threatening them with his trident. Of if they pass in another direction they make a sea-monster spring forward and squirt water in their faces. . . . In order to understand how the brain can be excited by external objects which affect the organs of sense, so that all the members can be moved in a thousand different ways, imagine that the delicate threads, which arise inside the brain and form the marrow of the nerves, are so disposed in all the parts which serve as the organs of any sense that they can easily be set in motion by the objects of the senses, and that whenever they are set in motion, even ever so little, they pull upon the parts of the brain whence they originate, and so open certain pores on the internal surface of the brain. Through these pores the animal spirits in the ventricles pass into the nerves and then into the muscles which carry out movements like those to which we are incited when our senses are affected in that way. If, for instance, fire comes near the foot, the minute particles of the fire . . . set in motion the skin of the foot and by thus pulling the delicate thread attached to the skin there they open the pore against which the thread ends, just as by pulling at one end of a rope one rings a bell at the other end" (*L'Homme*, Part II).

The mechanistic explanation of material bodies, even of living bodies, is, however, not the whole truth. For there are other substances than material or extended bodies, namely, minds or thinking substances, such as inhabit human bodies, for instance. Altogether unlike Hobbes, Descartes draws a sharp line between minds and bodies. Under the influence of his religious upbringing, he conceives them in such contrast that whatever he asserts of the one he denies of the other, except that both have been created by God. One result of this antithesis has already been referred to. Since mind is essentially active, body must be essentially inert, and consequently motion cannot be an intrinsic property of matter, but something added to it by God. Another result of the antithesis is the problem of explaining the apparent interaction between mind and body in the case of human beings, even if the lower animals be treated as mere automata. Descartes tries to get over the difficulty by supposing that the mind comes into contact with the body in the conarion or pineal gland "in the middle of the substance of the brain," and that from there "it radiates through the rest of the body by means of the animal's spirits, nerves, and even the blood." Reverting to the analogy of the mechanical toys in the royal gardens, he compares the function of the mind or soul residing in the conarion of the brain with that of "the fountaineer who has to take his place in the reservoir whence all the different tubes of the machines proceed whenever he wants to start them, to stop them, or to change them in any way." More particularly, Descartes thought that the conarion required but a minimum of influence to incline it one way or another, and that the "animal spirits" were such a fine sort of matter as almost to be non-material. But he could not consistently explain the apparent interaction between the body and soul of man. In the last resort he and his followers, the so-called "Occasionalists," could only appeal to divine intervention—the occurrences in bodies being made the occasion for divine communications to minds, and *vice versa*. Thus Descartes' philosophy finally ended in two distinct worlds, consisting respectively of material substances and of minds, held together somehow by the supernatural intervention of God.

SPINOZA

Benedict de Spinoza (1632–77) was born in Amsterdam, the son of Jewish refugees from Portugal. His father and grandfather were well-to-do merchants who at various times filled posts of honour in the Jewish community. Benedict attended the Jewish school, the curriculum of which included some of the writings of the Jewish philosophers as well as the Bible, and the Hebrew codes. Outside school hours he learned various languages, including Dutch, Latin, and probably some French, German, and Italian. Spanish was the vernacular used in his home and at school. He also studied mathematics and physics. In 1656 he was excommunicated by the Synagogue for his alleged heretical views. His father had died in 1654 and his mother long before that. So Spinoza had no strong attachments to the Jewish community. He earned his living sometimes by teaching at a school, sometimes by giving private lessons, and for the most part as an exceptionally skilful maker of lenses. His friends and acquaintances were mostly Quaker-like Collegiants and

Cartesians. Some of them formed a study-circle under his guidance. One of them left him an annuity of 500 florins, but he would not accept more than 300. In 1660 he moved to Rijnsburg, near Leiden, the headquarters of the Collegiants. Here, in 1661, Oldenburg, the prospective Secretary of the Royal Society, visited him. Here also he became friendly with Steno and others. In 1663 he removed to Voorburg, near the Hague, and there became acquainted with the philologist Vossius, with Christian Huygens and others. In the same year he published a geometric version of Descartes' *Principia*, Parts I and II, together with an appendix called *Metaphysical Thoughts*. Spinoza was not a Cartesian, but had to teach the Cartesian philosophy.

By this time he had already written a good deal of his own philosophy, namely, his *Short Treatise on God, Man and his Well-Being*, his *Treatise on the Improvement of the Understanding*, and Part I of his *Ethics*. In 1665 his greatest work, the *Ethics*, was near completion. But conditions were not favourable for its publication. Under the influence of the Calvinist clergy and the monarchists intolerance was on the increase. Spinoza thereupon conceived the idea of writing a defence of freedom of thought and speech, and a refutation of the alleged Biblical support for clerical interference in civil and political affairs. In 1670 his *Tractatus-Theologico-Politicus* was published anonymously, and it created such a storm that Spinoza abandoned the idea of publishing anything else. But he continued to write. In the same year he moved into the Hague where he stayed till the end. In 1673 the French army was at Utrecht, and Spinoza was invited to visit Prince Condé there. After consulting some influential people Spinoza went in the hope of advancing the cause of peace. But in vain. In the same year he was also offered a Professorship of Philosophy in the University of Heidelberg, which he declined. Among the distinguished people who visited Spinoza in the Hague were Tschirnhaus (1675) and Leibniz (1676). In February 1677 he died at the age of forty-four. His *Posthumous Works* were prepared for the press by his friends in great secrecy, and published in the same year, both in Latin and in Dutch, as the works of B.D.S.

The philosophy of Spinoza may be described as the fullest expression of the tendency of modern thought to rely on itself, unaided and unhampered by "authorities" of any kind. It also shows, in a grand manner, the new and friendly attitude towards Nature, and the growing suspicion of the need of the supernatural. Yet it is not merely enthusiastic, but strictly rational, though suffused with a moral glow. And it achieves its unity, not by ignoring anything that seems to have a *prima facie* claim to reality, but by its all-inclusive comprehensiveness. For Spinoza the world of reality is a real universe, one all-inclusive and intimately interconnected cosmos, in which the material and the mental, the human and the divine have all their proper place, and in which nothing is capricious or contingent, but everything is orderly according to immutable laws.

The way in which this conviction came to Spinoza may be briefly indicated as follows. In order to understand any object or event reference must be made to innumerable others with which it is connected; and each of these is, in its turn, dependent on innumerable others. Every finite object or event sends out countless tendrils, obtains support from many sources, and transmits influences in numerous directions. Can the whole of reality consist solely of such dependent things and events? No, there must be some self-existing, independent, or absolute Being at the basis of all that is dependent. This absolute ground of reality, however, was not conceived by Spinoza in the conventional manner as a Creator who made the world out of nothing at a time and in a manner arbitrarily chosen by Him. Spinoza rejected this conception of God as the alleged last link in a causal chain of similar and yet different links. He preferred to regard the entire system of reality as its own immanent ground, as at once Nature and God. This leaves no room for the supernatural; but it also needs no supernatural intervention to correlate mind with matter, for Nature is both at once. The philosophy of Spinoza is thus pantheistic, naturalistic, and rationalistic. Its Pantheism consists in its contention that God is All (that is the Universe in its entirety), and All is God. Its Naturalism consists in its exclusion of the supernatural by raising Nature to the level of Universe and identifying both with God. Its Rationalism consists in its rejection of whatever is arbitrary or capricious or merely accidental, and its insistence on the prevalence of law and order throughout the universe, even where man has not yet succeeded in discovering them. It is a common mistake to identify naturalism with materialism. Materialism, like that of Hobbes, no doubt is a form of naturalism; but not the only form; and Spinoza's naturalism was certainly not materialistic, for it not only admitted but emphasized the reality of God and of mind as well as matter. Such was the general framework of Spinoza's philosophy. Some of its details must be described next.

Spinoza describes the structure of the universe in terms of *substance*, *attributes*, and *modes*; but he employs these terms in a peculiar way, which must be carefully observed, for nothing but confusion and misunderstanding can result if these terms are taken in their vague popular meaning. Spinoza himself used the term substance in two somewhat different though intimately connected senses. But the explanation of this difference will make his main point clear. By substance he generally meant a self-existent reality, independent of anything else. For example, physical objects and events cannot, according to Spinoza, be understood without assuming some self-existing matter or physical force which expresses itself in all the changes which occur in space. This physical force or ultimate ground of all physical phenomena Spinoza, following Descartes, called *extension*, and at first described it as a substance. Similarly, transient mental experiences cannot be understood without assuming some self-existent eternal consciousness or mind-energy, which he called *Thought*, and also described at first as a substance. Each of these two substances was so called because neither was reducible to the other—each existing in its own right. In the life of man, however, body and mind appear to be so intimately connected that Spinoza felt it necessary to regard extension and thought not as detached substances but as constituting one organic whole or system. To express this view, Spinoza now restricted the term substance to the whole system, and applied the term *attribute* to extension and thought. He still regarded each of them as *infinite of its kind*, extension being the exhaustive ground or matrix of all physical phenomena; and thought, of all mental experiences. But substance was now conceived as *absolutely infinite*, that is to say as the exhaustive ground or matrix of *all* reality, as the system of all the "attributes." The "attributes" are not properties of substance, according to Spinoza; they are, or constitute, between them the whole of substance. Hence his use of the phrase "substance or the attributes." Substance is just the entire system of attributes; and there may be other attributes than extension and Thought, which are the only two known to human beings. Using the term "infinite" in the sense of "complete" Spinoza accordingly described substance as consisting of an infinity of attributes each of which is *infinite of its kind*, while substance is *absolutely infinite* and one. In this way also substance in Spinoza's special sense came to be identified with God (who is also usually described as the infinite ground of reality), and with Nature or the Universe.

God, Nature, or Substance, then, is the ultimate ground or matrix of all cosmic reality. For Spinoza, moreover, reality is essentially activity—to be is to be active. Substance, accordingly, is incessantly active, each attribute exercising its kind of energy in all possible ways. All objects and events of the physical world arise as modes (states or modifications) of Extension; and all minds and mental events are modes of Thought. The modes are not "thrown off" by the Attributes as external products, but are immanent states of them, just as air-waves are states of the air. The Attributes, however, do not manifest themselves as finite modes directly, but indirectly, through intermediate stages. Galilean and Cartesian physics induced Spinoza to regard all physical phenomena as varying manifestations of a constant stock of motion (or motion and rest). With his usual caution, however, Spinoza suspected that motion might be but one of several types of physical energy. He therefore did not identify Extension with motion, but described motion rather as an *infinite* and *immediate mode* of Extension—*infinite* as exhaustive of all finite modes of motion, and *immediate* as a direct manifestation or expression of Extension. Again, "the face of the [physical] world as a whole," preserves a certain sameness in spite of countless changes in detail. This, however, is the result of the conservation of motion. Spinoza consequently describes it as a *mediate* or indirect mode of Extension; but it is *infinite* inasmuch as it includes all things that can be reduced to motion. The physical phenomena of ordinary experience are *finite*, because each is limited or hedged in by other finite modes. This limitation is essentially negative in character—each finite mode is *finite* just because it is *not* also the other finite modes. But each mode is positively real and ultimate as part of the Attribute. Similarly with the modes of the Attribute Thought and the other Attributes. And the whole cosmos is conceived as an all-inclusive dynamic system of which the various Attributes are the several "world-lines" along which it expresses itself in an infinite variety of events.

Spinoza's conception of extension and thought as concurrent Attributes of Substance put a new complexion on the relation between the body and the soul. It has already been shown that the relation between body and soul presented a serious problem to the Cartesians, who never really solved it satisfactorily. Probably it was the attempt to get over this difficulty that led Spinoza to his conception of concurrent Attributes, which accounted for the apparent interaction between body and soul without explaining away either of them, and without having recourse to supernatural interaction. For, in Spinoza's cosmic scheme, man is a finite mode of God, and therefore participates at once in the Attributes of Extension and of Thought, and concurrently functions in both ways, physically and mentally. This solution of the problem committed Spinoza to the view that all bodies are animated, though in very different degrees. And Spinoza embraced this view.

The cosmic philosophy of Spinoza receives some additional light from his theory of knowledge with which it is intimately connected. It is therefore necessary to give some account of it here. Spinoza distinguished three grades of knowledge. The lowest grade he calls "opinion." It is pre-scientific in character, regards objects and events as detached, and is blind to their connections and laws. The second grade is called "reason." It is the stage of scientific insight into the relations and laws of things and events. It is rather abstract: it follows the course of single threads in the fabric of reality, but fails to take in the whole pattern; it traces "world-lines," but has no cosmic vision. The highest grade of knowledge Spinoza calls "intuition." It grasps the cosmic system as a whole. It is not a visionary substitute for the lower grades of knowledge, but their culmination. These three stages might be compared with the three stages in acquiring knowledge of a new language. First one learns the separate letters of the alphabet; next, their combination into words, and the combination of words in sentences, according to certain grammatical laws; finally comes the stage when the significance of a whole paragraph, chapter, or entire literary work can be seen in its entirety. So it is with the great book of Nature. First comes the perception of apparently isolated facts and events; next, the understanding of their relations and laws; finally, the intuition of the structure and significance of the whole cosmos—the vision of all things in God, and of God in all things.

With regard to the first two grades of knowledge it is important to appreciate Spinoza's way of distinguishing between "opinion" or perception, on the one hand, and "reason" or understanding, on the other. A percept or image is regarded by him as entirely different from an idea or concept. Hence his insistence that "we cannot *imagine* God, but we can *conceive* him." Conception has nothing to do with images; it is an activity which grasps connections—ideas, he insists, are activities, not like lifeless pictures on a panel. Even their laws are different: perception and imagination follow the laws of association; conception or understanding follows the laws of logic. This explains his rejection of Bacon's empiricism. From the observation of particulars as such, no laws can be derived concerning their interconnections. In the last resort, scientific laws, or the general truths of science, rest, not on the correspondence with objects of perception, but on their coherence in a system of truths. The ultimate test of truth is more truth, or the harmony of all that is known. The false betrays itself by its incoherence with what is already known. Spinoza, in fact, prefers to speak of the *adequacy* of ideas rather than of their truth, just to avoid the suggestion of external correspondence. Concepts, as acts of apprehending connections, are adequate in so far as they really help to systematize a certain range of facts. And until one has adequate concepts he cannot apprehend the facts in such a way as to see that the concept is also true, that is, in agreement with the facts. Finally, as regards the highest kind of knowledge, Spinoza's estimate of its cosmic significance is noteworthy. For Spinoza such knowledge is more than power, in the Baconian sense. It is life. For it is the means of so holding together the activities of life that they may constitute an harmonious unity and take their proper place in the cosmic system. In this way the effort after the highest knowledge is part of the cosmic activities by which the unity of the universe is maintained. It is, therefore, a part of the very life of God.

LOCKE

John Locke (1632–1704) was born at Wrington, in Somersetshire, and educated at Westminster School, London, and Christ Church, Oxford. He was a Puritan by upbringing, and thought of becoming a clergyman. But his growing love of freedom and tolerance led to his abandonment of the idea, in favour of medicine. In this way he came into contact with Sydenham and Boyle, and under the influence of their empiricism. In 1667 he moved to London, and for the next fifteen years he stayed at Exeter House with Lord Ashley, subsequently Earl of Shaftesbury, as his confidential secretary. It was here, in 1670, that Locke formed the project of writing his *Essay Concerning Human Understanding*, which it took him twenty years to complete. From 1675 onwards political troubles in England forced Locke to live abroad a good deal. He spent three years in France, and five years in Holland. Eventually he returned to England in 1689 in the same boat as Princess Mary, and about three months after the accession of William of Orange. In 1685 he had published his *Letter on Toleration* and *Two Treatises on Government*. In 1690 his *Essay* appeared at last. In 1691 he went to live with Sir Francis Masham at Oates Manor, in Essex, and spent there the rest of his life. Lady Masham was the daughter of his friend, Ralph Cudworth. These last fourteen years were spent for the most part in literary work, including some economic and theological essays; and during four or five years he also acted as Commissioner on the Board of Trade, in which capacity he visited London frequently. Locke's fame rests mainly on his great devotion to truth and his keen appreciation of the limitation of human knowledge. "To love truth for truth's sake," he wrote, "is the principal part of human perfection in this world, and the seedplot of all other virtues." Such a plea has often been made the excuse of fanaticism. It was his insight into the limitations of human knowledge, and the dubiousness of so many human convictions, that saved Locke from fanaticism and made him a champion of toleration.

The motive of Locke's philosophy is explained by him as follows. "Five or six friends" used to meet regularly, while he was staying at Exeter House, to discuss the "principles of morality and religion.

Henry More

John Locke

Gottfried Wilhelm Leibniz

They found themselves quickly at a stand by the difficulties that arose on every side." It consequently occurred to him "that before we set ourselves upon inquiries of that nature, it was necessary to examine our own abilities, and see what objects our understandings were or were not fitted to deal with." For, by "extending their inquiries beyond their capacities," people only "raise questions and multiply disputes, which never coming to any clear resolution, are proper only to continue and increase their doubts, and confirm them at last in perfect scepticism." This was in 1670, and what was then "begun by chance was continued by entreaty, written by incoherent parcels, and, after long intervals of neglect, resumed again as humour and occasions permitted." The final result was his *Essay Concerning Human Understanding* (1690). Locke's method consists in taking stock of human "ideas" and tracing their origin and growth. By "ideas" he meant any kind of cognition, including sensations and percepts as well as concepts or "ideas" in the more usual meaning of the term.

First of all, Locke denies the existence of "innate ideas." Descartes and some of the English Neo-platonists, like Herbert of Cherbury and Henry More, held that man has certain innate ideas— the idea of God, for instance. He argues that many people have no such idea at all, and the others have very different ideas of Him. Similarly with other alleged innate ideas or principles. He concludes, accordingly, that there are "no innate principles in the mind," and that the human mind is at the outset like a blank sheet of paper waiting for experience to write upon it, or like a dark cabinet waiting for the light to fill it with visions. Ideas, in other words, all depend upon experience. Locke's polemic against innate ideas was largely prompted, in all probability, by the fact that all sorts of mere prejudices were wont to masquerade as "innate" convictions.

In order to make good his contention that all ideas are ultimately of experiential origin, Locke distinguishes between simple ideas and complex ideas, and argues that all complex ideas are composed of simpler ideas. It is therefore only necessary to prove the empirical origin of the simple ideas. Now simple ideas, he contends, arise in one of two ways, namely, either from sensation or from reflection, that is to say, either from outer perception or from inner perception. "Ideas of sensation" arise when material objects stimulate the sense-organs. "Ideas of reflection" arise as the result of the mind's apprehension of its own activities in connection with ideas of sensation. The mind is therefore credited with the capacity of reflection, and, moreover, also with the power of combining the simple ideas into complex ideas, though the content of all its ideas is, according to

Locke, ultimately limited by the range of human sensations. And before he has exhausted his inventory of human ideas Locke has to admit that the mind can even invent ideas of its own, which are not mere complexes of simple ideas. Anyway, what kind of knowledge can the human understanding claim to possess? Locke set out with the dictum that any belief that could not be traced back to simple ideas of sensation and reflection had no claim to be regarded as knowledge of objective fact. It was this attitude that made him the philosopher of empiricism. But he failed to maintain this attitude consistently.

With regard to our knowledge of external objects, its basis is, of course, in ideas of sensation. Now, for Locke, these ideas have a twofold character. On the one hand, they are *direct* experiences; on the other hand, they are treated as *representing* "things," and things, that is external or material objects, are not ideas. Can one be certain that sensations give a knowledge of real things? Like his contemporaries, Locke distinguishes between primary and secondary qualities, that is, between what he calls the "original or essential qualities of matter" and "derived qualities." The primary qualities are solidity, extension, figure, and motion. They are quantities rather than qualities, are inseparable from matter, and "would be really in the world as they are, whether there were any sensible being to perceive them or not." The secondary qualities, on the other hand, are not physical properties of things, and would not exist if there were no conscious being to perceive them, "except perhaps as unknown modes of the primary, or if not, as something still more obscure." The reduction of the secondary qualities to mere experiences is consistent enough with the whole trend of Locke's thought. But why should the primary or mathematical qualities be regarded as objective, as independent of experience? Locke says that they are like the ideas we have of them. But how can that be known? Who can compare his "ideas of sensation" with the objective qualities which they are alleged to represent? Locke, moreover, accepts the reality of material things or substances as the supports of the primary qualities, though he cannot trace his complex ideas to any simple ideas of experience, admits that they are vague, and that we cannot know the "real essence" of substance. These and similar weaknesses in his empirical philosophy Berkeley and Hume were not slow to seize upon.

As regards our knowledge of mind, Locke is, of course, on safe ground in accepting the reality of mental experiences as such, and our knowledge of them by means of "ideas of reflection." But here again he passes beyond the bounds of his professed empiricism when he admits the reality of minds or souls or mental substances as the alleged bearers of the experiences, though he is candid enough to say that by "substance," physical or mental, he means "only an uncertain supposition of we know not what," and admits that it is impossible to say whether the soul is a spiritual substance or a material substance endowed with the capacity to think.

Locke's admission of the reality of substances and of the primary qualities of matter rests ultimately on his recognition of the category of causality. But what is the empirical justification of this idea of a cause or active power? He admits that it is not an idea of sensation, and Joseph Glanvill (1636–80) had already pointed out, in *The Vanity of Dogmatizing* (1661), that what is observed is *sequence*, not *causal connection*. Locke, however, claims that causality is an idea of reflection derived from "our consciousness of our own voluntary agency," which supplies an analogy for the interpretation of physical phenomena, which thereby become intelligible. And it is by means of the category of causation that Locke demonstrates the existence of God as the First Cause of all existing things.

The foregoing considerations naturally lead Locke to a very modest estimate of human knowledge. As we have no innate ideas, the only sources of human knowledge are ideas of sensation and ideas of reflection and combinations of these. And as we can never be sure how far ideas of sensation really represent external objects, many beliefs commonly accepted are matters of faith rather than of real knowledge. Though Locke maintains that we have an intuitive, irresistible knowledge each of his own mind or soul, yet he admits that we do not know what its essence is, not even whether it is material or not. Similarly, he maintains that we have a demonstrative knowledge of the existence of God, but admits that nothing is known about His nature. He also accepts the reality of material bodies or substances, but admits that nothing is known about their "real essences," only that they are bundles of certain primary qualities, and even these cannot be regarded as objective with absolute certainty. And for these reasons, though Locke recognizes mathematics and ethics as affording real knowledge, he does so on the seemingly paradoxical ground that these studies are concerned only with the relations between ideas as such, and not with any realities beyond them. But he is rather sceptical about physics, in so far as it professes to deal with the essential objective properties of material bodies. Three years after the publication of Newton's *Principia*, Locke, who was a great admirer of the genius of his great countryman and contemporary, expressed himself as "apt to doubt a science of physical bodies as out of our reach." And the net result of Locke's teaching was to discourage ambitious cosmic speculations. To some extent this attitude helped to reconcile people to their traditional theology as a matter of faith. It also encouraged the pursuit of science in a strictly empirical spirit. But the most valuable practical result of Locke's reflections was the discouragement of every kind of fanaticism and of the intolerance that is born of it.

LEIBNIZ

Gottfried Wilhelm Leibniz (1646–1716) was born at Leipzig, where he also studied law. He graduated in the University of Altdorf at the age of twenty, and was offered a Professorship there but declined it. Turning his attention to science, he felt "transported to another world." In 1672 he went on a diplomatic mission to Paris, where he met Gassendi, Huygens, Malebranche, and others. He also visited London, where he met Boyle and other Fellows of the Royal Society; and Holland, where he met Spinoza. In 1676 he was appointed by the Duke of Brunswick to the post of librarian at Hanover. He was also raised to the rank of Councillor of State, and was frequently occupied with legal and political problems. In 1700 he took a leading part in founding the Academy of Sciences in Berlin; but he remained at his post in Hanover till the end of his days. An account of his contributions to science, and more particularly of his part in the discovery of the differential calculus, has already been given in an earlier chapter. Here we shall deal briefly with his cosmic philosophy only. The most important philosophical works of Leibniz are contained in the following English translations: *The Monadology and other Philosophical Writings* (translated by R. Latta, Oxford, 1898); *Discourse on Metaphysics, Correspondence with Arnauld*, etc. (translated by G. R. Montgomery, Chicago, 1908); *New Essays Concerning Human Understanding* (translated by A. G. Langley, New York, 1896).

The leading motive in the philosophy of Leibniz is that of vindicating the reality and significance of the spiritual, and especially of finite spirits or souls, in the universe. His wide interests, his optimism, and his readiness to compromise encouraged him to attempt a synthesis in which all the different cosmic theories might be harmonized more or less. But his spiritual interest was the dominant factor. In this way, although he admits the existence of objects corresponding to the categories of mechanics (space, time, matter, motion) he treats them as phenomenal rather than as ultimate, that is, as expressions of the activity of spiritual entities which pursue ends by means of apparently mechanical aids.

The mechanistic philosophy, it seemed to Leibniz, was the result of treating atoms or similar extended objects as ultimate realities, and he challenged this view. What is extended, be it never so small, is divisible, and what is divisible must be made up of parts, and cannot therefore be an ultimate reality. The really essential thing in all material substances is force. Force is what persists in all of them, and is conserved in accordance with definite laws. Force, moreover, is something simple, unextended, and non-material. All material phenomena are the expression of units or centres of force. If matter were really inert no motion would be possible, for it is inconceivable how objects absolutely at rest can originate any activity. Things must be regarded as aggregates of units of activity or force. And such active units must be of the nature of mind or spirit, not of inert, extended matter. Leibniz applies to these units of activity the term "monads," which is found already in the writings of Bruno and even earlier. In accordance with the principle of continuity, he posited an infinite series of monads showing infinite degrees of development so that no two monads are alike. Even the lowest have some degree of consciousness or subconsciousness; and at the stage represented by the human soul there is self-consciousness. But the lower monads may be conceived after the analogy of the human soul, and regarded as experiencing some kind of conscious or subconscious activity.

Anxious to avoid both pantheistic and mechanistic philosophy, Leibniz tried to conceive the monads as standing in no direct connection with each other, as incapable of influencing each other. "They have no windows," he says, "by which anything can come in or go out." He must, however, admit one exception to this, namely God, who is conceived as the supreme monad, or the "Monad of monads." God has created all the other monads, the process of their creation being described as one of emanation from Him. This, of course, is not quite consistent with the principle of continuity, which permits no jumps or breaks; for the "Monad of monads" is thus conceived as different in *kind* from the other monads, and not only different in degree. Moreover, there is still the problem of accounting for the apparent interaction between the other monads. If these monads "have no windows," how does it come about that the assembly of the less developed monads constituting the apparent body seem to influence the higher monad called the human soul, and *vice versa*? His answer is that the monads do not really interact, but each is self-contained and self-sufficient. But since all have the same origin, namely, in the Monad of monads, or God, and all are ultimately similar in spiritual character and activity each monad repeats within itself and according to its level of development and its own limitations the experiences of the supreme monad. In this way, all the monads are so many mirrors each of which reflects the same ultimate reality (God) in accordance with its own powers and its peculiar position. They are consequently all in harmony without actually influencing one another. It is as though innumerable clocks of all sorts had been wound up and timed electrically from one central clock; they would all keep time together without acting on each other. There is, in other words, a "pre-established harmony" which has been planned by God, so that each monad in a sense mirrors every other monad, and therefore the entire universe from the point of view of that monad.

The philosophy of Leibniz is thus in some important ways the exact opposite to that of Hobbes. In contrast to the latter's materialism, the reduction of all reality to matter and motion, Leibniz upholds a spiritualism or Idealism which makes all reality consist of spiritual centres of psychical activity. The spatial extended-ness and motion of bodies are, according to Leibniz, only appearances resulting from the confused nature of the activity of the lowest monads. Space and time are consequently, for Leibniz, merely phenomenal orders of co-existence and sequence—forms of appre-hension, not ultimate or independent realities. But Leibniz succeeds as little in explaining how minds and mental activities can account for the appearance of matter and motion, as Hobbes succeeded in explaining how matter and motion can produce minds and mental activities.

Like Spinoza (whose *Ethica* Leibniz had studied in manuscript), Leibniz emphasized the dynamic or active character of reality. In opposition to Locke's contention that the mind is a passive blank tablet on which experience imprints a record, Leibniz vindi-cated the essential activity of the mind; and, indeed, Locke himself had to credit the mind with more active powers than he had intended. To the dictum of Locke and others that "there is nothing in the intellect but what has come through the senses," Leibniz rightly added "except the intellect itself." But Leibniz went to the opposite extreme of Locke's avowed empiricism. For whereas Locke denied all innate ideas, Leibniz by his conception of "window-less" monads whose activity is entirely immanent, though pro-gressive, he virtually reduced all ideas to the level of innate ideas—ideas which may not always (except in God) be clear and distinct from the beginning but which gradually unfold from more obscure perceptions which are innate.

In the last resort, however, Leibniz succeeded as little as did Hobbes in holding the world together in some sort of unity without the supernatural intervention of an external God. Thus, in the end, Leibniz, unlike Bruno and Spinoza, just fell back on the tradi-tional theology of his time.

MORE

The mechanistic trend of modern science, especially the extreme form in which Hobbes expressed it, caused considerable uneasiness among religious people of the orthodox type. Many attempts were accordingly made either to resist it, or at least to harmonize it with Christian doctrine. Of these defenders of the faith, the most interesting from the standpoint of the history of science was Newton. His views on these matters were, however, influenced to a great extent by Henry More, Robert Boyle, and Isaac Barrow. It is therefore necessary to begin with a brief outline of their philosophical views.

First, however, it is necessary to indicate the specific problems which were raised by mechanistic science. The tendency to explain physical phenomena by means of mathematical laws in terms of matter and motion, and the consequent tendency to reject teleological explanations, and to ignore the secondary qualities of things, involved an entirely new orientation. On the one hand, space and time as the necessary conditions of motion, were given far greater importance than they had before. On the other hand, the life of man which consists predominantly in the appreciation of secondary qualities seemed to be reduced to mere illusion, and ceased to be the main consideration that it was once believed to be in the economy of Nature. Nay, God himself, long conceived as the ultimate End towards which the whole creation moves, appeared to be threatened with the loss of His former place in the world.

Let us now see how these and related problems were dealt with by the above-mentioned group of thinkers.

Henry More (1614–87) was born in Grantham, Lincolnshire. The son of a Calvinist, he could never, he said, "swallow down that hard doctrine concerning Fate." After spending three years at Acton College, he went to Christ's College, Cambridge, where Milton was just finishing his studies. Four years' study of Aristotelian philosophy "ended in nothing, in a manner, but mere scepticism." He then turned his attention to the writings of the Neo-platonists, the German theosophists, and the Jewish mystics. Eventually, he joined the "Latitude-Men," who pleaded for reason in religion and the spirit of religion in the pursuit of knowledge, and were opposed to dogmatism and intolerance. They were subsequently known as the Cambridge Platonists. Though deeply religious, a mystic and a believer in ghosts and witches, More was also interested in science and philosophy, and was elected a Fellow of the Royal Society. Among his correspondents were Descartes, Van Helmont, Cudworth, and Glanvill. He died in Cambridge, and was buried in Christ's College Chapel. His chief philosophical works are his *Enchiridion Metaphysicum* (1671) and *The Immortality of the Soul* (1659).

The main motive of More's philosophy was threefold. In the first place he sought to vindicate the reality (and immortality) of spirits or spiritual substances as against the thoroughgoing materialism of Hobbes. In the second place, he sought to maintain a view of the world as a unity in which material and spiritual substances were not so sharply sundered as Descartes' dualism represented them to be; and in intimate connection with this contention, he also opposed the Cartesian identification of matter with extension, which he preferred to regard as essentially non-material, and as common to both matter and spirit, and as a kind of link between them. In the third place, he wanted to urge the necessity of a religious conception of the origin and guidance of the world. More of course does not keep these problems separate, but mingles them in all sorts of curious ways.

More agreed with Descartes in maintaining that souls or spirits are substances. But whereas Descartes regarded thought or consciousness as the characteristic property of a spiritual substance (*res cogitans*), More contended that the essence of spirit is self-activity. Some spirits are conscious, and in their case consciousness is accepted as evidence of self-activity. But there are spirits which are active, though they act and strive blindly, unconsciously. That there are self-active spirits is evident to all human beings because of their direct awareness of self-activity, which, according to More, "is a sufficiently clear argument to prove that there is something incorporeal in nature" (*Ench. Met.*, XXV, 7). Perceptual knowledge as such confirms this, for "the mundane material particles of animals are not in any way capable of the operations and functions of knowledge such as we experience in ourselves" (*Ibid.*, XXV, 1). The activities of memory, imagination, and thought are cited as additional evidence (*Ibid.*, XXV, 6). As regards the existence of other than human souls or spirits, More proves their existence by showing that there are many natural phenomena which cannot be explained mechanistically, that is, by means of matter and impact motion; and whatever is not material must be spiritual. The very union of material things in nature, the origin of motion, and the orderly occurrence of physical events cannot, according to More, be explained without reference to some self-active spirit or spirits (*Ibid.*, IX, 4–13). Having established the existence of spirits, More proceeds to enumerate many different grades of spirit, from God to the lowest "plastic" spirits, or "archei," which played such havoc in the chemistry and geology of the period. These details, however, need not detain us.

Now spirits, according to More, are extended. He agrees with Hobbes, in opposition to Descartes, that although all matter is extended yet extension is not identical with matter, for one can easily imagine extension without matter. More also agrees with Hobbes that whatever is nowhere is nothing. But instead of concluding, with Hobbes, that there are no spirits, More concludes that spirits are extended. "For," he argues, "to take away all extension is to reduce a thing only to a mathematical point, which is nothing else but pure negation or nonentity, and there being no medium betwixt entity and nonentity, it is plain that if a thing be at all it must be extended" (*Ibid.*, IX, 21). Spirit, then, is extended, and can freely penetrate bodies so as to set them in motion; it can also contract or dilate at will, according to More. In this way he tries to explain the activities of human beings. The soul, from its chief seat in the fourth ventricle of the brain, can spread all over the body and even a little beyond it, as a kind of effluvium; and having accomplished what it wanted, it can contract again and confine itself within the ventricle. This power of spiritual expansion and contraction More called "spissitude."

By analogy with the alleged happenings in the human body, More conceives of physical nature as a whole being likewise suffused by a spirit, namely the "spirit of nature" or the "universal soul of the world." More revived the ancient *anima mundi* as an auxiliary or supplement to the mechanistic explanation of physical phenomena. Like several of his contemporaries, he felt that many physical phenomena could not be accounted for by matter and motion alone—for instance, cohesion, magnetism, and electricity, even gravity. All such facts he tried to explain by means of the "spirit of nature," which he described as "a substance incorporeal, but without sense and animadversion, pervading the whole matter of the universe, and exercising a plastic power therein, according to the sundry predispositions and occasions in the parts it works upon, raising such phenomena in the world, by directing the parts of the matter, and their motion, as cannot be resolved into mere mechanical powers" (*Immortality*, III, xii, 1). In order to confine the concept within scientific limits, or to prevent its then common abuse in the interests of magic and hocus pocus, More further qualified the "spirit of nature" as "one and the same everywhere, and acting always alike upon the like occasions, as a clear-minded man, and of a solid judgment, gives always the same verdict in the same circumstances" (*Ibid.*, III, xiii, 7). Ultimately, however, the whole cosmic order is due to God. In the above analogy with a human being, the "spirit of nature" corresponds only to the "animal spirits" which are the unconscious agents of the soul; God Himself would correspond to the soul, but is, of course, much more, being Creator as well as Director.

God, then, according to More, extends throughout the universe. The next problem is to determine God's relation to space and time. As already remarked, the important place of motion in modern science appeared to confer a new status of independent existence upon both space and time as the background or scene of matter and motion, as frames of reference for the measurement of all motion. Moreover, though matter may be thought away, space cannot, for it is presupposed in any kind of existence. To More space appeared, indeed, to have many most remarkable properties. It is "one, simple, immobile, eternal, perfect, independent, existing by itself, subsisting through itself, incorruptible, necessary, immense, uncreated, uncircumscribed, incomprehensible, omnipresent, incorporeal, permeating and embracing all things, essential being, actual being, pure actuality" (*Ench'. Met.*, VIII, 7). It must, therefore, be a spiritual substance. Nay more, these attributes of space are among the attributes commonly ascribed to God. It must, therefore, be divine. Unlike Malabranche, More did not actually identify space with God, but he described it as "a certain rather confused and vague representation of the divine essence or essential presence, in so far as it is distinguished from his life and activities. For none of these attributes . . . appear to concern the divine life and activity, but simply his bare essence and existence" (*Ibid.*, VIII, 14). More thus identified space with the omnipresence of God. The origin of this conception of space must be sought in Jewish mystical literature, in which God is described as "the space of the world" (*Genesis Rabba*, 68, 9), and also as "filling the whole world, as the soul fills the body" (*Leviticus Rabba*, 4, 8). It has already been pointed out that More studied Jewish and other forms of mysticism.

BARROW

Isaac Barrow (1630–77) studied at Charterhouse, Felsted, and St. Peter's College, Cambridge. After travelling in France, Italy, and the Near East, he was appointed Professor of Greek at Cambridge in 1660. In 1662 he became Professor of Geometry in Gresham College; in 1663 a Fellow of the Royal Society; and in 1664 the first Lucasian Professor of Mathematics at Cambridge. In 1669 he resigned his chair in favour of his pupil, Newton. In 1672 he was appointed Master of Trinity College, Cambridge; and in 1675 he was elected Vice-Chancellor of the University. His contributions to mathematical science have already been dealt with in a previous chapter. The more speculative ideas referred to here are contained chiefly in his *Mathematical Lectures* (1669).

Barrow appears to have been influenced by More and other Cambridge Platonists. His views on geometrical concepts are essentially Platonic. Ideas of perfect geometrical figures are not derived from experience, for, he asks, "who ever saw, or distinguished by any sense, an exact straight line, or a perfect circle?" The ideas are already in the mind implicitly; diagrams and other objects of sense-perception only serve as occasions for their explicit recall. He also embraced the view that there actually exist perfect geometrical figures embodied in sensible objects, though they are not visible, except to the eye of reason. Now geometrical figures occupy space, and space cannot be regarded as existing independently of God. How, then, is space related to God? Regarding the existing world as the creation of God, and assuming the infinity and omnipotence of God, Barrow argues that God is capable of creating additional worlds. He must, therefore, reach out or extend beyond this world. And what is called space is just the presence and potency of God. This, as has already been shown, was also More's view of space. Barrow, however, was interested in time as well as in space. The Cartesian conception of geometrical figures as produced by motion, which involves time as well as space, made the nature of time also an urgent problem for the mathematician. And Barrow's conception of time is similar to his conception of space. "Just as," he writes, "there was space before the world was founded, and even now there is an infinite space beyond the world (with which God co-exists) . . . so before the world and together, with the world (perhaps beyond the world) time was, and is; since before the world arose, certain beings [God and the angels] were able continually to remain in existence, so now things may exist beyond the world capable of such permanence. . . . Time, therefore, does not denote an actual existence, but simply a capacity or possibility of permanent existence; just as space indicates the capacity of an intervening magnitude. . . . But does time not imply motion? Not at all, I reply, as far as its absolute, intrinsic nature is concerned; no more than rest; the quantity of time depends on neither essentially; whether things run or stand still, whether we sleep or wake, time flows in its even tenor . . . although that the quantity of time be distinguished by us, the aid of motion must be called in as a measure by which we judge temporal quantities and compare them with each other" (*The Mathematical Works of Isaac Barrow*, 1860, Vol. II, p. 160). For Barrow, it was just the divine nature of space and time, as the omnipresence and eternity of God, that accounted for the unusual lucidity and certainty of mathematics. And the Newtonian conception of absolute space and time is no doubt connected with these religious conceptions of More and Barrow.

GILBERT

More's conception of space and of the "spirit of nature" was mainly derived from earlier mysticism and philosophy; but it was also encouraged by certain influences nearer home. The chief of these was that of William Gilbert, of whose pioneer work in magnetism and electricity an account has already been given. His endeavour to *explain* magnetic phenomena, as well as to describe them, led him to the conclusion that magnetism is something animate, something like a soul, in fact, apparently superior in some ways to the human soul, to judge from the unfailing accuracy and regularity of a magnetic action as compared with the frequent blundering of mortal man. And as the Earth exercises a magnetic power, the Earth must have a soul. Nor did Gilbert's animism stop there. He says: "We consider that the whole universe is animated, and that all the globes, all the stars, and also the noble earth have been governed since the beginning by their own appointed souls and have the motives of self-conservation" (*On the Magnet*, The Gilbert Club, London, 1900, p. 209). By means of a "light and spiritual" effluvium which it emits the magnetic soul or force can act on objects at a distance. This view of Gilbert's, coupled with Descartes' use of ethereal vortices to account for the movement of inert material bodies, gave a certain vogue to the conception of an "ethereal spirit," which was essentially like More's "spirit of nature," and was resorted to for the explanation of action at a distance and for such phenomena as could not be accounted for by impact motion.

BOYLE

Robert Boyle, the severely empirical chemist and physicist, whose important contributions to science have already been described above, also showed occasionally some leaning towards More's ideas. But he expressed himself more cautiously, admitting only that the world behaves "as if there were diffused through the universe an intelligent being" (*Works*, ed. 1672, Vol. II, p. 39). In his chemical and physical researches Boyle followed very closely the principles of mechanistic explanation, and when More suggested that the action of the air-pump could not be explained mechanically, Boyle rejected the suggestion. But when dealing with problems outside his especial province, Boyle sometimes indulged in teleological explanations. For instance, in his *History of Fluidity and Firmness* (§ xix), speaking of "ducks, swans, and other water-fowl," Boyle explains that "Nature having designed [them] to flye sometimes in the air and live sometimes in the water, she providently makes their feathers of such a texture, that they do not, like the feathers of divers other birds, admit the water, which imbibed would make them unfit for the use of flying." And, in any case, he has no doubt about the need of a teleological and theological explanation of the physical world as a whole, even if all its parts could be explained mechanistically. First of all, the vast orderly machine must have been designed and created by a supremely intelligent and omnipotent creator. Moreover, Boyle contends "this most potent Author, and Opificer of the world, hath not abandoned a masterpiece so worthy of him, but does still maintain and preserve it, so regulating the stupendously swift motions of the great globes, and other vast masses of the mundane matter, that they do not, by any notable irregularity, disorder the grand system of the universe, and reduce it to chaos" (*Works*, ed. 1672, Vol. V, p. 519). Miracles are not impossible, according to Boyle. But the world does not normally need supernatural intervention, for "it is like a rare clock, such as may be at Strasbourg where all things are so skilfully contrived, that the engine being once set a-moving, all things proceed according to the artificer's first design" (*Ibid.*, p. 163). Boyle was thus well on the way towards the conception of an intrinsically orderly cosmos, which did not need incessant tinkering on the part of supernatural powers. In this respect, however, he lagged far behind Spinoza's conception of immanent cosmic order. How far Boyle lagged behind Spinoza may be seen from this. At the very time when Newton was about to embrace in one grand generalization (the principle of gravitation)all the physical phenomena of the universe—from the fall of an apple to the movements of the tides, the shape of the earth, the revolutions of Jupiter's satellites, the motions of the planets, and even such apparently erratic movements as those of comets—Boyle was still contemplating the possibility that in other worlds beyond ours the laws of motion might be different from what they are here (*Ibid.*, p. 139). His mind was apparently still haunted to some extent by the traditional belief in the distinction between sublunar and superlunar worlds, or something of the sort.

Boyle not only tried to find a place and function for God behind the mechanism of Nature, he also attempted to reinstate man in his proper place in the world. It has been pointed out above that the scientific tendency to stress the mathematical or primary qualities of matter, at the expense of the secondary qualities, seemed to reduce human life more or less to a life of illusions. Boyle made a praiseworthy defence on behalf of the secondary qualities. At one time he went so far as to contend that "they have an absolute being irrelative to us; for snow, for instance, would be white, and a glowing coal would be hot, though there were no man or any other animal in the world." Usually, however, he is on safer ground, and insists that "there are *de facto* in the world certain sensible and rational beings that we call men; and the body of man having several external parts, as the eye, the ear, etc., each of a distinct and peculiar texture, whereby it is capable of receiving impressions from the bodies about it, and upon that account is called an organ of sense; we must consider, I say, that these sensations may be wrought upon by the figure, shape, motion, and texture of bodies without them after several ways, some of those external bodies being fitted to affect the eye, others the ear, others the nostrils, etc. And to these operations of the objects on the sensories, the mind of man, which upon the account of its union with the body perceives them, gives distinct names, calling the one light or colour, the other sound, the other odour, etc." The secondary qualities, he admits, do not as such exist in the external body, except as "a disposition of its constituent corpuscles, that in case it were truly applied to the sensory of an animal, it would produce such a sensible quality which a body of another texture would not" (*Works*, Vol. III, pp. 22–36). Such dispositions, however, are quite real; and since men do actually exist, the effects of those dispositions on them are also quite real. And, after all, Boyle insists, human beings are not only as real as anything in Nature, but "the soul of man [is] a nobler and more valuable being, than the whole corporeal world" (*Ibid.*, Vol. IV, p. 19). For Boyle, indeed, not only secondary qualities were quite real, and the beauty and orderly harmony of Nature were among his main arguments in proof of the existence of "an Author supremely powerful, wise, and good" (*Ibid.*, Vol. IV, p. 515).

Mechanistic science, according to Boyle, furnished but a part of the explanation of natural phenomena; the complete explanation would have to include a reference to the Author of the universe and His design. Still, the problem of the man of science is to trace, as far as possible, the precise ways in which things happen. Granted that the physical world "is like a rare clock, such as may be at Strasbourg," it has a mechanism which should be studied, so that its action may be understood in detail. An intelligent being should not be content with the bare statement that it was made by a skilled clockmaker. "He must be a very dull inquirer," Boyle writes, "who, demanding an account of the phenomena of a watch, shall rest satisfied with being told that it is an engine made by a watchmaker; though nothing be thereby declared of the structure and co-aptation of the spring, wheels, balance, and other parts of the engine, and the manner, how they act on one another, so as to co-operate to make the needle point out the true hour of the day." So it is with all phenomena. "To explicate a phenomenon, it is not enough to ascribe it to one general efficient cause, but we must intelligibly show the particular manner, how that general cause produces the proposed effect" (*Ibid.*, Vol. V, p. 245). In this way it came about that Boyle in his experimental work was content to show that the phenomena he investigated were "explicable by the motion, bigness, gravity, shape, and other mechanical affections" (*Ibid.*, Vol. III, p. 608), and usually kept his theology and his belief in teleology out of his science.

NEWTON

The scientific work of Newton has already been described in earlier chapters. In the present chapter we are concerned only with the philosophic background of his thought. Broadly speaking, it may be said that most of the philosophic assumptions of the pioneers of modern science are to be found again in Newton. But the very confluence of several trends of thought necessitated a certain amount of mutual accommodation. This was accomplished by Newton, who also contributed something more than his mutual adaptation of different philosophical tendencies.

One of the greatest adepts of all times in wielding the mathematical method, Newton avoided Kepler's mistake of turning a scientific method into a cosmic philosophy. There is little, if anything, of the Neo-pythagorean mathematical enthusiasm to be found in Newton's writings. In fact, he did not even attach so much importance to mathematical deduction as Descartes, for instance, had attached to it. His scientific spirit was more akin to the empirical spirit of Bacon, Boyle, and Locke. He did not rely on mathematical deduction alone, but always invoked the aid of empirical verifications; and he admitted, moreover, that some problems cannot be resolved mathematically at all. He even went so far as to trace geometry to an empirical origin. "Geometry," he writes, "is founded in mechanical practice, and is nothing but that part of universal mechanics which accurately proposes and demonstrates the art of measuring" (*Universal Arithmetic*, Preface). It is this empiricism that accounts for Newton's hostility towards metaphysical hypotheses, that is to say, against theories which were not based on experience and verified by it. "The proper method for inquiring after the properties of things is to deduce them from experiments" (*Opera*, ed. 1779, Vol. IV, p. 320). The discoverer of the law of universal gravitation, and of the most important laws of optics, Newton yet refrained from definitely committing himself to any view about the essential nature either of gravity or of light. Light he describes merely as "something or other" that is propagated every way in straight lines from luminous bodies. The expression "something or other" savours of the empiricism of Locke when dealing with "substances." On the other hand, in spite of his strong empirical sympathies, Newton knew how to combine experiment with mathematical analysis and deduction so as to obtain far-reaching results. The happy result was largely due to his explicit realization that a knowledge of the exact laws of phenomena may be very valuable even in the absence of any real knowledge of the ultimate nature of those phenomena. "To derive two or three general principles of motion from phenomena, and afterwards to tell how the properties and actions of all corporeal things follow from those manifest principles, would be a very great step in philosophy [i.e. science] though the causes of those principles were not yet discovered" (*Opticks*, 3rd ed., p. 377).

It has already been pointed out several times that one of the consequences of the predominance of the mathematical method in modern science was the distinction between primary and secondary qualities of matter, and the comparative neglect of the latter. Newton embraced this distinction, though not without modification. To the primary qualities he added that of "mass." With regard to secondary qualities, he adopted the current conception that sounds and colours are not qualities of things, but are produced in living organisms by vibrations propagated by the external objects. "Sound in a bell or musical string, or other sounding body," he writes, "is nothing but a trembling motion, and in the air nothing but that motion propagated from the object, and in the sensorium 'tis a sense of that motion under the form of sound; so colours in the object are nothing but a disposition to reflect this or that sort of rays more copiously than the rest; in the rays they are nothing but this disposition to propagate this or that motion into the sensorium [i.e. the part of the brain in which the soul was believed to reside], and in the sensorium they are sensations of those motions under the forms of colours" (*Ibid.*, p. 110). Yet Newton did not favour the view that the so-called primary qualities (including mass) were the only objective properties of natural bodies. Probably he shared the above-mentioned ideas of Boyle in this regard, or he may even have gone beyond them. He certainly believed in the objective beauty and harmony of the world, and in their conservation by God.

The introduction of "mass" among the primary qualities of matter appears to have been suggested to Newton by Boyle's experiments on the density of air. The concept made it possible to work out the mechanical theory of Nature more satisfactorily than it was possible to do with the Cartesian vortices. This fact, coupled with the apparent relegation of all secondary qualities from Nature, helped to establish the mechanistic view of the world as the creed of science for nearly two centuries. Newton's own ideas on the matter were not altogether consistent. On the one hand, he was an orthodox Christian, and believed in a First Cause, which, as he remarked, "certainly is not mechanical" (*Ibid.*, p. 344), but is interested in the preservation of cosmic beauty and harmony. On the other hand, he not only applied successfully the mechanistic mode of explanation to a vast field of facts, but wished "we could derive the rest of the phenomena of nature by the same kind of reasoning from mechanical principles" (*Principles*, trans. by Motte, II, 9); and, in fact, he adopted the current idea of an all-pervading ether the pressure of which might help to account, in a more or less mechanical or quasi-mechanical manner, for the transmission of light, and for such other phenomena as could not be explained by reference to mass and motion. Moreover, unlike his more orthodox contemporaries, he practically relinquished the idea of a cosmic purpose apart from the actual cosmic order. The world is, indeed, a wonderful machine created by God. But God has performed his engineering feat so well that the machine does not need constant repairs, only just a little supervision to keep it in running order. God still functions as the resident engineer. But in all essentials the world is a block-universe in which everything is more or less predetermined. Man has only to learn what he can about this vast mechanism, and adore the mathematical genius and mechanical expertness of the Great Engineer.

For Newton the admission of the presence and influence of God in the universe was not a mere concession to popular belief. It was a vital part of his thought, and influenced his outlook considerably. It is no exaggeration to say that Newton's conceptions of absolute motion, space, and time were largely the outcome of his theological views as influenced by More and Barrow. The main points are these. First, as regards absolute motion, Newton says "the causes by which true [i.e. absolute] and relative motions are distinguished, one from the other, are the forces impressed on the bodies to generate motion. True motion is neither generated nor altered, but by some force impressed upon the body moved; but relative motion may be generated or altered without any force impressed upon the body. For it is sufficient only to impress some force on other bodies with which the former is compared, that by their giving way, the relation may be changed, in which the relative rest or motion of this other body did consist" (*Principles*, trans. by Motte, I, 10). Now, in the last resort, Newton's conviction of the reality of absolute motion was based on his belief that ultimately the energy of motion is exercised by God, and He knows exactly whether He has exercised energy, and how much. Again, absolute motion presupposes absolute space and absolute time, in which absolute motion takes place. Newton accordingly accepted both these concepts. "Absolute, true, and mathematical time, of itself, and from its own nature, flows equably without regard to anything external, and by another name is called duration; relative, apparent, and common time is some sensible and external (whether accurate or unequable) measure of duration by means of motion, which is commonly used instead of true time; such as an hour, a day, a month, a year." Similarly, "absolute space, in its own nature, without regard to anything external, remains always similar and immovable. Relative space is some movable dimension or measure of the absolute spaces; which our senses determine by its position to bodies, and which is vulgarly taken for immovable space; such is the dimension of a subterraneous, an aerial, or celestial space, determined by its position in respect of the earth. Absolute and relative space are the same in figure and magnitude; but they do not remain always numerically the same. For if the earth, for instance, moves, a space of our air, which relatively and in respect of the earth always remains the same, will at one time be one part of the absolute space into which the air passes; at another time it will be another part of the same, and so, absolutely understood, it will be perpetually mutable" (*Principles*, trans. by Motte, I, 6). But what justification is there for assuming the reality of absolute time and space, instead of resting content with relative space and time, of which alone we appear to have any real knowledge or use? Newton was well aware of the difficulties of defending them on purely scientific grounds. But his ultimate justification of them was theological rather than scientific. God, according to traditional theology, "endures for ever, and is everywhere present." And Newton, accepting the views of More and Barrow, added significantly that God "by existing always and everywhere, he constitutes duration and space" (*Principles*, trans. by Motte, II, 311).

The religious convictions of Newton and kindred spirits saved them from the risk of converting mechanical science into a mechanistic cosmic philosophy, after the manner of Hobbes and some later thinkers. Leibniz, as has already been seen, attempted to remove the very foundations of materialism by means of his idealistic philosophy of monadism. Whether he was any more successful in constructing an all-comprehensive and satisfying philosophy is more than questionable. In some ways he seemed to favour a more rigorously mechanistic view of Nature than did Descartes, Boyle, or Newton, by confining God's activity in the world so as not to extend beyond its creation and pre-established harmony. He almost jeers at the views of his more orthodox contemporaries. "The machine of God's making," he says, "is so imperfect, according to these gentlemen, that he is obliged to clean it now and then by an extraordinary concourse, and even to mend it as a clock-maker mends his work" (Brewster's *Newton*, II, 285).

For Leibniz, however, the whole of physical nature had no ultimate reality, and was only an appearance of spiritual monads. But even so, when one considers the predetermined destiny of the windowless monads, and their arbitrarily conceived relation to the "Monad of monads," in the system of Leibniz, there seems to be very little, if any, real difference between the spiritualistic philosophy of Leibniz and the materialistic philosophy of Hobbes, let alone the religious compromise of Descartes, Boyle, and Newton. As a system of philosophy, the pantheism of Spinoza was superior to all these extremes and compromises. But even the age of genius was not yet ripe for it.

(See E. A. Burtt, *The Metaphysical Foundations of Modern Science*, 1925; J. E. Erdmann, *History of Philosophy*, Vol. II, 1892, etc.; W. Windelband, *History of Philosophy*, New York, 1901; Bertrand Russell, *History of Western Philosophy*, London, 1948; A. Wolf, "Descartes" and "Spinoza" in the *Encyclopaedia Britannica*, 14th ed.; S. V. Keeling, *Descartes*, London, 1934; P. H. Osmond, *Isaac Barrow*, London, 1944; L. T. More, *Life and Works of the Honourable Robert Boyle*, New York and London, 1944.)

INDEX

Abacus, 556 f.
Abel, N. H., 191
Abraham, J. J., 429
Absolute motion, space, time, 673 f.
Académie des Sciences, 8 f., 54, 63 ff., 69, 147, 162, 165, 176 f., 232, 234, 260, 272 f., 280, 286, 452, 473
Accademia del Cimento, 8, 54 ff., 64, 87, 89, 112, 258, 278 f., 303, 306 f., 312
Acids, 331, 339, 499
Acosta, G. di, 443
Acugua, 440
Adams, F. D., 371
Adams, J. C., 151
Adelhard of Bath, 188
Aether, 161, 164 f., 257, 260 f., 266 f., 280
Africa, exploration of, 379 f
Agathodaemon, 384
Agricola, G., 350, 353 ff., 325, 430, 445, 486 ff., 505 f., 512, 521 ff., 537 ff.
Agriculture, 453 ff.
Air, 50, 60, 101, 105, 237 f., 339 ff.
Air-pump, 9 f., 43, 56, 60, 62, 64, 93, 99 ff., 235 ff., 277, 288
Air vessel to force pumps, 527
Al-Battani, 21
Albertus Magnus, 365
Albinus, P., 440
Alcazar water supply, 526
Alcohol, 442
Aldrovandi, U., 402
Alembic Club Reprints, 332 f., 342, 344 ff.
Alexandrians, 7, 15, 24, 189
Alexandro, Alexander ab, 365
Algaroth, 439
Alhazen, 244 f., 248
Alkali, 339
Allen, W. G., 482
Almagest, see Ptolemy
Almagro, D. de, 373
Alum, 500
America, exploration of, 372 ff., 380 f.
Ammonia, 440

Amontons, G., 85 f., 94, 307
Anaesthetics, 437
Anatomy, 62, 65, 359, 365, 403, 406 ff., 418 f., 422 f., 444
Anchor-escapement, 113 f.
Andrade, A. de, 379
Angelo, Michael, 27
Ango, 264
Animals as automata, 568
Anne, Queen, 147
Antimony, 495
Antimony cup, 439
Antwerp, 500
Apian, Peter, 381 f., 388
Apian, Philip, 381 ff.
Apollonius of Perga, 6
"Applied science," 451
Aqua fortis, 499
Aqua regia, 499, 504
Aqua valens, 499
Aqueduct, 526
Arabs, 7, 71, 188 ff., 290
Arch, theories of the, 478 ff.
Archimedes, 2, 6, 39, 48, 202, 204 f., 324, 526, 544
Architecture, 477 ff.
Arderon, 289
Aristarchus of Samos, 24
Aristotelian system of nature, 14 f., 17, 28 f., 32 ff., 39, 45, 48, 124, 222, 245, 269, 275, 286, 392 (*see also* Scholasticism)
Aristotle, 4, 17, 34, 47, 244, 281, 287, 296, 306, 361, 398 f., 403, 408, 417, 452, 564, 582, 629, 633, 643
Arthur, G., 381
Artificial gems, 326
Artificial parts of the body, 437, 442, 444
Ashton, T. S., 542
Asia, exploration of, 378 f.
Assaying, 489
Association of ideas, 566
Aston, 153
Astrology, 122, 132, 306, 426 f.
Atmosphere, height of, 93, 314 ff.

Atmosphere, pressure of, 10, 56, 84 f., 90 ff., 100 f., 105, 224 f., 235 ff., 314
Atmospheric pressure engine, 549 f.
Attention, 565
Augsburg waterworks, 525 f., 532
Augustine, St., 582
Aurora Borealis, 302 f.
Auzout, A., 66, 80, 162, 165, 168, 170, 172
Avicenna, 365
Axles, 507 f., 518, 520
Ayscough, W., 146

Bachmann, A. Q., 401
Bacon, F., 25, 54, 58 f., 68, 84, 275, 279, 293, 318, 452, 614, 630, 632 ff., 644, 646, 655, 671
Bacon, R., 8, 75, 188, 245, 248, 273
Baffin, W., 377
Bagrow, L., 385
Baillou, G. de, 443
Baily, F., 178, 181 f., 184
Baker, J. N. L., 381
Balance, 431, 434
Balance-spring, 114, 117
Ball, W. W. R., 154, 218
Banzer, M., 437
Barbon (*or* Barebone), N., 619, 620 f., 623 f., 626
Barbosa, D., 378
Barents, W., 376
Barlow (*or* Barlowe), W., 298
Barometer, 9, 10, 56, 63, 91 ff., 105, 107, 224 f., 236 ff., 242, 306, 311 f., 317
Barrow, I., 146, 178, 209, 211, 248, 269, 273, 663, 666 ff.
Bartholin, T., 413
Bartholinus, E., 261 f., 368
Bartisch, G., 443
Bate, J., 533
Batts, T., 381
Bauer, G., *see* Agricola
Bauer, L. A., 302
Bauhin, K., 397 f., 400
Bayer, J., 187
Beams, strength of, 467 ff.

Beazley, C. R., 388
Beck, T., 525 f., 540
Beet sugar, 451
Belidor, 536
Bell, W. G., 628
Bellosta, A., 437
Bellows, 524
Belon, P., 403
Bentekoe, 442
Bentley, R., 353
Berg, Sir J. C. van, 458
Berlichingen, G. von, 437
Berlin Academy, 67 ff.
Bernoulli, Daniel, 223
Bernoulli, Jakob, 274
Bernoulli, Johann, 46,
  216, 223, 228, 274
Beroald, 537
Berry, A., 26
Berthollet, 451
Bertrand, J. L. F., 70
Bessel, F. W., 35
Besson, J., 456 f., 537,
  540, 544
Bianconi, G. L., 287
Bible of Nature, 419
Bifilar pendulum, 111
Bignon, Abbé, 67
Bills of mortality,
  588 ff.
Binomial nomenclature,
  397 f., 400
Binomial theorem, 146,
  209, 213, 215
Biology, 394 ff., 430, 445
Birch, T., 70, 280, 477,
  482, 485
Biringuccio, V., 486
Bismuth, 495, 499, 504
Bitumen, 496, 500
Black, J., 279
Blackborrow, P., 301
Blainville, 525 f.
Bland, E., 380 f.
Blast furnace, 495
Bleaching, 451
Bligh, E. W., 449
Blind spot, 65, 272
Blondel, F., 473
Blood, 407, 410 ff., 415,
  418, 422, 443
Bobbing-wheel, 459
Bock, H., 395
Böckler, 541
Bodin, J., 390, 583 ff.,
  628
Boehme, J., 4
Boerhaave, H., 419
Bolton, H. C., 83, 87
Bonar, J., 628
Bond, H., 301
Bonomo, 444
Borelius, P., 72
Borelli, G. A., 55, 58,

231, 286, 287, 394,
  415 ff., 445
Borough, W., 300
Borri, 292
Bosse, A., 199
Botanical gardens, 394 ff.,
  402, 423
Botany, 394 ff., 402
Botero, G., 582
Boyle, R., 4, 56, 60, 62,
  85, 87 f., 93, 94,
  102 ff., 107, 120,
  235 ff., 275 ff., 286,
  288, 305, 314,
  336 ff., 348 f., 370 f.,
  415, 425, 442, 449
  489, 504 f., 548, 575,
  656, 663, 668 ff., 674
Boyle's law, 61, 85, 93,
  235, 314 ff.
Bradley, J., 158, 259
Brahe, Tycho, 4, 24, 26,
  35, 67, 121 ff.,
  131 f., 135 ff., 140,
  145, 168, 177, 181 f.
Brain, 444
Brake, 508 f., 520 f.
Branca, 545 f.
Brand, 348 f.
Brass wire, 468
Brett, G. S., 581
Brewster, Sir D., 161,
  267, 675
Bridge waterworks, 532 ff.
Briggs, H., 195
British Museum, 532
Brouncker, Lord, 60, 178,
  209, 239, 477
Brown, H., 70
Browne, Sir T., 3
Bruce, Alexander, Earl of
  Kincardine, 116 f.
Brudzewski, A., 11
Brunfels, O., 395
Bruno, G., 5, 25 f., 29,
  366, 630 ff., 662
Bryant, W. W., 53
Buckingham, Duke of, 63
Building problems, 467 ff.
Bürgi, J., 140, 194, 195
Burnet, T., 351 f., 353
Burning-glasses, 64 f., 71,
  273, 279 f.
Burrough, S., 376
Burtt, E. A., 675
Button, T., 377
Buys-Ballot, C. H., 320
Bylot, R., 377

Cabeo (or Cabeus), N.,
  298, 303
Cabot, J., 373
Cabot, S., 376
Cabral, P. A., 372

Cajori, F., 151, 193, 218,
  317, 563
Calcination, 60, 64 f.,
  332 ff., 340, 345
Calculating machines,
  556, 560 ff.
Calculators, mechanical,
  556 ff.
Calculus, 200, 202, 210,
  213, 214 ff.
  (see also Fluxions
  and Infinitesimals)
Calomel, 440
Calvin, 410 f.
Cam, 515
Cambridge Platonists,
  663
Camerarius, R. J., 422 ff.
Campani, G., 74
Campden House steam
  pump, 553 f.
Canizares, 440
Cannan, E., 628
Canton, J., 58
Capillarity, 56, 58 f.
Cardan, G., 191, 198,
  526 f., 537, 543
Careil, F. de, 68
Carlos, E. S., 76
Carpenter, N., 388 ff.
Cartier, J., 375, 380
Cartography, 362 f.,
  381 ff.
Cascara, 442
Cassini, G. D., 55, 67,
  162, 165, 175 f., 183,
  286
Castelli, B., 83, 222, 540
Catenary, 482
Caus, S. de, 545
Caustics, 273 f.
Cavalieri, B., 192, 201 f.,
  204, 206 f., 208, 248
Cavallo, T., 91
Cellini, B., 615
Cellular structure, 61
Celsius, A., 91
Cementation, 500
Centre of the universe,
  631
Cesalpini (Caesalpino),
  A., 398 f., 402
Cesarini, 83
Cestoni, 444
Chain of dippers, 512 f.
Chain-drive to machinery,
  540
Champlain, S. de, 380
Chancelor, R., 376
Chandler, J., 329
"Chaos," 327
Charles I, 60
Charles II, 60, 178 f.,
  181, 272

Charles V, German Emperor, 354, 374, 381, 383
Chasles, M., 199, 200
Chemical affinity, 331
Chemistry, 325 ff., 444 f.
Chérubin d'Orléans, 74
Chesne, J. de, 440
Child, Sir J., 626 f.
Child, J. M., 218
Chinese looms, 460 f.
Chlorine bleaching, 451
Chouart, M., 380
Christian Church, 1 ff., 8 f., 25, 28, 37 f., 54, 131
Christian IV of Denmark, 177
Christin, 91
Christina, see Queen Christina
Chromosphere, solar, 187
Chuquet, N., 192
Ciermans, J., 560
Cinchona, 440 ff.
Circular motion, laws of, 150, 163 f., 228 ff.
Clairaut, A. C., 59
Clausius (l'Eclus), C., 396
Clay, R. S., 120
Clement, 113
Clepsydras, 41 f., 109, 111, 127
Clinical thermometer, 432
Clock-mechanism in lifting tackle, 512 f.
Clocks, 109 ff., 528
Clockwork figures, 528
Clüver, P., 385 f.
Cobalt-blue glass, 504
Colbert, J. B., Marquis de, 64, 67, 615
Collegium Curiosum sive Experimentale, 67
Collegium Naturae Curiosorum, 67
Collins, J., 178, 212
Colour, 146, 245, 251, 255, 256 ff., 264 ff., 269, 271
Columbus, C., 291, 372 f., 387, 633
Columbus, R., 411
Columna, F., 440
Combustion, 339 ff., 344 f.
Comets, 25, 34, 36, 124 f., 143, 159 f., 183 f., 381 f.
Compass, magnetic, 493
Compass, mariners', 290 f.

Conic sections, 6, 197 ff., 205, 208 f.
Conservation of energy, 506
Cook, Captain J., 378
Co-ordinate geometry, 197 ff., 208
Copper, 488, 494 f., 498, 542
Copernican system, see Heliocentric system
Copernicus, N., 4, 6, 11 ff., 30, 121, 130, 133, 135, 145, 409, 443, 445
his De Revolutionibus, 13 ff., 35
Cordova, 527
Coriolis, G. G., 46
Corona, solar, 187
Coronado, F. de, 373
Cortes, H., 373
Cosmography, 382, 387 f.
Court, T. H., 120
Cowell, P. H., 184
Cowl, ventilating, 521, 523
Crabtree, W., 143
Craig, J., 217
Crank, 515, 517 f.
Crew, H., 52
Crommelin, A. C., 184
Crosthwait, J., 180
Croune, W., 168
Crystallography, 263, 350, 368 ff.
Ctesibus, 527, 531
Cudworth, R., 663
Cusa, N. de, 432

D'Acres, R., 541
Dael, J. van, 609
Dalencé, 89
Dampier, W., 319, 378
Dannemann, F., 102
Dante, 27
Darmstädter, L., 542
Davenant, C., 608, 616 ff., 623, 626
Davis, J., 377
D'Avity, P., 582
Decimals, 193
Declination, magnetic, 183, 291 f., 295, 300 ff.
Delamain, R., 560
Delisle, J. N., 186
Deluc, J. A., 307
Deluge, Noachian, 352, 366, 367
Democritus, 5, 399
Demography, see "Political arithmetic"
Derand, F., 479

Derham, W., 287 f., 311
Desaguliers, 536
Desargues, G., 199 f., 208
Descartes, R., 3, 4, 25, 56, 63, 66, 68, 76, 80, 93 f., 155, 157, 164, 192, 193, 196 ff., 208, 225, 231 f., 236, 248, 250 ff., 258, 269 ff., 284, 299 ff., 306, 350 ff., 390, 391 f., 394, 415, 480, 567 ff., 575, 628, 640 ff., 657, 663 ff., 671, 674 f.
Desmarest, 452
Determinants, 217
Deventer, H. van, 437, 444
Diffraction of light, 156, 254 ff., 258, 260, 271
Digby, K., 440
Digester, Papin's, 548
Digestion, 395 ff.
Digges, Leonard, 75
Digges, Thomas, 75
Diophantus of Alexandria, 189 f.
Dip, see Inclination, magnetic
Dipping needle, 114 f., 119, 292, 294 f.
Disease, 435 f., 438, 442 ff.
Dissections, 62, 65
Divining rod, 487 ff., 511
Dobbin, L., 349
Doctors, 445 ff.
Dodonaeus, R., 440
Dollond, J., 82
Dominis, A. de, 269
Donne, 151
D'Orville, A., 379
Dover clock, 109
Dowser, see Divining rod
Drake, Sir F., 375
Dreyer, J. L. E., 26, 144
Dry analysis of metals, 498 f.
Duclos, S. C., 64
Dudley, D., 64
Duns Scotus, 629
Dynamics, 35, 39 ff., 113, 148 ff., 154 ff., 222 f., 225 ff.

Ear, 435, 437, 443 f.
Earth, age of, 322 f.
Earth, shape of, 25, 67, 157 f., 164, 176, 230 f., 303

Earth, size of, 6, 150 ff., 174
Eccentrics, see Planetary theory
Economics, 613 ff.
Effluvia, 297, 303, 305
Einstein, A., 161
Elasticity, 484 f.
Elder oil, 437, 447
Electrical machine, 304 f.
Electricity, 7, 56, 58, 105, 293, 296 f., 299, 303 ff.
Elements, 326, 329, 336 ff
Elixir, 440, 442
Elizabeth, Queen, 293, 620, 632
Energy, 506
Engineering, mechanical, 505 ff.
Engineering sketches, 536
Ent, G., 59
Epicureans, 244
Epicycles, see Planetary theory
Epsom salt, 441
Equations, theory, of, 188, 190 ff., 196, 198 f., 214, 560
Erasmus, D., 354
Erdmann, J. E., 675
Escosura, L. de la, 528
Ether, 442
Euclid, 6, 200, 205
    Elements of, 188, 201
    Optics of, 244
Eudoxus of Knidos, 14, 15
Euler, L., 82, 227, 283, 467
Evaporation, 320 ff., 392
Evelyn, J., 60
Ewbank, T., 525, 534, 536
Exploration, geographical, 372 ff., 383

Fabri, H., 89
Fabricius, H., 397, 408, 411, 419, 443, 445
Fabricius, J., 30 f., 79
Fahie, J. J., 53
Fahrenheit, D. G., 90 ff.
Fallam, R., 381
Falling bodies—
    deviation of, 34 f., 152
    laws of, 28, 34 f., 39 ff., 165, 222, 226 f.
Fallopia, G., 440
Fan, ventilating, 522 f.
Fatio de Duillier, N., 216
Felber, H., 525

Ferdinand, King of Austria, 354
Ferdinand II, Grand Duke of Tuscany, 55, 87, 312, 358
Fermat, P. de, 63, 200 ff., 208, 252 f.
Fermentation, 444
Fernel, J., 443
Ferrari, L., 191
Fever, 440 ff., 449
Field, J., 25
Fire, 338 ff.
Fire-engine, 542
Flame, 339 ff.
Flamsteed, J., 144, 147, 161 f., 178 ff., 286
Florence glass factories, 500
Fludd, R., 83
Fluents, 211 ff., 215
Fluxions, 146, 147, 155, 187, 209 ff., 215
    (see also Calculus and Infinitesimals)
Flyer for twisting yarn, 459
Flywheel, 505, 519
Force, 39, 45, 47, 148, 154 f.
Force pumps, 515, 526
Ford, Sir E., 534 f.
Forster, W., 560
Fossils, 350, 358, 362, 365 ff., 407
Foster, S., 59
Foucault, L., 253
Foxe, L., 377
Foyer, J., 433
Franklin, B., 451
Fracastorius, G., see Fracastoro, H.
Fracastoro, H., 365 f., 433 ff.
Frederick II of Denmark, 122
Frederick I of Prussia, 69
Frederick William I of Prussia, 70
Freewill, 574, 581, 640
Freezing, 56 f., 64, 277
Fritz, S., 381
Frobisher, Sir M., 376 f.
Fuchs, L., 395
Fulling mill, 463
Furnaces, 495 ff.

Galen, 403, 406 ff., 410 f., 571
Galilean telescope, 76 f., 82
Galilei, Galileo, 4 f., 25 ff., 54 f., 58, 72, 76 f., 79, 82 ff., 92,

111 f., 114, 131, 145, 147 f., 155, 163, 176, 202, 219, 222, 224 f., 228, 231, 238, 246, 254, 258, 281 f., 318, 412, 415 ff., 431, 433, 448, 452, 468 ff., 541, 632, 640 f., 646
    his Sidereus Nuntius, 76 f.
    his Two Chief Systems, 32 ff., 36
    his Two New Sciences, 37 ff.
Galilei, Vincenzio (father of Galileo), 27
Galilei, Vincenzio (son of Galileo), 44, 112
Gama, Vasco da, 372
Garrison, F. H., 449
"Gas," 327
Gascoigne, W., 77, 82, 168 ff.
Gassendi, P., 63, 275, 286 f., 288, 646
Gauge-cocks to steam boiler, 559
Geikie, Sir A., 371
Gellibrand, H., 300
Gemma Frisius, 382, 383
Gems, artificial, 504
Geocentric system, 5, 14 f., 17, 33 f., 36, 125, 134 ff., 386, 389
Geogony, 350 ff., 359 ff.
Geology, 350 ff., 430, 445
Geometry, analytical, see Co-ordinate geometry
Gerbert, 543, 556
Gerbillon, J. F., 379
Gerland, E., 120, 274
Germ theory of infection, 443
Gesner, C., 402, 440
Gilbert, Sir H., 376
Gilbert, W., 4, 25, 142, 246, 291, 292 ff., 300 ff., 389, 430, 445, 668
    his De Magnete, 293 ff.
Girard, A., 191 f.
Girard, P. S., 473
Glaisher, J. W. L., 151
Glanvill, J., 659
Glassmaking, 500 ff.
Glauber, J. R., 329 ff., 440 f., 445, 504
Glisson, F., 413, 437, 444
Goddard, J., 59
Goes, B. de, 379
Gold, 488, 495, 498, 504 f.

Gould, R. T., 120
Gout, 444, 449
Graaf, R. de, 419
Grafenberg, J. S. von, 437
Graham, G., 183
Grandi, G., 473
Gras, N. S. B., 466
Graunt, J., 587, 588 ff.,
    599 f., 602, 608 f.
Gravitation, 140, 144 ff.,
    157, 160 f., 174,
    180, 230, 267, 353,
    671
Gravity, 39, 41, 45, 61,
    142, 148 ff., 157,
    164 f., 223, 226 f.,
    297, 389, 671
Gray, S., 74 f., 97 f.
Greeks, 2, 4 ff., 71, 188 f.,
    196, 198, 203, 244,
    290, 296, 365
Greenwich Observatory,
    9, 162, 175, 178 ff.,
    183
Gregory, D., 82, 482
Gregory, J., 80
Gresham, Sir T., 620
Gresham's law, 619 f.
Grew, N., 417. 422 f., 441
Grimaldi, F. M., 254 ff.,
    258, 271
Grollier de Servière, 539
Grotius, 222
Grueber, J., 379
Guaiacum, 443
Guericke, O. von, 85,
    92 ff., 99 ff., 106 f.,
    273, 288 f., 304 f.
Guldinus, P., 207
Gunter, E., 151, 300, 559
"Gunter's scale," 559 f.
Gunther, R. T., 70, 120,
    310 f., 485
Günther, S., 383
Gwilt, J., 478, 528

Haak, T., 59
Hadley, G., 318 ff.
Haemorrhage, 437, 447
Hafenreffer, S., 444
Haldane, E. S., 642
Hales, J., 615
Hall, Chester More, 81 f.
Hall, J. W., 542
Halley, E., 82, 89, 93 f.,
    144, 147, 152 f.,
    157, 159, 161 f., 176,
    180 ff., 247 f., 278,
    286, 301 ff., 315 ff.,
    320 ff., 362, 393,
    609 ff.
Halos, 271 f.
Hantsch, V., 388
Harmonics, 283 ff.
Harriot, T., 189, 192, 245

Harris, W., 364
Hart, I. B., 467
Hartmann, G., 292
Hartogszoon, D., 378
Harvey, W., 3, 4, 6, 408,
    411 ff., 415, 417,
    419, 420, 425, 430,
    445, 634, 648
Hauksbee, F., 107, 288 f.,
    303
Heart, 444
Heat, 58, 64, 89 f., 275 ff.
    (see also Thermom-
    eter)
    specific, 278 f.
Heliocentric system, 6,
    12 f., 24 f., 28 f.,
    34 ff., 121, 125,
    131 f., 134 ff., 145,
    157, 296, 386, 390 f.
Helioscope, 79
Hellmann, G., 92 f., 324
Helmont, J. B. van, 298,
    325 ff., 427, 444 f.,
    663
Hennepin, L., 380
Henry IV of France, 189
Heraclides of Pontus, 15
Herbals, 395
Hérigone, 193
Hermann, Landgrave of
    Hesse, 312
Hero of Alexandria, 2, 7,
    83, 252 f., 543
Herschel, Sir W., 187
Hertel, C. G., 74
Hessus, E., 542
Hevelius (Hevel), J. 80,
    82, 162 f., 181 ff.,
    273
Hicetas, 15
Hilden, F. von, 435, 443
Hipparchus of Rhodes,
    21, 144, 158
Hippocrates of Cos, 438,
    449, 585
Hire, P. de la, see La
    Hire
Hobbes, T., 64, 564 ff.,
    628, 640 ff., 646,
    649, 662 ff., 674 f.
Hobson, E. W., 195
Hoffmann, F., 442
Holbach, 504
Hollerius, 437
Hollow cylinders as
    beams, 473
Hondius, J., 385
Hooke, R., 61 f., 72, 82,
    87 f., 95 ff., 102,
    105, 113 f., 117 ff.,
    151 ff., 169, 178,
    183, 235, 239,
    241 ff., 256 ff., 266,
    271, 275, 278, 280,

289, 307 ff., 314,
    319, 341 ff., 366 ff.,
    370, 415, 417 f.,
    422 f., 425, 476 f.,
    482, 484 f.
Hoover, H. C., and L. H.,
    357, 487
Hoppe, E., 305
Horrebow, P., 172, 174,
    177
Horrocks, J., 143 f., 178,
    186
Horror Vacui, 51, 92 f.,
    101, 224 f.
Horsburgh, E. M., 563
Horsley, 310
Hospitals in London and
    Paris, 429 f.
Houtman, F., 378
Hudde, J., 609
Hudson, H., 294, 376,
    377
Hull, C. H., 601, 628
Humours, 427, 442
Hunt, 321
Hutten, U. von, 443
Hutton, 451
Huygens, Christian, 44,
    64, 66, 80, 89, 94,
    107, 112 ff., 150,
    155, 157, 162 ff.,
    170, 175, 214,
    225 ff., 231 ff., 250,
    258, 260 ff., 268,
    271, 273, 286, 368,
    609, 615
    his gunpowder engine,
    548
    his Horologium Oscil-
    latorium, 113, 163 f.,
    226 ff.
    his Traité de la Lu-
    mière, 64, 260 ff.
Huygens, Constantijn
    (father of Chris-
    tian), 162
Hydrodynamics, 49, 66,
    156, 222 f., 234
Hydrography, 391 ff.
Hydrometer, 115, 120
Hydrostatics, 48 ff., 66,
    219, 220 ff., 223 ff.,
    234
Hygrometer and hygro-
    scope, 63, 306 ff.,
    311
"Hypothesis," 630
Hypsometer, 91 f.
Hysteria, 444

Idealism, 662
"Idols," 635
Impact, 47 f., 155, 231 ff.
Inclination, magnetic,
    119, 292, 295, 301

Inclined plane, motion on, 41 ff., 47, 219 f.
Indices, 193, 196
Inertia, law of, 35, 39, 45
Infinitesimals, 66, 202 ff., 206 f., 209, 211 ff., (*see also* Calculus *and* Fluxions)
Innate ideas, 575 f.
Innocent XI, Pope, 359
Inquisition, 25, 36 f., 55
Insolation, 323 f.
Interest on money, 191, 626 f.
Internal sense, 577
Ipecacuanha, 442
Iron, 481, 495, 498 f., 507, 512, 527, 542
Irradiation, 144
Iva, 442

Jablonski, D. E., 69
Jackman, C., 376
Jacobi, J. C., 442
James II, 147
James, T., 377
James, W. S., 243
Jansen, Z., 72, 76
Janszoon, W., 378
Jeffreys, Judge, 147
Jenkins, R., 534
Jenkinson, A., 379
Jesuits' bark or powder, 441
Jewish mystics, 663, 666
Joliet, L., 380
Jones, W., 193
Jordan, W., 563
Jordanus Nemorarius, 188 f.
Juanelo, T., 528 f., 536
Jungius, J., 67, 399 f.
Jupiter, satellites of, 29 f., 32 f., 36, 76, 81, 141, 169, 175 f., 259
Jürgen, J., 459
Jurin, J., 314
Justell, H., 609

Kanold, J., 314
Karg, L., 525
Keill, J., 216
Kepler, J., 3 f., 14, 23 ff., 29 f., 77, 79 f., 123, 130 ff., 143 ff., 194 f., 201 ff., 206 f., 244 ff., 258, 296 ff., 671
his *Ad Vitellionem Paralipomena*, 245 ff.
his *Astronomia Nova*, 140

his *Dioptrice,* 77, 245 ff.
his *Mysterium Cosmographicum,* 29, 123, 131, 133 ff.
his *Stereomatria,* 203 ff.
his *Tabulae Rudolphinae,* 132, 140, 195, his laws of planetary motion, 140 f., 150, 152, 157, 181, 186
Keplerian (*or* astronomical) telescope, 77, 79, 82, 167
King, G., 587, 602 ff., 618, 623
Kirby, R. S., 537
Kirch, G., 187
Kircher, A., 74, 85, 298, 351, 425, 443 f.
Knitting, 463 ff.
Knolles, R., 583
Knowledge, grades of, 572 ff., 654 f.
Krafft, 348 f.
Kunckel, J., 340, 504 f.

La Condamine, C. M. de, 287
Lagrange, J. L., Comte de, 286
La Hire, P. de, 273 f., 483
Language and knowledge, 566
Langley, A. G., 660
Lansberg, P. von, 143 f.
Laplace, P. S., Marquis de, 25, 59, 286
Larynx, 444
La Salle, R., 380
Latham, M. L., 196, 642
Latham, R. A., 438
Lathes, 537 f.
Latta, M., 660
Laurson, P. G., 537
Lavoisier, A., 415
Law, J., 621, 622 f.
Law of continuity, 580
Lead, 488, 495, 497
Lead pipes, 527, 542
Least time, principle of, 252 f.
Leblanc, 451
Lederer, J., 381
Lee, W., 465
Leeuwenhoek, A. van, 71 f., 74, 369, 413, 417, 420 ff., 425
Le Gras, 442
Leibniz, G. W., 68 ff., 98, 147, 192, 202, 212 ff., 228, 233 f., 253, 272, 312, 352,

477, 562 f., 579 ff., 660 ff., 674 f.
Le Maire, J., 378
Lemery, N., 364, 440
Le Monnier, 168
Lenses, aberrations of, 80 ff., 161, 248, 252, 264, 268
Lenses, achromatization of, 80 ff., 268
Leo Africanus, 379
Leonardo da Vinci, *see* Vinci, Leonardo da
Leonardo of Pisa, 188, 189
Lettsom, J. C., 429
Leviathan, 564, 567
L'Hôpital, G. F. A., Marquis de, 274
Libavius, A., 325 f., 504
Life (or Mortality) tables, 608 ff.
Ligature, 436, 447
Light, 7, 53, 80 ff., 146, 156, 161, 198, 244 ff., 671
Light, velocity of, 53, 58, 67, 251, 253, 257 ff.
Lightning conductor, 451
Linacre, T., 426
Link polygon, 482 f.
Linnaeus, C., 398 f., 401, 407
Lintlaer, 533
Linus, F., 238 f., 266
Lippershey, H., 76
Liquation, 500 f.
Lister, M., 362 ff., 430, 445
Lluyd, E., 367
Lobelius (l'Obel), M., 396, 398
Locke, J., 431, 445, 575 ff., 621, 623, 626, 656 ff., 662, 671
Locy, W. A., 424
Logarithms, 140, 193 ff., 209, 558 f.
London waterworks, 532 f.
Longitude, determination of, 31 f., 176, 178, 183 f., 291 f., 301, 382, 393
Longomontanus (C. S. Longberg), 135, 177
Loom, weaving, 459
Louis XIV, 64, 67
Louvois, F. M., 67
Lower, R., 62, 343 f., 425, 444 f.
Lucas, A., 266
Lunar theory, 22, 31, 130 f., 143 f., 156,

159, 161, 178, 180, 183 f., 187
Luther, M., 25

Mach, E., 243, 256, 274, 281
Machinery in mines, 489
Maffei, G. P., 442
Magati, C., 437
"Magdeburg hemispheres," 101
Magellan, F., 374
Magic, 426
Magnan, E., 307
Magnetism, 7, 25, 53, 56, 58, 105, 142, 290 ff. terrestrial, 291 f., 294 ff., 300 ff., 389
Mairan, J. J., 288
Maitland, W., 532
Malpighi, M., 413, 417 ff., 445
Maps, see Cartography
Marchetti, A., 473
Marci, M., 231
Margraff, 451
Marine clock, 114 ff.
Marine instruments, 114 ff.
Mariotte, E., 64, 65 f., 94, 232, 234 f., 242 f., 271 f., 279 f., 312, 314 f., 317, 319, 321, 362, 474 ff.
Marius, S., 31
Marquette, J., 380
Mass, 154
Mästlin, M., 131
Materialism, 641
Materials, strength of, 53, 61, 467 f.
Mathematics, 14, 188 ff., 643
Matthesius, 544
Mattioli, P. A., 396 f., 439
Maunder, E. W., 181
Maupertuis, P. L. M. de, 253
Maurice, P., 532
Maurolycus, F., 245 f., 248 f., 273
Maxima and minima, 201 f., 205, 252 f.
Mayow, J., 344 ff., 415, 425, 445
Mechanical engineering, 505 ff.
Mechanical toys, 528
Mechanics, 477 ff.
"Medicean stars," 30
Medici, Leopold de, 55
Medicine, 7, 395, 425 ff.

Meikle, A., 458
Mela, 387
Melanchthon, P., 354
Mendana, A. de, 375
Mendelssohn, M., 575
Mendoza, G. H. de, 373
Menzzer, C. L., 13
Mercantilism, 615 ff., 628
Mercato, L., 444
Mercator (G. de Cremer), 292, 383 ff 388
his projection, 302, 384
Mercury, 439, 443, 494 f.
Merret, C., 59, 500
Mersenne, M., 52, 63, 86, 92 f., 102, 200, 225, 228, 282 ff., 286
Meteorology, 306 ff.
Metallurgy, 486 ff.
Metius, J., 76
Meyer, E. von, 504
Michael Angelo, see Angelo, Michael
Micrographia, 61, 72, 241, 256, 341 f., 423
Micrometers, 66, 77, 82, 98, 163, 168 ff., 178
Microscopes, 9, 10, 58, 61, 71 ff., 98, 278, 394, 407, 417 f., 420 f.
Middleton, H., 534
Milburne, W., 560
Milky Way, 30 f.
Milton, J., 37 f., 663
Mind, 641
Minderer, R., 440
Mineralogy, 350, 354 356 ff., 363 f., 368, 370 f.
Mineral waters, 326
Mines, ventilation of, 521 ff.
Mining, 7, 61, 325, 354, 355, 486 ff.
Misselden, E., 617
Misson's Travels, 525
Molyneux, W., 307
Momentum, 154, 155
Monads, 579 f., 631, 661 ff.
Monardes, N., 440
Money, 617 ff.
Monsoons, 419
Montchrétien, A. de, 613
Montgomery, G. R., 660
Montmort, 63
Moon, librations of, see Lunar theory

Moon, mountains of, 30, 32
Moore, Sir J., 178 f., 181
Morales, A., 528
Moray, Sir Robert, 60, 89, 588
More, H., 657, 663 ff., 668
More, L. T., 161
Morel, 437
Morgan, A. de, 216, 217
Morland, Sir S., 94, 541, 551, 561 f.
Morrison, R., 400
Morton, R., 444
Motion—
    laws of, see Newton's laws of motion
    circular, laws of, see Circular motion, laws of
    pendular, laws of, see Pendular motion, laws of
    perpetual, 219, 228.
    quantity of, 154, 232, 235
Motte, A., 149, 674
Mottelay, P. F., 305
Moxa, 440
Moxan, J., 480
Mucous membrane, 444
Mun, T., 615, 617, 626
Münster, S., 387 f.
Musgrave, W., 89
Mynsicht, A. van, 439

Napier, J., 140, 193 ff., 558
"Napier's bones," 556, 558 f., 562
Nasturtium, 440
"Nature," 631, 637
Nebulae, 31, 187
Needham, J., 381
Neo-Platonism, 7, 631
Neri, A., 500, 504
Newcomen Society's Transactions, 534, 541 f.
Newcourt, R., 597
Newsham, R., 542
"New stars," 29, 32, 34, 122, 124, 143, 187
Newton, Sir Isaac, 4, 25, 26, 38, 45, 59, 80 f., 89 f., 140, 143, 145 ff., 162, 164, 174, 176, 178, 180 f., 183 f., 186, 192 f., 202, 208 ff., 215 ff., 229, 231, 235, 243, 257, 258. 264 ff., 280, 286,

90,

f.,

270 f.

567
particles,

., 284 f.
129
nskiöld, E., 424
olk plough, 455
rfolk system of agri-
culture, 454
Norman, R., 292, 294
North, Sir D., 618 f.,
627, 628
Novara, Domenico di, 11
Novum Organum, 633 ff.
Numbers, theory of, 202
Numerals, 6, 188
Nunez, P., 129
Nürnberg iron-mill, 542
"Nürnberg scissors," 528

"Occasionalists," 650
Odhner, W. T., 563
Oldenburg, H., 63, 168,
178, 213 ff., 229,
232, 264, 266, 308,
359, 370 f., 651
Oliva, A., 55
Optics, *see* Light
Oresme, N., 193
Ornstein, M., 70
Ortelius (Örtel), A., 383,
385
Osiander, A., 13 f.
Ostwald's *Klassiker*, 102,
203
Oughtred, W., 168,
192 f., 558 f.
Ovals, Cartesian, 198
Overall against infection,
436
Overtones, *see* Harmonics

Pacific Ocean, explora-
tion of, 378
Pacioli, L., 189
Packe, C., 329 f.
Paddle-boats, 550 f.
Paez, P., 379

Paget, 153
Palaeontology, 350, 358,
362, 365 ff.
Palissy, B., 365
Palladio, A., 478
Pantheism, 631, 652 f.
pin, D., 107, 288, 361,
548 ff.
appus of Alexandria,
196 ff., 200, 207
Paracelsus, T. B., 325,
344, 426 ff., 439,
445, 448
Parallax, stellar, 17, 34 f.,
124 f., 143, 176
Parallelogram law, 45,
219 f.
Pardies, I. G., 264, 266
Paré, A., 437, 443, 445,
447 ff.
Paris Observatory, 55,
67, 114, 162, 163,
165 ff., 172, 175 f.,
179, 183, 259
Paris waterworks, 532,
535 f.
Partridge, S., 560
Partsch, J., 386
Pascal, B., 49, 58, 63,
92 f., 200, 202, 208,
221, 223 ff., 240,
560 ff., 563, 608
"Passions," 568 ff.
Paul III, Pope, 13
Paul V, Pope, 36
Peach, C. S., 482
Pearson, K., 485
Pecquet, J., 413
Pellikan, C., 387
Pelvis, 444
Pemberton, H., 148,
150 f.
Penck, A., 386
Pendular motion, laws of,
28, 39, 42 ff., 52, 67,
111 ff., 156, 163 f.,
225 ff., 229 f.
Pendulum clock, 9 f., 44,
66, 109 ff., 115 ff.,
165, 172, 179 f.,
431 ff.
Penot, G. B., 437
Peppermint, 442
Pepys, S., 62
Périer, 93
Perolle, 289
Perrault, Charles, 64
Perrault, Claude, 66 f.
Perrault, Pierre, 321,
361 f.
Peruvian bark, 440, 445
Pet, A., 376
Peter the Great, 70
Petrarch, 27
Petrus Peregrinus, 291

Petty, Sir W., 60, 429 ff.,
445, 477, 484 f., 587,
597 ff., 609, 613,
616 ff., 621 f., 624 f.,
626 f.
Philipsen, E., 177
Philo of Byzantium, 83
Philolaus, 15
"Philosophical furnaces,"
504
Philosophy, 1, 54, 431,
445, 564, 629 ff.
Phosphorus, 348 f.
Phthisis, 443
Physical geology, 350,
353 ff.
Physics, 244 ff., 430, 445,
448
Physiology, 407, 409,
415
Picard, J., 66 f., 114,
151 f., 162, 165, 168,
170, 172, 174 f.,
176 f., 259, 286, 303
Pigot, T., 284 f.
Pillars, strength of, 467,
481
Pinto, M., 378 f.
Pitch of notes, 52 f.,
281 ff., 286, 288
Pitfield, A., 65
Pizarro, F., 373
Pizarro, G., 373
Planetary theory, 14 f.,
18 ff., 22 f., 34, 121,
131 ff., 143 f., 181
(*see also* Geocentric
system *and* Helio-
centric system)
Plant-analysis, 65 f.
Plant anatomy, 60
Plat, Sir Hugh, 457
Plato, 5, 14, 361, 568,
582, 643
Platonic system of nature,
5, 275
Pliny, 395 f., 403
Ploughs, 455 ff.
Plummet-level, 492
Pneumatics, 7, 50 ff., 56,
92 ff., 99 ff., 105,
156, 223 ff., 235 ff.
Poggendorff, J. C., 274,
540
Polarization of light, 271
Poleni, J., 562
"Political arithmetic,"
587 ff., 614, 628
Poncelet, J. V., 200
Poncet, C., 379
Pope, A., 582
Porta, G. B., 245, 249,
279, 293, 298, 544 f.
Potash, 442
Power, the desire of, 567

Precession of the equinoxes, 21, 33 f., 130, 156, 158 f.
"Pre-established harmony," 580
Prices, 621 ff.
Priestley, J., 289
Principle of work, 541
"Principles," 326, 329, 336 ff.
Probability, 191, 202, 608, 611 ff.
Projectiles, 39, 44 ff., 58, 148 f., 223
Protheroe, R. E., 466
Protozoa, 421 f.
Psychology, 430, 445, 564 ff.
Ptolemaic system, see Geocentric system
Ptolemy, 6, 7, 11, 15, 20 ff., 24, 121, 129, 130, 137, 144, 187, 244, 383, 384, 387
his Almagest, 6, 11, 22, 23, 24, 129
Pulleys, 47, 66, 219
Pulsilogy or pulsimeter, 111, 432 f., 448
Pumps, 512, 515, 532 f., 539
Pythagoras, 17, 22, 52, 281, 282
Pythagoreanism, 4, 11, 14, 17, 133, 141, 643

Quast, M. H., 378
Queen Christina, 642
Queen Elizabeth, 293, 632
Quincy, J., 433
Quinine, 440
Quiros, P. de, 378

Radisson, P. E., 380
Raemdonck, J. van, 385
Rag and chain pumps, 518
Rahn, J. H., 192
Railway lines, 511
Rainbow, 269 f., 272
Rainfall, 94, 310, 314, 321 f., 361 f.
Rain-gauge, 306, 310 f., 321
Raleigh, Sir W., 374
Ramazzini, B., 94, 444
Ramelli, A., 515, 528, 531, 538 ff.
Ramsey, D., 545
Rannequin, 536
Raphael, 27
Ray, J., 353, 367, 399 ff., 406 f., 442

Real, V., 444
Reaumur, R. A. F. de, 91
Recorde, R., 192
Redi, F., 55, 420, 422
Reflection of light, 244, 251 f., 261 f., 264
Reformation, 8
Refraction of light, 6, 156, 244 ff., 251 f., 258, 260 ff., 264 ff., 272, 368
Refraction, atmospheric, 66, 129, 140, 176, 246, 393
Regiomontanus (J. Müller), 189
Regular solids, 133 f.
Reinhold, E., 24, 121
Reizen and Salva, 451
Remontoire, 117
Renaissance, 1, 8
Renaldini, C., 89
Rent, 614, 624 f.
Repsold, J. A., 120
Resistance of beams, etc., 469 f., 472
Respiration, 339 ff., 415, 418 f., 437
Rey, J., 86, 332 ff.
Rheticus (G. Joachim), 13, 22
Ribbon-loom, 462
Ricciolus, G. B., 238
Richer, J., 67, 157, 175, 176
Rickets, 437, 444
Rigaud, S. P., 168
Rivault, D., 545
Rivinus, see Bachmann
Roberts, Lord, 588
Roberval, G. P. de, 207 f.
Rohault, J., 299
Roilau, J., 444
Rolling mill for metals, 542
Roman aqueduct at Toledo, 526
Römer, O., 67, 162, 172 ff., 177, 180, 259 f., 286
Rondelet, G., 403, 480, 482
Rooke, L., 60, 232
Rosa, F. da, 445
Rosenberger, F., 274
Royal Society of London, 8, 54, 59 ff., 64 f., 69, 81, 90, 107, 117, 146 f., 152 f., 162, 178, 181 ff., 208, 214, 216, 231 f., 239, 242, 272, 280, 303, 310 f., 314, 418, 420, 423, 448, 477, 552, 598

S
Sag
3
St. Paul
480 ff
St. Petersbu
70
St. Pierre, Le S
178
Sal-ammoniac, 45
Salisbury Cathedral,
Salt, 500
Salusbury, T., 32
Salva and Reizen, 451
Salviati, 32 f., 38 f.
Salvio, A. de, 52
Sanctorius (Santorio), S., 84, 431 ff., 445, 448
Sansovino, F., 582
Saturn, rings of, 30, 163, 175
Sauveur, J., 285
Savery, T., 542, 550 f., 553
Saxony wheel, 459
Scales, graduation of, 128 f.
Scaliger, J., 385
Sceptical Chymist, The, 337 ff.
Schaep, H. C., 378
Scheiner, C., 31, 36, 77, 79, 167, 249
Scheuchzer, J. J., 317
Schneider, C. V., 444
Scholasticism, 2, 4, 5, 33 ff., 51, 54, 629, 633
Schopper, H., 537
Schott, K., 102, 559
Schouten, W. C., 378
Schürer, C., 504
Schwenter, D., 298
Science and philosophy, 629 f.
Science and technology, 450 ff.
Science Museum, London, 547, 561, 563
Scientific methods, 638 ff.
Screw-cutting lathe, 538
Screw-jack, 540

Sea-sounding, instrument for, 114, 117 f.
Sea-water sampler, 114, 118 f.
Secondary qualities, 565, 577, 658, 669 f., 672
Servetus, M., 5, 408, 410 f.
Servus, H., 120
Severino, M. A., 437
Shafts of mines, 490 f.
Sharp, A., 179, 180, 182
Shaw, P., 337
Shore, J., 283
Silchester pump, 532
Silver, 494 f., 498
"Simplicio," 32 f., 38 f.
Singer, C., 414, 424, 449
Six, J., 91
Slide-rule, 192, 556, 559 f.
Slitting-mill for metals, 542
Smelting, 494 ff.
Smith, D. E., 196, 218, 642
Snell, W., 174, 250
Snell's law, 250 ff., 262
Societas Ereunetica, 67
Societas Meteorologica Palatina, 312
Socrates, 5, 582
Soda, 451
Sodium sulphate, 441
Solinus, 387
Somerset House water tower, 534 f.
Soto, H. de, 373
Sound, 52 f., 105, 107, 281 ff.
Sound, velocity of, 58, 156 f., 285 ff., 289
Sowing, 457
Space, absolute, 154
Spafarik, N., 379
Spanheim, E., 69
Specific gravities, 48 f., 107, 109, 120, 230
Spectrum, 264 ff., 267 f.
Speculum, 435, 443
Spinning, 458 f.
Spinoza, B. de, 25, 272, 358, 571 ff., 628, 641, 650 ff., 660, 662, 669, 675,
Spirit of salt, 329 ff.
Spirit of wine, 442
Spiritus silvester, 327
Spontaneous generation, 420, 422
Sprat, T., 70, 312
Springs, origin of, 321, 361 f., 392
Stahl, G. E. 438, 442, 445

Stamp mill, 494 f., 515
Star-catalogues, 24, 129 f., 140, 178 ff., 181 ff.
Stars, proper motions of, 187
Statics, 7, 46, 49, 219 f.
Statistics, see "Political arithmetic"
Steam, 543, 551
Steam-engine, 543 ff.
Steel, 498, 508, 512
Steel furnace, 495
Steichen, M., 222
Steiner, J., 200
Stellati, F., 417
Steno, N., 55, 64, 353, 358 ff., 365 f., 368 ff., 419
Stetten, P. von, 525
Stevin, S., 191, 193, 219 ff., 224
Stifel, M., 189, 192
Stillman, J. M., 335
Stimson, D., 26
Stisser, 442
Stocking frame, 465
Stöffler, J., 387
Stow, 534
Stratigraphy, 351, 354, 355 ff., 359 ff., 363 ff.
Structural mechanics, 477 f.
Stuart, R., 543
Stubbs, S. G. B., 449
Sturm, C., 67
St. Vitus dance, 444
Suction pump, 512
Sulphur, 496, 500
Sulphuric acid, 442
Sun, distance of, from the earth, 22, 67, 130, 144, 175, 186
Sun, rotation of the, 25, 31, 142
Sun-spots, 30 f., 32, 34, 36, 79, 142 f.
Swammerdam, J., 417, 419 ff.
Sydenham, T., 425, 431, 438, 440, 442, 444 f., 448 f., 575, 656
Sylvius, F., 442, 444
Symbols—
  algebraic, 188 ff., 196
  geometrical, 193
  operational, 189, 192
Syphilis, 443

Tabernaemontanus, J. T., 440
Tacitus, 386
Tagliacozza, C., 437
Talbor, R., 441

Tape-worm, 444
Tappets worked by cams, 515
Tartaglia, N., 191
Tasman, A. J., 378
Taylor, A. J., 642
Taylor, B., 283
Tea, 442
Technology, 7, 61, 66, 354, 450 ff.
Teixeira, P., 381
Telescopes, 9 f., 22, 29 ff., 58, 66, 75 ff., 146, 161, 162, 165 ff., 182, 246, 264, 268
Tenacity of solids, 468
Textile problems, 458 ff.
Theodoric of Saxony, 269
Theophrastus, 365, 395
Thermometers and thermoscopes, 9 f., 58, 63, 82 ff., 278, 279, 306, 311, 393, 431 f., 448
Thevenot, M., 63 f.
Thomas Aquinas, St., 2
Thomas, de Colmar, 562 f.
Thompson, S. P., 293
Thornton, R., 541
Threshing, 458
Thurston, R. H., 549
Tides, 34, 144, 156, 158 f.
Tilly, J. T., Count of, 99
Time, absolute, 154
Time-measurement, 6, 10, 41 f., 57, 109 ff., 127 f. (see also Pendulum clock)
Tin, 488, 495, 498
Todhunter, I., 485
Toledo aqueduct, 526 f.
Tomatoes, 440
Tools, 489
Toothed wheels, 507
Torraneo, L., 445
Torres, L. V. de, 378
Torricelli, E., 37, 54 ff., 58, 92 ff., 208, 222 f., 316
"Torricellian vacuum," 56, 92, 236 ff.
Touchstone and needles, 494
Tournefort, J. P. de, 401 f.
Towneley (or Townley), Christopher, 143
Towneley, Richard, 168 f., 178, 235, 239, 241 f., 243, 310
Townshend, C., 454

Tradesmen's equipment, 537
Trade-winds, 34, 317 f.
Transit-instrument, 177, 183
Transits of planets across the sun, 142 f., 184, 186
Transport at mines, 511
Traumüller, F., 120
Treadmill, 506 ff., 512, 519
Trembley, 398
Trigonometry, 6, 189 f., 194 f., 203, 208, 213 f., 559, 562
Trocar, 448
Tschirnhaus (or Tschirnhausen), E. W. von, 272 ff., 651
Tull, J., 455, 457
Turbines, 543, 545 f.
"Turnip Townshend," 454
Tycho Brahe, see Brahe, Tycho
Tychonic planetary system, 125, 131, 136
Tyson, E., 444

Universities, 8 f., 29, 54 f., 306
Uraniborg, 67, 122 ff., 126, 176 f.
Urban VIII, Pope, 36
Urdaneta, A. de, 374 f.
Uroscopy, 428
Usher, A. P., 466
Ussher, Archbishop, 388

Vacuum theory of tenacity, 468
Valdivia, P. de, 373
Valerian, 440
Vallisnieri, A., 362
Valturius, R., 528
Value, 619, 620 ff., 624 f.
Varenius, B., 317 f., 322, 390 ff.
Varignon, P., 46
Varthema, L. de, 378
Velocity ratio, 512
Venereal disease, 443, 449
Venice glass factories, 500
Ventilation of mines, 521 ff.
Venus, phases of, 30, 81
Veranzio, F., 540
Verney, G. J. de, 444
Vernier, 129
Versailles waterworks, 536

Vesalius, A., 6, 403, 406, 408 ff., 412, 425, 445, 447
Vespucci, A., 372 f., 387
Vibration, sympathetic, 281, 283
Vieta, F., 189 f., 192 f., 214
Vigo, G. da, 436
Vinci, Leonardo da, 5, 8, 27, 39, 58, 249, 254, 365, 408, 459, 467, 531, 536 f., 540, 544
Vinta, B., 30
Virtual velocities (or displacements), Principle of, 46 f., 49 f., 219, 224
Vision, 82, 244 ff., 248 ff., 252, 272
Vis viva, conservation of, 228, 231, 233 f.
Vitellio, 245
Vitriol, 499 f.
Vitruvius, 2, 281, 477, 527, 531 f.
Viviani, V., 37, 44, 54 f., 83, 92, 112, 286, 287
Vlacq, A., 195
Volume of steam, 551
Vortices, Cartesian, 151, 157, 164, 251, 299, 305, 392, 647, 672
Vries, M. G. de, 378

Wages, 622, 625 f.
Wallenstein, A. W. E. von, 132
Waller, R., 56, 258, 279, 342
Wallis, J., 59, 105, 155, 193, 195, 208 f., 213 f., 231 f., 237, 284 f.
Ward, S., 60, 105, 237
Ware, I., 478
Washing machine, 463
Water, 58, 61, 327 f.
Water-clock, 432 f.
Water-commanding engine, see Worcester
Water mains, 512, 528
Water-pumps, 50, 512 ff.
Water-wheel, 516, 518, 520, 532 f., 539
Waterworks, 524 ff.
Wealth, 614 ff.
Weather-clock, 306, 310 ff.
Weaving, 459 ff.
Wechsler, A., 642
Weighing-chair, 434, 448
Wepfer, J. J., 444

Westergaard, H. L., 628
Westminster Abbey, 481
Weston, Sir R., 454
Wharton, T., 413
Wheels, toothed, 507
Whim, 507 f.
Whiston, W., 148, 150 f., 353
Whitehead, A. N., 2
Whittaker, E. T., 267, 274
Whooping cough, 443
Widman, J., 192
Wierus, J., 425
Wilhelm IV, Landgrave of Hesse, 122, 140
Wilkins, J., 59, 448, 545
Williamson, Sir J., 181
Willis, T., 415, 440, 444
Willoughby, Sir H., 375 f.
Willow-tree experiment, 328
Wilson, J., 74
Winch, see Windlass
Windelband, W., 675
Wind-gauge, 115, 119 f., 306, 309, 311
Windlass, 505 f.
Windmill, 523, 540
Wind-scoops, 521
Winds, 119, 316 ff., 354 f., 393
Winter, J. G., 359
Witchcraft, 3
Witt, J. de, 609
Wolf, A., 675
Wolf, C., 168, 175
Wolf, R., 26
Wollaston, W. H., 91
Wood, A., 380 f.
Woodward, J., 352 f., 364 f., 366, 429 f., 445
Wootton, A. C., 449
Worcester, Marquis of, 545, 547, 551, 553
Wotton, E., 402
Wounds, 447
Wren, Sir C., 60, 63, 105, 151, 152, 155, 178, 179, 231, 232, 237, 243, 310, 341, 344, 480 ff.
Wren, S., 481
Wright, E., 384

Yarrow (Iva), 442

Zeising, 541
Zinc, 495
Zinner, E., 26
Zittel, K. A. von, 371
Zonca, V., 540
Zoological gardens, 394
Zoology, 402 ff.